Railwa Restored 2000

THE BEST-SELLING GUIDE TO HERITAGE RAILWAYS

Edited by Alan C. Butcher

Ian Allan PUBLISHING

Contents

Front cover: Great Western 2-6-2T No 4141 soaks up the sun at Llangollen on 5 September 1999. *ACB*

Back cover: Henschel-built 0-4-0WT No 14 *Helen Kathryn* in action on the South Tynedale Railway. *STR*

Previous page: Caledonian Railway 0-6-0 No 828 stands at Aviemore on the Strathspey Railway with the 10.00 from Boat of Garten, 10 June 1999. *Alan P. Barnes*

Right: The restored station building at Bickleigh, Devon Railway Centre . *DRC*

First published 1980
Twenty first edition 2000

ISBN 0 7110 2709 9

© Ian Allan Publishing Ltd 2000

Published by Ian Allan Publishing

an imprint of Ian Allan Ltd, Terminal House, Shepperton, Surrey TW17 8AS
Printed by Ian Allan Printing Ltd, Riverdene Business Park, Hersham, Surrey KT12 4RG

Code: 0003/D

The publishers, the railway operators and the Heritage Railway Association accept no liability for any loss, damage or injury caused by error or inaccuracy in the information published in *Railways Restored 2000*. Train services may be altered or cancelled without prior notice, and at some locations diesel traction may be substituted for scheduled steam workings.

Foreword

Amazingly, the number of heritage railway projects continues to grow, especially in the north of England, where there are well-established schemes for the reopening of the Wensleydale and the Weardale lines and the Eden Valley Railway between Appleby and Warcop (and eventually Kirkby Stephen). This new generation is inspired as much by the desire to promote public transport opportunities as to preserve our steam — or diesel — heritage. Some projects are little more than a glint in the eye and as such will not appear in these pages but I have been involved in heritage railways too long to know better than to write off as impossible some ideas that seem 'crackpot'. Whether such growth is necessarily desirable is another matter but no one can doubt the commitment or the resilience of their promoters.

It is partly this ever-changing scenario that makes the purchase of *Railways Restored* on a regular basis so indispensable. It has grown in size over the years to match the subject it covers and is now supplemented by a useful timetable of passenger trains on heritage lines.

However comprehensive such guides and timetables may be, they cannot, of course, provide specific details of special events which is why the provision of telephone numbers in the entries of this book is so invaluable. Many railways, for example, will be participating in the European Steam Weekend on 10/11 June 2000, and the Heritage Open Weekend on 9/10 September 2000, when visitors will be able to see behind the scenes in areas normally barred to the public, such as engine sheds, free of charge.

A growing number of 'rail-buffs' (if you will excuse the slang) are taking an interest in steam overseas, particularly in Europe where so many already go on holiday. I hope next year that we can provide contact addresses of the national organisations representing heritage, museum or historic railways throughout Europe for those interested in honing up before going on their travels on what our continental colleagues are doing. In the meantime, more information may be gleaned from the secretary of our European 'umbrella'. FEDECRAIL (the European Federation of Museum & Tourist Railways): Livius Kooij at De Akker 25, 7481 GA Haaksbergen, The Netherlands (tel: 00 31 53 57 27357) (e-mail: fedecrail@worldonline.nl). Like most Dutchmen, he speaks fluent English!

Happy travelling.

David Morgan
Chairman, HRA

Editor's Comment

Welcome to the 21st edition of *Railways Restored*. As ever it is packed with essential information.

There are several arrivals and departures to announce for this edition. Liverpool Museum has closed for redevelopment, presumably awaiting the result of a Lottery Grant application. Westrail, in County Galway, will be undergoing extensive repair work and will not be operating services this year. Hopefully Westrail will reappear in the next edition of *Railways Restored*. Tiverton Museum is closed during 2000 and will reopen in 2001 following redevelopment again hopefully to reappear in these pages.

On the arrivals side is the Exmoor Steam Centre, ideal for a family day out. It gives the opportunity to ride out and walk back, the walk back is a lot shorter than the ride! Pay a visit and find out why. Also new is the Great Northern & East Lincolnshire Railway based at Ludborough, near Grimsby.

In his Foreword David Morgan mentions three embryonic schemes; on top of these are numerous others. A number of these schemes were sent requests for information in order that they could be included in *Railways Restored*; sadly most could not be bothered to respond. To save their embarrassment I will not list them, but they range from central southern England to north of Wales, on to Scotland and back to London. If the publicity officers would care to the drop me a line via the publishers, or indeed fax their details direct, then they will be contacted in the autumn for inclusion in the next edition of *Railways Restored*.

Editor's Notes

On the following pages will be found a guide to the major preserved railways, railway museums and preservation centres in the British Isles. Information for visitors has been set out in tabular form for easy reference, together with a locomotive stocklist for most centres.

Many preservation centres and operating lines provide facilities for other groups and organisations to restore locomotives and equipment on their premises. It has not been possible to include full details of these groups, but organisations which own locomotives are shown under the centres at which they operate. In addition, a full list of member societies of the AIRPS is given elsewhere. In the case of most operating lines their length is given, but there is no guarantee that services are operated over the entire length.

Within the heading to each entry a heading block has been incorporated for easy reference as to what each site offers in the way of passenger service to visitors. These are as follows:

Timetable Service: Railways providing a passenger service between two or more stations with public access; eg Mid-Hants Railway.

Steam Centre: A railway or preservation site offering a passenger service on a short length of line, on a regular basis, with public access at only one point; eg Lavender Line.

Museum: A museum or site that does not offer a passenger service on a regular basis, if at all; eg Science Museum, London. Some sites may however offer rides on miniature railways.

As well as a guide as to what to expect on each site, this year's *Railways Restored* shows what, if any, particular professional body the Companies or Societies belong to. These are:

HRA: Indicates that the organisation is a member of the Heritage Railway Association (HRA).

TT: Indicates that the organisation is a member of the Transport Trust (TT).

Membership of the HRA and TT is open to both organisations and private individuals. Private members are able to take advantage of concessions offered to them by the organisations that subscribe to these two bodies.

The concessions range from a discount on the admission price to free entry. The TT's Travel Back leaflet provides details.

Details given under **Access by public transport** should be checked beforehand to ensure services shown are operating. Unless the Heritage Railway, Steam Centre or Museum has identified the privatised train company operating the service, the phrase 'by rail', or 'main line', has been used to identify access by train.

Visitors wishing to see specific items of rolling stock or locomotives are advised to check before their visit that the exhibit is available for inspection. It should be stressed that not all items are usually available for inspection due to restoration, operating or other restrictions.

Ian Allan National Heritage Awards

The Awards have been made annually since 1979 with the object of encouraging high standards of structural restoration and environmental care, thereby promoting public recognition and awareness of historic railway structures and their place in the environment. We aim to promote careful design and quality workmanship in restoration, modernisation and maintenance, after taking full account of all relevant factors, particularly, of course, manpower and finance. In this way, we encourage both public and private railways to present their operational premises as an attractive 'shop window', while occupiers of former railway buildings now used for other purposes are similarly encouraged to retain as much as possible of the original character.

The organisers are the HRA and the main sponsors are Ian Allan Ltd, together with British Rail through their Community Unit and the Railway Heritage Trust. Judging is done from the beginning of May through to the end of August and the results are notified at the beginning of October. The Awards are presented in late November at a prestigious location by a well-known public figure, with full media coverage.

1992 saw the inclusion of Ireland in the Awards initially with the addition of a special Premier Award and up to three Certificates of Commendation in each sector.

WHAT IS ELIGIBLE?

1 Any present or former railway structure such as a station, warehouse, bridge, viaduct, tunnel or signalling installation, that has been sympathetically restored for whatever purpose.
2 A replica structure intended to recreate or augment some aspect of the railway heritage.
3 A new structure designed in traditional style in order to blend with or complement the local environment.

WHO CAN ENTER?

Any group in Great Britain and Ireland involved in railway preservation, whether as a private railway company or as a less formal organisation. Railtrack, Irish Rail, Northern Ireland Railways (NIR). Other public or commercial organisations. Private individuals.

The scheme is divided into:
(a) The Volunteer Sector for organisations run wholly or largely by volunteers.
(b) The Public & Commercial Sector. In cases of doubt, the awards committee decides which sector is appropriate.

For application forms apply to:
Arthur Harding,
6 Ullswater Grove
Alresford, Hants
SO24 9NP
Tel: (01926) 733327.

The HRA Annual Award

This, the premier award made by the HRA, is for a group or organisation making an outstanding contribution to railway preservation during the year of the Award.

The Award takes the form of a Royal Train Headboard from the London, Brighton & South Coast Railway, which is on loan to the HRA from the National Railway Museum. The Award is held for one year and the winning group also receives a commemorative plaque. The Award is announced and presented at the Association's Annual General Meeting which is held on the last weekend of January each year.

Standard Abbreviations

AEC	Associated Equipment Co
AEG	Allgemeine Elektrizitaets Gesellschaft
A/Barclay	Andrew Barclay
A/Porter	Aveling & Porter Ltd
A/Whitworth	Armstrong Whitworth
B/Drewry	Baguley/Drewry
B/Peacock	Beyer Peacock & Co
B/Hawthorn	Black, Hawthorn & Co
BRCW	Birmingham Railway, Carriage & Wagon
BTH	British Thomson Houston
Buch	23 August Locomotive Works
D/Metcalfe	Davies & Metcalfe
E/Electric	English Electric Ltd
F/Jennings	Fletcher Jennings & Co
F/Walker	Fox Walker
G/England	George England & Co
GRCW	Gloucester Railway, Carriage & Wagon
H/Leslie	Hawthorn Leslie & Co
H/Hunslet	Hudson Hunslet
H/Clarke	Hudswell Clarke & Co Ltd
K/Stuart	Kerr Stuart & Co Ltd
M/Cam	Metropolitan Cammell
M/Rail	Motor Rail Ltd
M/Vick	Metrovick (Metropolitan-Vickers)
M/Wardle	Manning Wardle & Co Ltd
N/British	North British Locomotive Co Ltd
N/Wilson	Nasmyth Wilson & Co Ltd
O&K	Orenstein & Koppel
P/Steel	Pressed Steel Co Ltd
RSH	Robert Stephenson & Hawthorn Ltd
R/Hornsby	Ruston Hornsby
R/Proctor	Ruston Proctor
S. F. Belge	Société Franco Belge
YEC	Yorkshire Engine Co

Company abbreviations

BR	British Railways
DB	German Federal Railway

DSB	Danish State Railways
GWR	Great Western Railway
JZ	Yugoslav Railways
LMS	London Midland & Scottish Railway
LNER	London & North Eastern Railway
MoS	Ministry of Supply
NSB	Norwegian State Railways
RR	Rhodesian Railways
SJ	Swedish Railways
SAR	South African Railways
SNCF	French National Railways
SR	Southern Railway
USATC	United States Army Transportation Corps
WD	War Department

Other abbreviations

BE	Battery-electric
DE	Diesel-electric
DH	Diesel-hydraulic
DM	Diesel-mechanical
DMU	Diesel multiple-unit
E	Overhead electric
EMU	Electric multiple-unit
F	Fireless
G	Geared
GH	Gas-hydraulic
IST	Inverted saddle tank
LRO	Light Railway Order
PM	Petrol-mechanical
PH	Petrol-hydraulic
ParM	Paraffin-mechanical
PT	Pannier tank
R	Railcar
ST	Saddle tank
STT	Saddle tank and tender
T	Side tank
VB	Vertical boiler
WT	Well tank

Faces on engines ensures that children bring their parents to Thomas the Tank Engine events on heritage railways. A scene at Shepherdswell on the East Kent Railway. *EKR*

NORTH

SEA

INVERNESS
Alford
Strathspey

Caledonian Rly
(Brechin)
Kerr's

Mull Rail

Summerlee
Bo'ness   Prestongrange
GLASGOW   EDINBURGH
Museum

Scottish Ind.Rly Museum
Dalmellington

Leadhills

Foyle
South Donegal

North Tyneside
(North Shields)

CARLISLE

Bowes
Tanfield   Beamish

South Tynedale

Rly Pres.
Society of
Ireland

Ulster Folk & Transport
Museum
BELFAST

Downpatrick

Darlington
North Yorkshire

Snaefell
Mountain

Ravenglass &
Eskdale

Lakeside & Haverthwaite

Lightwater Valley
(Ripon)

Groudle Glen
Manx Electric
DOUGLAS

I.O.M. Railway

IRISH

Embsay
Keighley & Worth Valley

National Rly Mus.
YORK

Mus of Army Transport (Beverley)

Blackpool

West Lancs
East Lancs (Bury)

LEEDS
Middleton
Leeds Industrial

DUBLIN

SEA

Great Orme

Penrhyn
Castle

Kirklees

South Yorkshire

MANCHESTER
Museum

Cleethorpes
Light Rly

Great Northern

Wells & Walsingham
North Norfolk Rly

Irish Steam Pres. Society

Llanberis
Snowdon Mountain

Conwy Valley

Churnet Valley

Crich (Nat. Tramway)
Peak Rail
Midland Rly

Ffestiniog
Welsh Highland

Llangollen
Cambrian Rlys
(Oswestry)

Railway Age

Foxfield

Nottingham

Great Central   Abbey

Bure Valley

Corris

Bala

Chasewater

Rutland Rly Mus.

PETERBOROUGH   Mid-Norfolk

East Anglia
Transport

Fairbourne

Welshpool
& Llanfair

Telford
Ironbridge

Battlefield
(Shackerstone)

Nene Valley Rly

Bressingham

Colne Valley

Mid-Suffolk

Talyllyn

Vale of Rheidol

Severn
Valley

BIRMINGHAM   Cadeby

Railway Museum
Kidderminster
Airfield Line

Northampton
Steam
Northampton
Ironstone   Irchester

East Anglian Rly

Teifi

Gwili

Brecon

Dean
Forest

Pontypool

Vale of
Glamorgan

Bristol Ind.
Avon Valley

Glouc. & Warks. Rly
Winchcombe
National
Waterways
Swindon &
Cricklade

Swindon
GWR Mus.

Leighton
Buzzard   Buckinghamshire

Princes Risborough
Didcot   Ruislip Lido
Cholsey

LONDON

Audley
End

Mangapps Farm
N. Woolwich

Kew Bridge
London Transport
Science Museum

Sittingbourne

Swansea Vale
+ Maritime & Ind

Exmoor
West Somerset

East Somerset

Great Cockcrow

Mid-Hants

Spa

Bluebell Rly

East Kent

K&ESR

Romney

Bideford

Gartell

Hollycombe

Amberley

Lavender Line

Launceston

Bicton

Moors Valley (Ringwood)

Bodmin
Dobwalls

South Devon
Plymouth
Plym Valley

Seaton

Paignton
& Dartmouth

Swanage   Isle of Wight

Alderney

ENGLISH

CHANNEL

7

England

Museum — Abbey Pumping Station — Leicester

Members: TT

Narrow gauge site railway (2ft gauge) formerly part of a sewage pumping station that now forms museum site. Railway relaid in concrete by MSC scheme during early 1980s to original track layout. New track layout as an extension to original laid with 35lb rail on wooden sleepers. All the railway system is now run by volunteers. Original Simplex locomotive kept on site in operational condition. A Planet petrol locomotive and a Ruston diesel are used to demonstrate the railway with typical tipper wagons and mine tubs. Line originally used for transferring solid material from screens to tip (about 100yd).

Location: Abbey Pumping Station, Corporation Road, off Abbey Lane, Leicester LE4 5XP

Operating group: Leicester City Council Museum, Arts & Records Service and Leicestershire Museums Technology Association

Telephone: (0116) 299 5111

Fax: (0116) 299 5125

Car park: Free on site

Access by public transport: Main line Leicester (London Road).

Industrial locomotives

Narrow gauge:

Name	No	Builder	Type	Built
—	—	Motor Rail (5260)	4wPM	1931
—	—	Hibberd (1776)	4wPM	1931
—	—	R/Hornsby (223700)	4wDM	1944

Stock

3 new passenger vehicles based on Leicester & Swannington coaches. 10 skip wagons, 6 mine tubs, 2 flats, bomb wagon chassis, various miscellaneous

Leicester City Bus route 54 or 54K from city centre (alight at Beaumont Leys Lane)

Length of line/gauge: About 300yd, 2ft gauge. Passenger carrying on special open days (small fare payable on Free-entry days)

Period of public opening: Daily from 9 April, 10.00 to 17.30 Monday to Saturday and 14.00 to 17.30 Sunday

On site facilities: Museum/shop/toilets/car park. Refreshments only on Special Event Days

Facilities for disabled: Access to museum lower floor and grounds. Steps to Engine House and refreshments on event days

Volunteer contact: Tony Kendal, c/o Abbey Pumping Station

Museum contact: Mr C. Stevens, c/o Abbey Pumping Station (Tel: 0116 299 5111)

Other attractions: Museum holds various transport, steam navvy, beam engines. Some items only viewable by appointment or on Special Event Days

Special events: Children's Steam Day — 16 April; Longest Steam Day (Wednesday)* — 21 June; A Journey into the Past — 17 September; Railway Day* — 8 October; Hubble Bubble Toil & Trouble* — 29 October; Craft & Art Day* — 12 November; Christmas Toy Steam Day — 10 December (*free entry)

Museum — Airfield Line — Warwickshire

Member: HRA

The railway is the only standard gauge line in Warwickshire and has been constructed on a 'greenfield' site by members of The 1857 Society, work beginning in 1983. Originally known as the Coventry Steam Railway Centre, the public were first admitted in 1988, after which time the marketing name —

Multiple-units

Name	No	Origin	Class	Type	Built
—	61684*	BR	2EPB / 416/2	MBS	1955
—	75736*	BR	2EPB / 416/2	DTC	1955
—	65323††	BR	2EPB / 416/2	DMBSO	1955
—	77112††	BR	2EPB / 416/2	TSO	1955
—	75407**	BR	2HAP / 414	DTC (L)	1948
—	61287**	BR	2HAP / 414	MBS	1948
—	12799†	BR	4SUB / 405	MBS	1948
—	12796†	BR	4SUB / 405	MBS	1948

Airfield Line — was adopted.
Development continues and the site
now houses ex-MR Little Bowden
Junction signalbox, and the rebuilt
118-yea- old LNWR North
Kilworth station building, to be
renamed Thistledown Halt on
completion. Work is on-going to
convert the six acre site to an
authentic railway setting. The site
also contains a collection of vintage
road rollers
Location: Within the boundary of
Coventry Airport, south of the city.
Easily reached via Rowley Road,
junction with A45/A46, Coventry
eastern bypass — M6/M69/M1 link
road. Follow Coventry Airport
direction signs — entrance is
adjacent to Emergency Exit Gate 2
OS reference: SP 349750
Access by public transport: BR
Coventry, West Midlands bus route
20/21 from city centre to Toll Bar
end
Operating society/organisation:
Coventry Steam Railway Centre in
conjunction with Carrick Wardale
Steam Crane Group, The 1857
Society and Suburban Electric
Railway Association
Telephone:(0121) 708 2815
evenings only and/or answerphone
Length of line: Third of a mile
(under construction)
Public opening: Every Sunday and
bank holiday from Easter to

Name	No	Origin	Class	Type	Built
—	12354†	BR	4SUB / 405	TS	1948
—	10239†	BR	4SUB / 405	TOS	1948
—	29720	LMS	503	TSO	1938
—	28690	LMS	503	DMBSO	1938
—	7	LOR•	—	Trailer	1895

•Liverpool Overhead Railway, built by Brown Marshall & Co
* unit No 6142, later 930053, †unit No 4732,
**unit No 6089, ††unit No 5793

Industrial locomotives

Name	No	Builder	Type	Built
—	1	A/Barclay (1772)	0-4-0F	1922
Spondon No 1	—	E/Electric (EE905)	4wBE/WE	1935
Southam	—	H/Clarke (D604)	0-4-0DM	1936
C. P. May	—	Hibberd (2895)	4wPM	1944
—	L14	R/Hornsby (235515)	4wDM	1954
Mazda	—	R/Hornsby (268881)	0-4-0DE	1950
Crabtree	—	R/Hornsby (338416)	4wDM	1953
—	L7	R/Hornsby (349038)	4wDM	1954

Rolling stock
1 BR Mk 1 Res/buffet (TSO conversion), 1 Liverpool Overhead Railway
coach, 1 steam crane, 1 crane, 2 fitted vans, 1 LNER brake van, 1 SR brake
van, 4 other vehicles

Owners
Class 503 vehicles the Electric Train Preservation Ltd
2EPB — the Suburban Electric Railway Association

October, 11.00-17.00, static
display. See press for operating
days and special events. Other
times and party visits by prior
arrangement. (No access at other
times.)

Car park: On site, access off
Rowley Road
Facilities for disabled: Site
relatively flat. Members willing to
assist if prior notice given. No
access to buffet coach, no toilets

Steam Centre	# Amberley Museum	West Sussex

Member: HRA, TT

**Narrow Gauge and Industrial
Railway Collection (incorporating
the Brockham Museum of
Narrow Gauge Railways)**
The NG&IR Collection is part of an
open air industrial museum set in 36
acres of the former Pepper & Co
chalk pits. A 2ft gauge line has been
constructed and this is used for
carrying passengers in genuine
workmen's vehicles
Museum Director: Robert Taylor
Location: Houghton Bridge,
Amberley, West Sussex (3 miles
north of Arundel) on B2139.
Adjacent to Amberley main line
station

Locomotives
(2ft or 60cm unless otherwise indicated)

Name	No	Builder	Type	Built
Polar Bear	—	Bagnall (1781)	2-4-0T	1905
Peter	—	Bagnall (2067)	0-4-0ST	1918
Townsend Hook	4	F/Jennings (172L) (3ft 2.25in gauge)	0-4-0T	1880
Scaldwell	—	Peckett (1316) (3ft 0in gauge)	0-6-0ST	1913
—	23†	Spence (1ft 10in gauge)	0-4-0T	1921
—	—	Decauville (1126)	0-4-0T	1950
—**	—	Baldwin (778)	4-6-0T	1917
Monty	(6)	O&K (7269) (3ft 2.25in gauge)	4wDM	1936
The Major	(7)	O&K (7741)	4wDM	1937
—	2	Ransomes & Rapier (80)	4wDM	1937
—	—	Hudson-Hunslet (3097)	4wDM	1944
—	2	R/Hornsby (166024)	4wDM	1933

OS reference: TQ 030122
Operating society/organisation: Amberley Museum Trust, Amberley Museum, Houghton Bridge, Amberley, Arundel, West Sussex BN18 9LT
Telephone: Bury (01798) 831370 (Museum office)
Internet address: *web site:* www.amberleymuseum.co.uk
e-mail (general museum enquiries): office@amberleymuseum.co.uk
e-mail (specific railway enquiries): gerryac@fastnet.co.uk
Car park: Adjacent to Amberley station
On site facilities: Shop, café, audio-visual show
Public opening: Wednesday to Sunday (inclusive) each week, and Bank Holiday Mondays, (open all week in school holidays) 10.00-last entry 17.00, 15 March-29 October 2000
Special events: Railway Gala Weekend — 8/9 July. Please see press for details of further activities
Special notes: Displays include working potter, blacksmith, boatbuilder and printer, stationary engines, historic radio collection and vintage Southdown garage and buses. A 2ft 0in gauge industrial railway system is demonstrated when possible, and a 3ft 2.25in gauge line is under construction. In addition, a 2ft 0in gauge 'main line' has been constructed. The 500yd line was officially opened by HRH Prince Michael of Kent on 5 June 1984. The railway is operated every day the museum is open (subject to mechanical availability), with steam locomotive haulage on certain days — for details contact the museum office. Wheelchairs can normally be accommodated on the train. A Narrow Gauge & Industrial Railway Introductory Exhibition sets the scene for these and other set-piece display areas
Membership details: Friends of Amberley Museum, c/o above address
Membership journal: *Wheelbarrow* — bi-monthly

Name	*No*	*Builder*	*Type*	*Built*
		(3041)		
—	3101	M/Rail (Simplex) (1381) Armoured	4wPM	1918
Peldon	—	John Fowler (21295)	4wDM	1936
Redland	—	O&K (6193)	4wDM	1937
—	—	Lister (35421)	4wPM	1949
—		(LR 2593)		
—	—	M/Rail (Simplex) (872)	4wPM	1918
—	27	M/Rail (Simplex) (5863)	4wDM	1934
—	—	M/Rail (Simplex) (10161) (2ft 11in gauge)	4wDM	1949
Ibstock	—	M/Rail (Simplex) (11001)	4wDM	1951
*Burt**	—	Simplex 9019))	4wDM	1959
CCSW	—	Hibberd (1980)	4wDM	1936
Thakeham Tiles	No 3	Hudson-Hunslet (2208)	4wDM	1941
Thakeham Tiles	No 4	Hudson-Hunslet (3653)	4wDM	1948
—	—	H/Clarke (DM686)	0-4-0DM	1948
Star Construction	—††	Hudson-Hunslet	4wDM	c1941
—	18	R/Hornsby (187081)	4wDM	1937
—	—	Lister (33937)	4wDM	1949
—	—	Hibberd 'Y-type Planet' (3627)	4wPM	1953
—	WD904	Wickham (3403/04)	2w 2PMR	1943
—	2	W&R (5031)	4wBE	1953
—	—	W&R (5034)	4wBE	1953
—	—	W&R (4998)	4wBE	1953
—	—	W&R (T8033)	0-4-0BE	1979

†† not on site
** on loan to Leighton Buzzard Railway for restoration
* standard gauge
†Includes hoist and 'haulage truck' for conversion to 5ft 3in gauge from Guiness Brewery

Stock
2 Penrhyn Quarry Railway 4-wheel coaches (2ft gauge, ex-1ft 10.75in gauge); RAF Fauld bogie coach (1940) (2ft gauge); Rye & Camber Tramway bogie (incomplete) (1895) (3ft gauge); Post Office Railway unit No 808 of 1930; 4 Groudle Glen Railway 4-wheel coaches (1896 and 1905) (2ft gauge); 60 other varied pieces of rolling stock of 12 different gauges ranging from 1ft 6in to 3ft 2.25in plus numerous miscellaneous exhibits including track, signals, etc

Steam Centre — Amerton Railway — Staffordshire

Construction of the Amerton Railway started in June 1990. Over the following two years volunteers of the Staffordshire Narrow Gauge Railway Society Ltd constructed a new 2ft gauge railway on a greenfield site. Work undertaken in this period consisted of building a trackbed, laying a quarter mile of track and building a stock shed and station facilities. The railway opened to the public on 14 July 1992. The railway is currently constructing an extension, which should hopefully be fully open early in the season, with the final phase towards the later part of the season. This will give a line of one-mile in length with a further station, Chartley Road, situated at a proposed picnic area.

The former Great Northern Chartley station building is now being erected following restoration. It will become a museum of Staffordshire narrow gauge railway history

Location: Amerton Railway, Amerton Farm, Stowe-by-Chartley, Stafford ST18 0LA (situated between Stafford and Uttoxeter, signposted off A51 at Weston)

Operating company: Staffordshire Narrow Gauge Railway Society Ltd, c/o above address

Telephone: (Railway only) (01785) 284388. Farm (01889) 270294

OS reference: SJ 993278

On site facilities: Car park at Working Farm. Museum under construction; licensed tearoom and bakery (not operated by railway). Souvenir shop in railway ticket office. The railway is one of the main attractions at the farm; admission to most other attractions is free

Access by public transport: By rail to Stafford, then Stevenson's of Uttoxeter Ltd bus to Weston, then a mile walk to Amerton (no Sunday service)

Period of public operation: Sundays from mid-March to end of October. Saturdays from Easter until August Bank Holiday. Bank Holiday Mondays. Trains run 12.00 until 17.00. Subject to availability *Isabel* or *Pearl 2* will be in steam

Industrial locomotives

Name	No	Builder	Type	Built
Isabel	—	Bagnall (1491)	0-4-0ST	1897
Pearl 2	—	T. D. A Civil (1)	0-4-2IST	1997
—	746	M/Rail (40SD501)	4wDM	1975
—	—	M/Rail (7471)	4wDM	1940
—	—	Baguley (3024)	0-4-0DM/SO	1939
Dreadnought	—	R/Hornsby (221623)	4wDM	1943
—	Yard No 70	R/Hornsby (506491)	4wDM	1964
—	—	Hunslet (8561)	4wDH	1978

Rolling stock

4 toastrack coaches, 3 by Baguley, 1 ex-WHR, SNGRS-built passenger brake van and various wagons

Sundays and Bank Holidays. Diesel haulage generally on Saturdays

Special events: Goods trains will run during the summer. Santa Specials in December. Footplate experience courses. Please contact for details

Membership details: Membership Secretary, c/o above address

Membership journal: *Isabel Gazette*, quarterly

Timetable Service	Avon Valley Railway	South Glos

Member: HRA

Progress on the AVR's southern extension towards Bath continues, and the section from Barrow Hill to the River Boyd is expected to be open from Easter. This extension will give the AVR an operating line of over two miles. Planning permission has recently been granted for the construction of a platform and run-round loop at the end of the current extension towards Bath at the River Avon. RSH No 7151 has recently returned to steam

Headquarters: Bitton Railway Company Limited, Bitton Station, Willsbridge, Bristol BS30 9YZ

Telephone: (0117) 329 7296 for timetable information. (0117) 329 5538 weekends

Main station: Bitton

OS reference: ST 670705

Car park: Bitton

Access by public transport: Main line train service to Keynsham. Badgerline service No 332 (Bristol-

Locomotives

Name	No	Origin	Class	Type	Built
Sir Frederick Pile	34058	SR	BB	4-6-2	1947
—	44123	LMS	4F	0-6-0	1925
—	48173	LMS	8F	2-8-0	1943
—	D2994	BR	07	0-6-0DE	1962
—	51909	BR	108	DMBS	1958
—	54271	BR	108	DTC	1958

Locomotive notes: All steam locomotives undergoing restoration.

Industrial locomotives

Name	No	Builder	Type	Built
Edwin Hulse	2	Avonside (1798)	0-6-0ST	1918
Littleton No 5	—	M/Wardle (2018)	0-6-0ST	1922
—	—	RSH (7151)	0-6-0T	1944
—	—	R/Hornsby (235519)	4wDM	1945
—	—	Baguley/Drewry (2153)	0-4-0	1941
—	2*	Bagnall (2842)	0-4-0ST	1946
General Lord Robertson	610	Sentinel (10143)	0-8-0DH	1961
Kingswood	—	Barclay (446)	0-4-0DM	1959
—	D1171	H/Clarke (D1171)	0-6-0DM	1959

*on display at Warmley station, Bristol

Locomotive notes: R/Hornsby (235519) and Bagnall (2842) undergoing restoration. D1171 undergoing overhaul off-site.

England

Bath), No 558 (Bristol-North Common) (tel: 0117 955 3231 for details).

Access by bike: Bitton station is on the Bristol/Bath Railway Path (route 4 of the National Cycle Network)

Catering facilities: Buffet is able to provide hot and cold snacks, confectionery, hot and cold drinks and ice creams

On site facilities: Station buffet open every weekends and all operating days, toilets, picnic area, children's play area close by

Public opening: Open every weekend for static viewing. Trains operate 2, 21-24, 30 April; 1, 6/7, 14, 21, 28/29 May; 4, 11, 18, 25 June; 2, 9, 16, 23, 30 July; 2, 6, 9, 13, 16, 20, 23, 27/28, 30 August;

Stock
16 ex-BR Mk 1 coaches (9 stored off-site); 1 ex-BR Mk 1 Restaurant Coach; 1 ex-BR Mk 1 sleeper; 1 ex-LMS brake composite corridor; 2 cranes; 2 Wickham trolleys; numerous assorted wagons

Owners
44123 the London Midland Society
48173 the Bitton 8F Locomotive Group

3, 10, 17, 24, 30 September; 1 October and Santa/Mince Pie Specials

Special events: Mother's Day, Sunday Lunch — 2 April; Easter Weekend — 21-24 April; Day Out with Thomas — 6/7 May and 30 September/1 October; Children's Fun Day — 4 June; Father's Day, Sunday Lunch — 18 June; Teddy Bears' Picnic, Sunday Lunch —

16 July; Santa Specials 2-4, 9/10, 16/17, 23/24 December; Mince Pie Specials 31 December/1 January 2001

Facilities for disabled: Coach converted for disabled use (no toilet facilities)

Membership details: Membership Secretary, c/o Bitton station

Membership journal: *Semaphore* — quarterly

| Steam Centre | **Barrow Hill Roundhouse Railway Centre** | Derbyshire |

Member: HRA

In 1839 the North Midland Railway devised an arrangement of stabling locomotives around a turntable within a polygonal building with a conical roof, hence roundhouse. In 1864 locomotives began to be housed in buildings of a square nature (retaining the name) and in 1870 Barrow Hill was built to this design. Retained in use following the end of steam, Barrow Hill remained in use until 1991. Saved from demolition at the 11th hour, the Grade 2 listed building is unique in Great Britain as the last surviving working roundhouse.

The roundhouse can accommodate up to 24 main line locomotives, and includes maintenance pits and ancillary services

Location/headquarters: Barrow Hill Roundhouse Engine Shed, Campbell Drive, Barrow Hill, Nr Staveley, Chesterfield, Derbyshire S43 2PR.

Situated near junctions 29/30 on M1

OS reference: SK 4175

Project manager: Mervyn Allcock

Contact address: Barrow Hill Engine Shed Society, 266 Williamthorpe Road, North Wingfield, Chesterfield, Derbyshire S42 5NS

Locomotives

Name	No	Origin	Class	Type	Built
Kolhapur	5593	LMS	'Jubilee'	4-6-0	1934
—	2700	LMS	5P4F	2-6-0	1934
—	27505	NLR	2F	0-6-0T	1880
—	03066	BR	03	0-6-0DM	1959
—	03094	BR	03	0-6-0DM	1960
—	07001	BR	07	0-6-0DE	1962
—	07013	BR	07	0-6-0DE	1962
—	08507	BR	08	0-6-0DE	1958
—	08668	BR	08	0-6-0DE	1960
—	08818	BR	08	0-6-0DE	1960
—	12082	BR	11	0-6-0DE	1950
—	20056	BR	20	Bo-Bo	1961
—	20094	BR	20	Bo-Bo	1961
—	20096	BR	20	Bo-Bo	1961
—	20135	BR	20	Bo-Bo	1966
—	25067	BR	25	Bo-Bo	1963
—	D5300	BR	26	Bo-Bo	1958
—	26011	BR	26	Bo-Bo	1959
—	37111	BR	37	Co-Co	1963
Sherwood Forester	45060	BR	45	1Co-Co1	1961
—	45015*	BR	45	1Co-Co1	1961
—	45105	BR	45	1Co-Co1	1961
—	E3003	BR	81	Bo-Bo	1960
—	82008	BR	82	Bo-Bo	1961
—	83012	BR	83	Bo-Bo	1961
—	85101*	BR	85	Bo-Bo	1961

*expected to arrive early 2000

Industrial locomotives

Name	No	Builder	Type	Built
Henry	—	H/Leslie (2491)	0-4-0ST	1901
Marstons	—	— (2553)	0-4-0	—

England

Telephone: (01246) 472450
Fax: (01246) 472450
Car park: Adjacent to site
Access by public transport: Train to Chesterfield, Stagecoach bus Nos 80/90/56
On site facilities: Refreshments, souvenir shop and museum. Toilets
Refreshment facilities: Drinks and light refreshments
Public opening: Open most weekends — 4 major open days a year
Special events: Easter, summer, autumn and Christmas open days. Other dates to be confirmed
Membership details: MArtyn Brailsford, 18 Queen Street, Brimington, Chersterfield, Derbyshire S43 1HT
Socety journal: *The Roundhouse* — three times a year

Name	No	Builder	Type	Built
—	—	Drewry (2589)	0-4-0	—
—	—	RR/Sentinel (10254)	0-4-0DE	1967
—	D3	T/Hill	0-4-0DH	1974
—	—	E/Electric (1205)	0-4-0DE	—

Stock
1 ex-BR Mk 1 BSK coach, 1 ex-BR Mk 2 coach, 1 ex-MR brake van, 3 Tunny wagons, 3 Chub wagons, 2 ex-BR bogie vans, 1 dynamometer car, 1 ex-BR Lowmac, 1 ex-LMS brake van, 1 ex-BR brake van, 1 ex-SR brake van, 1 ex-GWR Toad brake van

Owners
2700 on loan from the National Railway Museum
27505 on loan from the Bluebell Railway
20094, 20135 and 37111 the Class 20 Work Group
45060 and 45105 the Pioneer Diesel Group
E3003, 82008 and 83012 the AC Loco Group
45015 the 3rd 45/0 Group
07001, 07013, 12082, Sentinel (10254) Harry Needle Industrial Locomotives

---

Timetable Service	**The Battlefield Steam Railway**	Leicestershire

Members: HRA, TT
A quiet country railway operated by the Shackerstone Railway Society Ltd.
Headquarters: Shackerstone station (3 miles north of Market Bosworth in Leicestershire)
Address: Shackerstone Station, Shackerstone, Nuneaton CV13 6NW
Telephone: Timetable enquiries: (01827) 880754, other enquiries (0116) 291 7460
Operating Manager: D. Weightman
Main station: Shackerstone
Other public station: Shenton
OS reference: SK 379066
Car park: Shackerstone (free), Shenton (council car park)
Access by public transport: No services to either Shackerstone or Shenton
Refreshment facilities: Tea rooms on Shackerstone station. Buffet/bar on most trains
Souvenir shop: Shackerstone
Museum: Shackerstone
Depot: Shackerstone
Length of line: 4.5 miles (8km)
Passenger trains: Shackerstone-

Locomotives and multiple-units

Name	No	Origin	Class	Type	Built
—	20048	BR	20	BO-BO	1959
—	D5518	BR	31	A1A-A1A	1958
—	31130	BR	31	A1A-A1A	1959
—	11215	BR	04	0-6-0DM	1956
—	D3236	BR	08	0-6-0DE	1956
—	D3429	BR	08	0-6-0DE	1958
—	51131	BR	116	DMBS	1958
—	51321	BRCW	116	DMS	1959
—	54289	P/Steel	121	DTS	1960
—	55005	GRCW	122	DMBS	1958
—	59496	P/Steel	117	TCL	1959
—	59522	P/Steel	117	TSL	1959
—	59791†	P/Steel	107	TSL	1960

†converted to locomotive-hauled vehicle
Ex-BR locomotives are expected to pay a visit during 1998

Industrial locomotives

Name	No	Builder	Type	Built
Linda	—	Bagnall (2648)	0-4-0ST	1941
Victor	—	Bagnall(2996)	0-6-0ST	1950
Waleswood	—	H/Clarke (750)	0-4-0ST	1906
—	11	Hunslet (1493)	0-4-0ST	1925
Dunlop No 7	—	Peckett (2130)	0-4-0ST	1951
—	3	RSH (7537)	0-6-0T	1949
Lamport No 3	—	Bagnall (2670)	0-6-0ST	1942
William	—	Sentinel (9656)	4wVBT	1956
—	—	R/Hornsby (235513)	4wDM	1945
—	—	R/Hornsby (263001)	4wDM	1949
—	—	R/Hornsby (347747)	0-6-0DM	1957

Market Bosworth-Shenton
Period of public operation: Steam service: weekends and Bank Holiday Mondays March-October. Midweek diesel railcar: Wednesdays in July and August
Special events: Not advised, please contact oe see leaflets and press for further details
Special notes: Family tickets available. 'Tudor Rose' dining train. Must book for dining trains. Scenic countryside views including Ashby Canal. Shenton station is adjacent to Bosworth Battlefield (1485) Country Park. 20 minute walk along 'Battlefield Trail' to visitor centre, return by later train

Name	No	Builder	Type	Built
—	—	R/Hornsby (393304)	4wDM	1956
—	—	R/Hornsby (423657)	0-4-0DE	1958
—	—	R/Hornsby (420142)	0-4-0DE	1958
—	—	S/Crossley (7697)	0-6-0DM	1953
—	RS/140 Planet (3892)		4wDM	1958

Stock
7 ex-BR Mk 1 coaches (including Griddle Car); 5 passenger-rated vans; 2 rail-mounted steam cranes; 2 rail-mounted diesel cranes; 35 wagons (inc 3 goods brake vans SR, MR, BR); 2 LNER ballast brakes

Operating company/ preservation society contact: The Secretary, Shackerstone Railway Society, Shackerstone Station, Shackerstone, Nuneaton CV13 6NW

Membership journal: *Shackerstone News* — 3/4 times/year
Marketing name: The Battlefield Line

Museum — Beamish — County Durham

The railway station, signalbox and goods shed have been completely re-created along with the other exhibits to show a way of life long past. There are some very old locomotives in the collection.
Museum Director: Peter Lewis
Location: The North of England Open Air Museum, Beamish, County Durham DH9 0RG.
OS reference: NZ 214548
Telephone: Stanley (01207) 231811
Fax: (01207) 290933
Car park: At museum
Access by public transport: Bus service from Eldon Square, Newcastle upon Tyne; bus service Nos 775 and 778 from Sunderland via Chester-le-Street; bus service 720 from Milburngate, Durham City
On site facilities: This 200-acre open air museum vividly recreates life in the North of England in the early 1800s and 1900s. The Town has dentist's surgery, solicitor's office, Co-op shops, garage, sweet shop and sweet factory. The Colliery Village has pit cottages, village school and chapel, 'drift' mine and pithead. Home Farm with farm house, livestock and exhibitions. Railway station complete with goods yard and signalbox, locomotives and rolling stock on static display. Pockerley Manor and Horse Yard illustrates the lifestyle of a yeoman farming family in the early 1800s.

Early Railways — opened in 1999, near Pockerley Manor, a large stone engine shed with displays illustrating the development of railways in the early 1800s. Visitors will also be able to take a short ride in recreated carriages of the period pulled by the replica *Locomotion*
Public opening: Summer (April-October) daily 10.00-17.00, last admission 15.00. Extended summer

Locomotives

Name	No	Origin	Class	Type	Built
—††	876	NER	C	0-6-0	1889
Locomotion	1*	—		0-4-0	1975

*Replica

Industrial locomotives

Name	No	Builder	Type	Built
Twizell†	3	Stephenson (2730)	0-6-0T	1891
—††	14	H/Leslie (3056)	0-4-0ST	1914
South Durham Malleable††	No 5	Grange Ironworks	0-4-0ST	c1880
Coffee Pot†††	—	Head Wrightson	0-4-0VB	1871
—*	E1	Black, Hawthorn (897)	2-4-0CT	1883
Hetton Loco	—	G. Stephenson	0-4-0	1822
Wellington	—	B/Hawthorn (266)	0-4-0ST	1873
Jacob†††	680	McEwan Pratt	0-4-0P	1916
—**	18	Lewin (693)	0-4-0WT	1877

†on long term loan to Tanfield
*in store
††on static display
** undergoing major rebuild
†††under repair

Locomotive notes: No 3 in working order. R/Hornsby not usually on display. Others usually on display

Owner
Hetton Loco on loan from National Railway Museum
Locomotion the Locomotion Trust

Note
Not all exhibits on display

England

opening (15 July-3 September) – daily 10.00-18.00, last admission 16.00. Winter (November-March) 10.00-16.00, last admission 15.00, closed Mondays and Fridays. Please check for Christmas opening times

NB: A winter visit to Beamish is centred on the Town and Tramway other areas of the museum are closed and admission charges are, consequently, reduced

Special events: A full programme of events is planned for 2000, including:
The History of Meccano — 21-24 April; Dog Agility Festival — 6/7 May; Morgan Car Meet — 11 June; School Sports Day — 11 June; The History of Meccano — 24/25 June; World Championship Quoits — 8/9 July; Beamish Classic Car Day — 24 September

Length of line: Rebuilt NER station, colliery sidings
Facilities for disabled: Not ideal for wheelchairs. One carriage at 1825 Railway suitable foe wheelchairs. Advanced notice for parties to Bookings Officer preferred

---

Bicton Woodland Railway

Steam Centre / Devon

A passenger-carrying line of 18in gauge with stock mainly from the Woolwich Arsenal Railway and of World War 1 vintage
Location: Bicton Park, near Budleigh Salterton
OS reference: SY 074862
Operating society/organisation: Bicton Woodland Railway, Bicton Gardens, East Budleigh, Budleigh Salterton, Devon
Telephone: Colaton Raleigh (01395) 568465
Car park: On site
Access by public transport: Buses pass half-hourly from Exeter, Exmouth, Sidmouth in season
On site facilities: Indoor and

Locomotives

Name	No	Builder	Type	Built
Woolwich	1	Avonside (1748)	0-4-0T	1916
Bicton	2	R/Hornsby (213839)	4wDM	1942
Carnegie	3	Hunslet (4524)	0-4-4-0DM	1954
Clinton	4	H/Hunslet (2290)	0-4-0	1941
Budleigh*	—	R/Hornsby (235624)	4wDM	1945

*static exhibit

Stock
4 open bogie coaches; 5 closed bogie coaches

outdoor play areas, glass houses, palm house, Grade 1 gardens, museum and restaurant
Length of line: 3,250yd
Public opening: Open all year

Facilities for disabled: Toilets, wheelchairs available. Special carriage for wheelchairs

---

Bideford Railway Museum

Museum / Devon

Based at the former LSWR/SR station on the now closed Barnstaple-Torrington line, the site is undergoing restoration. The former signalbox has been rebuilt, double track laid throughout and signals erected. A growing collection of rolling stock is being gathered. Funds are being raised for an ex-BR shunter to give brake van rides, expected to commence summer 2000
Headquarters: Bideford Station, Railway Terrace, East-the-Water, Bideford, Devon EX39 4BB
OS reference: SS 456263
Operating society: Bideford & Instow Railway Group
Access by public transport: By

Rolling stock
BR Mk 1 TSO No 4489, ex-SR Parcels Van No S2142, ex-BR brake van, ex-LMS closed box van, platelayer's trolley
2 18in gauge skip (ex-Peters Marland Clay Works)

train — Barnstaple 9 miles. Station is within walking distance from the town of Bideford and its bus stops
On site facilities: Museum, souvenir shop, book shop, refreshments, visitor centre, rolling stock under restoration
Period of public opening: Easter to end October — Sundays, Tuesdays, Thursdays and Bank Holidays 14.00-17.00; November to Easter - Sundays & bank holidays only
Special events: Annual open day — to be confirmed; Santa's Grotto — 16, 23 December
Membership details: Mr R Dark, 11 Swanswood Garden, Westward Ho!, Bideford, Devon EX39 1HP
Membership journal: *Atlantic Coast Express* (quarterly)

Member: HRA
Location: 670 Warwick Road (A41), Tyseley, Birmingham B11 2HL
OS reference: SP 105841
Operating organisation: Tyseley Locomotive Works Ltd
Supporting society: Friends of Birmingham Railway Museum
Telephone: (0121) 707 4696
Fax: (0121) 764 4645
Car park: Site
Access by public transport: Travel West Midlands route No 37 from city centre. Main line rail service to Tyseley station (Central Trains and Chiltern Railways)
On site facilities: The Museum is on the site of a former GWR/BR steam shed and has been equipped with specialised railway engineering machinery. Souvenir shop, restaurant, passenger demonstration line and station, viewing gallery, schools' education service
Refreshment facilities: Available in 'Chuffs' restaurant
Length of line: Third of a mile
Public opening: Static display daily 10.00-17.00 except Christmas and New Year. Engines in steam days almost every weekend on driving courses. Brake van rides on first Sunday of month between April-October. Visitor facilities available weekends only
Special events: Galas and Santa trains (phone for details)
Special notes: Tyseley is a centre for 'Steam on the Main Line' railtours over former BR lines to Stratford-upon-Avon and Didcot (via Oxford). Full education service providing guided tours, worksheets and live presentation. The Museum is noted for its driving experience courses where members of the public can actually drive and fire a steam locomotive. These courses mainly feature *Clun Castle* and range from four hours to all day. Please contact for prices
Membership details: Membership is available to the public, providing free entry to site events, four copies of *Steam in Trust* magazine
Note: All attractions and facilities are advertised subject to availability

Locomotives

Name	No	Origin	Class	Type	Built
Rood Ashton Hall	4965	GWR	'Hall'	4-6-0	1931
Earl of Mount Edgcumbe	5043	GWR	'Castle	4-6-0	1936
Defiant	5080	GWR	'Castle'	4-6-0	1939
Clun Castle	7029	GWR	'Castle'	4-6-0	1950
—	5553	GWR	4575	2-6-2T	1928
—	7752	GWR	5700	0-6-0PT	1930
—	7760	GWR	5700	0-6-0PT	1930
—	9600	GWR	5700	0-6-0PT	1945
Kolhapur	5593	LMS	'Jubilee'	4-6-0	1934
Galatea	5699	LMS	'Jubilee'	4-6-0	1936
Canadian Pacific	35005	SR	MN	4-6-2	1941
—	13029	BR	08	0-6-0DE	1953
—	08631	BR	08	0-6-0DE	1959
—	31105	BR	31	A1A-A1A	1959
—	31106	BR	31	A1A-A1A	1959
—	31128	BR	31	A1A-A1A	1959
—	31186	BR	31	A1A-A1A	1960
—	31289	BR	31	A1A-A1A	1961
—	31301	BR	31	A1A-A1A	1962
—	31415	BR	31	A1A-A1A	1961
—	31452*	BR	31	A1A-A1A	1961
—	31459	BR	31	A1A-A1A	1961
—	31462	BR	31	A1A-A1A	1962
—	31468*	BR	31	A1A-A1A	1962
—	31524	BR	31	A1A-A1A	1959
—	31526	BR	31	A1A-A1A	1960
—	31549*	BR	31	A1A-A1A	1962
Eastleigh	33026	BR	33	Co-Co	1961
—	33103	BR	33	Co-Co	1960
—	40118	BR	40	1Co-Co1	1961
—	47488	BR	47	Co-Co	1964
Waverley	47701	BR	47	Co-Co	1966
—	47703	BR	47	Co-Co	1967
—	47709	BR	47	Co-Co	1966
—	47710	BR	47	Co-Co	1966
—	47712	BR	47	Co-Co	1966
—	55034	BR	121	DMBS	1958

*31452 formerly 31552, 31468 formerly 31568, 31549 to be renumbered 31449

Note: Not all locomotives are on site, and some are undergoing restoration. Contract restoration work includes Nos (GWR) 4936 *Kinlet Hall*; (LMS) 6201 *Princess Elizabeth*
Locomotives away on loan include 7752 and 5593 (Barrow Hill), 7760 (Avon Valley)

Industrial locomotives

Name	No	Builder	Type	Built
Cadbury No 1	—	Avonside (1977)	0-4-0T	1925
—	1	Peckett (2004)	0-4-0ST	1942
—	—	Baguley (800)	0-4-0PE	1920
Henry	—	H/Leslie (2491)	0-4-0ST	1901

Stock

Various passenger, goods and departmental vehicles, including buffet car, engineer's saloon and steam crane

16

| Timetable Service | # Blackpool & Fleetwood Tramway | Lancashire |

The Blackpool & Fleetwood Tramway is the sole surviving traditional street tramway system in the United Kingdom and attracts visitors from all over the country. During the autumn the streets are illuminated and several specially decorated trams are used.

Operating organisation: Blackpool Transport Services Ltd, Rigby Road, Blackpool, Lancashire FY1 5DD
Telephone: (01253) 473001
Managing Director: Anthony Depledge
Operations Director: David Eaves

Marketing Manager: Liz Eshohf
Length of line: 11.5 miles, standard gauge
Period of public operation: Daily throughout the year
Number of trams: 78 double and single-deck trams.

| Timetable Service | # Bluebell Railway | East Sussex |

Member: HRA, TT
This famous steam railway was the first standard gauge passenger line to be taken over by enthusiasts. It derives its name from the bluebells which proliferate in the woodlands adjoining the line. A strong Victorian atmosphere pervades this branch line which has a large collection of Southern and pre-Grouping locomotives and coaches.
Contact: Mr John Potter
Headquarters: Bluebell Railway Preservation Society, Sheffield Park Station, Uckfield, East Sussex TN22 3QL
Telephone: Newick (01825) 722370 for travel information (24hr talking timetable); (01825) 723777 for general enquiries etc during office hours. (01825) 722008 – Golden Arrow Pullman (reservations and Catering Department)
Main station: Sheffield Park
Other public stations: Horsted Keynes and Kingscote
Car parks: Sheffield Park, Horsted Keynes
OS reference: Sheffield Park TQ 403238, Horsted Keynes TQ 372293
Access by public transport: Bus service 473 between main line East Grinstead and Kingscote (2 miles) connects with all Bluebell trains
Refreshment facilities: Sheffield Park restaurant/bar/self-service;

Locomotives

Name	No	Origin	Class	Type	Built
Stepney	55	LBSCR	A1X	0-6-0T	1875
Fenchurch	72	LBSCR	A1X	0-6-0T	1872
Birch Grove	473	LBSCR	E4	0-6-2T	1898
—	27	SECR	P	0-6-0T	1910
—	65	SECR	O1	0-6-0	1896
—	263	SECR	H	0-4-4T	1905
—	323	SECR	P	0-6-0T	1910
—	592	SECR	C	0-6-0	1902
—	1178	SECR	P	0-6-0T	1910
—	96	LSWR	B4	0-4-0T	1893
—	120	LSWR	T9	4-4-0	1898
—	488	LSWR	0415	4-4-2T	1885
—	58850**	NLR	2F	0-6-0T	1880
Earl of Berkeley	3217	GWR	9000	4-4-0	1938
—	541	SR	Q	0-6-0	1939
—	830*	SR	S15	4-6-0	1927
—	847	SR	S15	4-6-0	1937
Stowe	928	SR	V	4-4-0	1934
—	1618	SR	U	2-6-0	1928
—	1638	SR	U	2-6-0	1931
—	30064	SR	USA	0-6-0T	1943
—	C1	SR	Q1	0-6-0	1942
Blackmore Vale	21C123	SR	WC	4-6-2	1946
Sir Archibald Sinclair	34059	SR	BB	4-6-2	1947
Port Line	35027††	SR	MN	4-6-2	1948
Camelot	73082	BR	5MT	4-6-0	1955
—	75027	BR	4MT	4-6-0	1954
—	78059†	BR	2MT	2-6-0	1956
—	80064	BR	4MT	2-6-4T	1953
—	80100	BR	4MT	2-6-4T	1954
—	80151	BR	4MT	2-6-4T	1957
—	92240	BR	9F	2-10-0	1958

*purchased without tender, in store
†purchased without tender, for conversion to tank engine, work in hand
**on loan to Barrow Hill Roundhouse Railway Centre
††expected to leave by Easter 2000

England

Horsted Keynes – Victorian bar/buffet. The line's 'Golden Arrow' Pullman operates a dinner service most Saturday evenings and Pullman luncheon service most Sundays.

Telephone (01825) 722008 during normal office hours for details.
Souvenir shops: Sheffield Park, Horsted Keynes
Museum: Sheffield Park
Depots: Sheffield Park (locomotives), Horsted Keynes (stock)
Length of line: 9 miles
Passenger trains: Sheffield Park-Horsted Keynes-Kingscote
Period of public operation: Weekends all year round; daily May-September; additional trains run in school half-term weeks and in the lead-up to Christmas. Museum, locomotive sheds, buffet and shop at Sheffield Park open daily except Christmas Day
Special events: Victorian Evenings — 17 May, 7 June (evenings); Yetties Concert — 10 June (evening); Friends of Thomas the Tank Weekend — 17/18, 24/25 June; Toy & Collector's Fair — 22/23 July; Steam Fair — 29/30 July; 40th Anniversary Steam Gala — 5/6 August; 1930s Evening — 20 September (evening); Starlight Special — 21 October (evening);

Industrial locomotives

Name	No	Builder	Type	Built
*Blue Circle	—	A/Porter (9449)	2-2-0TG	1926
Baxter	3	F/Jennings (158)	0-4-0T	1877
†Stamford	24	Avonside (1972)	0-6-0ST	1927
Sharpthorn	4	M/Wardle (641)	0-6-0ST	1877

*on long-term loan to the Buckinghamshire Railway Centre
†on long-term loan to the Rutland Railway Museum

Stock
Substantial collection of pre-Nationalisation coaches including SECR, LSWR, Bulleid, Maunsell and Chesham vehicles. Also freight stock and engineers' vehicles plus 45ton steam crane

Owners
592 the Wainwright C Class Preservation Society
541, 830, 847 and 1618 the Maunsell Locomotive Society Ltd
96 and 21C123 the Bulleid Society Ltd
263 the H Class Trust
73082 the Camelot Locomotive Society
C1, T9 on loan from the National Railway Museum
928 on loan from Montagu Ventures Ltd
35027, 1178 Southern Locomotives Ltd
80064 the 80064 Group
80151 the 80151 Group

Giants of Steam — 22 October; LBSCR Weekend — 18/19 November; Santa Specials 2/3, 9/10, 16/17, 21-24 December. Further details of events available on request
Facilities for disabled: All station facilities are on the level and ramps available for placing wheelchair visitors into trains. Special toilets in buffet at Sheffield Park and at Kingscote. New 'multi-purpose vehicle' for use by groups, please telephone to confirm availability
Membership details: Membership Secretary, c/o above address
Membership journal: Bluebell News — quarterly

Bodmin & Wenford Railway

Timetable Service — Cornwall

Member: HRA
The Bodmin & Wenford Railway typifies the bygone branch railways of Cornwall. The terminus, close to Bodmin town centre, has an interesting collection of small standard gauge locomotives and rolling stock, and the operating line winds down to a junction with main line rail services at Bodmin Parkway. Passengers can alight at the intermediate Colesloggett Halt from where a footpath (not suitable for wheelchairs or the infirm) leads to Cardinham Woods (FC) with waymarked trails, picnic areas, a café and cycle hire facilities. From the train there are scenic views across the beautiful valley of the River Fowey. A second line circles

Locomotives and multiple-units

Name	No	Origin	Class	Type	Built
—	3802	GWR	2884	2-8-0	1938
—	5552	GWR	4575	2-6-2T	1928
Wadebridge	34007	SR	WC	4-6-2	1945
Triumph	50042	BR	50	Co-Co	1968
River Fowey	20166	BR	20	Bo-Bo	1966
—	20197	BR	20	Bo-Bo	1967
—	33110	BR	33	Bo-Bo	1960
—	D3452	BR	10	0-6-0DE	1957
—	D3559	BR	08	0-6-0DE	1958
—	51947	BR	108	DMBS	1960
—	52054	BR	108	DMCL	1960
—	53980	BR	108	DMBS	1960

Industrial locomotives

Name	No	Builder	Type	Built
—	—	Bagnall (2766)	0-6-0ST	1944
—	19	Bagnall (2962)	0-4-0ST	1950
Alfred	—	Bagnall (3058)	0-4-0ST	1953

England

Bodmin to Boscarne Junction where it meets the Camel Trail, a recreational path for cyclists and walkers. A visit can be made to the nearby Camel Valley Vineyard (July and August only). Most trains are steam-hauled except Saturday
Location: Bodmin General station, on B3268
General Manager: Mr R. Webster
Operating society/organisation: Bodmin & Wenford Railway, Bodmin General Station, Bodmin, Cornwall PL31 1AQ
Telephone: All enquiries (01208) 73666
Website: e-mail: http://members.aol.com/bodwenf
Web site: http://www.zyworld.com.bodwenfn ews
Car park: Bodmin General only, no parking permitted at Bodmin Parkway
Access by public transport: Interchange at Bodmin Parkway arrivals by main line train only, through tickets available from most stations. Local bus services to Bodmin
Refreshment facilities: Light refreshments at Bodmin General and on most trains
On site facilities: Railway shop, limited display of historic artefacts, toilets

Name	No	Builder	Type	Built
—	—	Bagnall (3121)	0-4-0F	1957
Peter	—	Fowler (22928)	0-4-0DM	1940
Progress	—	Fowler (4000001)	0-4-0DM	1945
Swiftsure	—	Hunslet (2857)	0-6-0ST	1943
Lec	—	R/Hornsby (443642)	4wDM	1960
—	—	RSH (7597)	0-6-0ST	1949
Ugly	62	RSH (7673)	0-6-0ST	1950

Stock
9 BR Mk 1 coaches; 3 BR Mk 2 coaches; 1 Mk 3 Sleeper, 6-wheel 10-ton steam crane, 4 GWR coaches; 2 GWR Siphon G; Various freight wagons

Owners
34007 the Wadebridge 34007 Ltd
3802 GW 3802 Ltd
7597 Railway Vehicle Preservations Ltd

Length of lines: 3.5 miles General-Parkway; 3 miles General-Boscarne
Passenger trains: 25/26, 29 March; 2, 5, 9, 12, 16-30 April; 1-3, 7, 9/10, 14, 16/17, 21, 23/24, 27-31 May; daily June to end September; 1, 3/4, 7/8, 10/11, 15, 17/18, 22-29 October; 2/3, 9/10, 16/17, 23/24, 26/27, 31 December; 1 January 2001
Special events: Diesel Weekend — 25/26 March; Everything Goes Easter Weekend — 23/24 April; Steam/Diesel Weekend — 27-29 May; Steam Gala — 2/3 September; Diesel Gala — 7/8 October
Driving experience courses:

Courses held in spring and autumn. Please apply for details
Facilities for disabled: Yes
Membership details: Mr J. Tizzard, Bodmin Railway Preservation Society, c/o above address
Special notes: Reduced fares for family groups and for passengers arriving at Bodmin Parkway in possession of a valid main line ticket
Membership journal: *Bodmin & Wenford News* — 3 issues/year

Bowes Railway

Steam Centre   County Durham

Members: HRA
The railway includes the only preserved rope-hauled standard gauge inclines, whose operation requires considerable skill and dexterity. You should not miss the opportunity of inspecting the inclines and winding house and haulage engine when you can
Chairman: Phillip Dawe
Location: Bowes Railway, Springwell Village, near Gateshead, (on B1288)
OS reference: NZ 285589
Operating society/organisation: Bowes Railway Co Ltd
Telephone: Tyneside (0191) 416 1847
Car park: Springwell
Access by public transport: Northern Buses services Nos 184

Industrial locomotives

Name	No	Builder	Type	Built
WST	—	Barclay (2361)	0-4-0ST	1954
—	22	Barclay (2274)	0-4-0ST	1949
—	20/110/709	Barclay (613)	0-6-0DH	1977
—	—	Hunslet (6263)	0-4-0DH	1964
-	503	Hunslet (6614)	0-6-0DH	1965
Norwood	77	RSH (7412)	0-6-0ST	1948
—	101	Planet (3922)	4wDM	1959
—	2207/456†	E/Electric (2476)	4wBE	1958
Victoria	2216/286†	H/Clarke (DM842)	0-6-0DMF	1954
BO3	20/122/514*	Hunslet (8515)	Bo-BoDMF	1981
—	—*	EIMCO (LD2163)	Rockershovel	1959
—	DB965071	Wickham (7586)	2w-2PMR	1957

†2ft gauge
*2ft 6in gauge
Owners
WST on loan from British Gypsum Ltd
Barclay 0-6-0DH on loan from Mr P. Dawe
DB965071 on loan from Mr M. Smith & Mr N. Whaler

Washington/Birtley, 187/188
Gateshead Metro/Sunderland, 189
Washington (Brady Sq)-Gateshead
638 Ryton/Sunderland
On site facilities: Exhibition of
Railway's history, wagon
exhibition, workshop displays. On
operating days — shop,
refreshments and guided tours. One
of the last operational Strowger
mechanical telephone exchanges
still in daily use. Steam-hauled
brake van rides. Rope haulage
demonstration trains. Tarmac car
park available for helicopter
visitors (prior permission required,
phone site)
Public opening: Bank Holidays,
also second and fourth Sunday in
each month, Easter-September.
Santa specials week prior to
Christmas. Disabled Children's
Day — mid July. Guided tours
Saturdays, out of season can be
accommodated with prior notice
(not trains)
Length of line: 1.25 miles total
length; 1.25 miles of rope haulage;
three-quarter-mile used for
passenger trains (extension in hand)
Special notes: Preserved section of

Stock
20 Ordinary 10-ton wooden hopper wagons (Springwell built); 16 other
wooden hopper wagons (of various pedigrees); 3 steel 14-ton hopper, 2 steel
16-ton hopper wagons; 7 wagons; 7 steel 21-ton hopper wagons; 1 reel
bogie (for rope replacement); 1 drift bogie (for shunting by rope); 1 loco
coal wagon; 7 material wagons; 2 tool vans; 4 brake vans; 4 flat wagons; 1
17-ton wooden hopper (ex-NER); 1 18-ton wooden hopper (ex-Ashington);
1 21-ton wooden hopper (ex-Seaham); 2 steel ballast Hopper Wagons; 1
tank wagon; 1 wooden side door coal wagon; Londonderry Chaldron
wagons, 1 Wickham trailer, 2ft gauge 4-wheel manrider, 2ft 6in gauge R. B.
Bolton-type bogie manrider; Easington Colliery weights wagon

Stationary haulage
Met-Vick/Wild, 300bhp electric (Blackham's Hill) 1950
BTH/Robey, 500bhp electric (Black Fell) 1950
Clarke Chapman, 22hp electric (Springwell Yard)
14ft Diam, Gravity Dilly Wheel (Springwell)

the Pontop & Jarrow Railway;
designed G. Stephenson; opened
1826; largest collection of colliery
wagons in country, the only
preserved standard gauge rope-
hauled incline railway in the world;
Railway's own historic workshops
preserved, with examples of all of
the Railway's wagon types
Facilities for disabled: Toilet and
refreshment room
Membership details: Dr Peter

Norman, Railway Secretary, c/o
above address
Membership journal: *The Incline*
— quarterly
Disclaimer: The Bowes Railway
Co Ltd wish to point out that all
advertised facilities are subject to
alteration without prior notice. The
company can therefore not be held
responsible for any loss or expense
incurred

Steam Centre — Bredgar & Wormshill Light Railway — Kent

Member: HRA
A short, 2ft gauge, private railway
constructed and operated to a very
high standard
Location/headquarters: The
Bredgar & Wormshill Light
Railway, The Warren, Bredgar, Nr
Sittingbourne, Kent ME9 8AT
Contact: Bill Best, David Best
Telephone: (01622) 884254
Access by public transport: Main
line trains to Sittingbourne
(5 miles) and Hollingbourne
(3.5 miles)
OS reference: TQ868579
Car park: On site (300 places)
On site facilities: Souvenir shop,
museum, light refreshments, toilets,
picnic sites, traction engines, 7.25in
and 15in gauge model locomotives,
beam engine. Largest UK
collection of Bean motor cars.
Steam-hauled train rides from
Warren Wood to Stony Shaw
(1km).

Industrial locomotives
(2ft gauge)

Name	No	Builder	Type	Built
Bronhilde	1	Schwartzkopf (9124)	0-4-0WT	1927
Katie	2	Arn Jung (3872)	0-6-0WT	1931
Harrogate	3	Peckett (2050)	0-6-0ST	1944
Armistice	4	Bagnall (2088)	0-4-0ST	1919
Bredgar	5	Baguley/Drewry (3775)	0-4-0DH	1983
Eigiau	6	O&K (5668)	0-4-0WT	1912
Victory	7	Decauville (246)	0-4-2ST	1897
—	8	O&K (12722)	0-4-0WT	1936
No 1	—	Hunslet (1429)	0-4-0ST	1922

(2ft 6in gauge)

Name	No	Builder	Type	Built
—	6	La Meuse (3355)	0-4-0T	1929
—	105	Henschell (29582)	0-6-0WT	1956

Rolling stock
3 bogie coaches, 1 four-wheel coach, 6 four-wheel wagons, 1 four-wheel
tank wagon, 1 four-wheel works truck, 1 four-wheel guards van

Public opening: First Sunday in
each month May to September
(11.00-17.00)
Special events: Steam locomotive

driving courses/Santa Specials
Note: A private site with no 'out of
hours' access, but groups by
arrangement

Bressingham Steam Museum

Member: TT

Five miles of various gauges of railway running through extensive gardens and a collection of well-maintained and impressive main line locomotives. All the fun of the fair, with something for everyone; a great day out for all the family

Location: Two miles west of Diss on the A1066

OS reference: TM 080806

Operating society/organisation: Bressingham Steam Preservation Co Ltd, Bressingham Hall, Diss, Norfolk IP22 2AB

Telephone: Bressingham (01379) 687386. 24hr hotline (01379) 687382

Car park: Steam Centre (free)

Access by public transport: Diss main line station (3 miles)

On site facilities: 10.25/15/24in and standard gauge lines, totalling nearly 5 miles. Museum, steam roundabout, fire museum, souvenir shop and restaurant, extensive gardens and plant centre

Public opening: Open daily from April to October. Full steam days every Sunday and Thursday, August, and Bank Holiday Mondays, 10.30-17.30 on all open days. Christmas events in December (dates to be confirmed). Education services for schools are available with pre-booking in March-October period

Special events: Please contact for details

Facilities for disabled: Toilets, wheelchairs available. Able to take wheelchairs on Nursery Line

Locomotives

Name	No	Origin	Class	Type	Built
Martello	662	LBSCR	A1X	0-6-0T	1875
Thundersley	80	LTSR	3P	4-4-2T	1909
Granville	102	LSWR	B4	0-4-0T	1893
—	490	GER	E4	2-4-0	1894
Henry Oakley	990	GNR	C2	4-4-2	1898
Royal Scot	6100	LMS	7P	4-6-0	1927
Oliver Cromwell	70013	BR	7MT	4-6-2	1951
Peer Gynt	5865	NSB	52	2-10-0	1944
King Haakon VII	377	NSB	21c	2-6-0	1919

Industrial locomotives

Name	No	Builder	Type	Built
Beckton	1	Neilson (4444)	0-4-0ST	1892
Beckton	25	Neilson (5087)	0-4-0ST	1896
William Francis	6841	B/Peacock (6841)	0-4-0+0-4-0T	1937
Millfield	—	RSH (7070)	0-4-0CT	1942
Bluebottle	—	Barclay (1472)	0-4-0F	1916

2ft gauge locomotives

Name	No	Builder	Type	Built
Gwynedd	—	Hunslet (316)	0-4-0ST	1883
George Sholto	—	Hunslet (994)	0-4-0ST	1909
Bronllwyd	—	H/Clarke (1643)	0-6-0WT	1930
Toby	—	M/Rail (22120)	4wDM	1964

15in gauge locomotives

Name	No	Builder	Type	Built
Rosenkavalier	—	Krupp (1662)	4-6-2	1937
Mannertreu	—	Krupp (1663)	4-6-2	1937
Flying Scotsman	4472	W. Stewart (4472)	4-6-2	1976
Works Loco	—	Diss	0-4-0DM	1992

10.25in gauge locomotives

Name	No	Builder	Type	Built
Alan Bloom	1	BSM	0-4-0ST	1995

Owners

80, 490, 990, 70013 on loan from the National Railway Museum

Railway

Special notes: Reduced rates for coach parties. Prices on application

Bristol Industrial Museum

The Museum houses machinery and vehicles associated with Bristol's industrial past, from horse-drawn vehicles to aircraft

Location: Princes Wharf, Bristol

OS reference: ST 585722

Operating society/organisation: Bristol Industrial Museum, Princes

Industrial locomotives

Name	No	Builder	Type	Built
Portbury	—	Avonside (1764)	0-6-0ST	1917
Henbury	—	Peckett (1940)	0-6-0ST	1937
—	3	F/Walker (242)	0-6-0ST	1874
—	—	R/Hornsby (418792)	0-4-0DM	1958

England

Wharf, Bristol BS1 4RN
Telephone: (0117) 925 1470
Fax: (0117) 929 7318
Car parks: Available nearby
Access by public transport: Buses to centre of city, 1km from Temple Meads station
On site facilities: Shop

Length of line: Half-mile, extension of one-mile open on special occasions only
Public opening: November-March — Saturdays & Sundays only 10.00-17.00; April-October — Saturday to Wednesday 10.00-17.00

Facilities for disabled: Reasonable access
Special notes: Operation of railway on advertised weekends only, 12.00-17.30
Membership details: Officer in charge — D. Martin, Bristol Harbour Railway c/o above address

Steam Centre — Buckinghamshire Railway Centre — Bucks

Member: HRA

The Buckinghamshire Railway Centre is situated at Quainton Road on the freight-only Aylesbury-Calvert line, once part of the Metropolitan and Great Central line from London to Verney junction. Quainton Road station is also the old junction for the Brill Tramway closed in 1935

Location: Adjacent to Railtrack goods-only line to Aylesbury. Turn off A41 at Waddesdon 6 miles NW of Aylesbury, Bucks

OS reference: SP 738190

Operating society/organisation: Quainton Railway Society Ltd, The Railway Station, Quainton, near Aylesbury, Bucks HP22 4BY

Telephone: Quainton (01296) 655450

Car park: Quainton Road — Free parking

Access by public transport: Main line Aylesbury station. Local bus Monday-Saturday only

On site facilities: Souvenir bookshop, light refreshments, toilets, steam-hauled train rides. Museum of small relics, secondhand bookshop, miniature railway

Catering facilities: Hot snacks and light refreshments available

Length of line: Two half-mile demonstration lines

Public opening: Sundays and Bank Holidays: April-end October. Wednesdays in July and August. Limited opening (no engines in steam) daily from 1 March-Christmas

Special events: A series of special events is held throughout the year including Thomas the Tank Engine weekends

Facilities for disabled: Access to most of site including special toilets

Locomotives and multiple-units

Name	No	Origin	Class	Type	Built
—	1	Met Rly	E	0-4-4T	1898
—	0314	LSWR	0298	2-4-0WT	1874
Wightwick Hall	6989	GWR	'Hall'	4-6-0	1948
—	7200	GWR	7200	2-8-2T	1934
—	7715	GWR	5700	0-6-0PT	1930
—	9466	GWR	9400	0-6-0PT	1952
—	41298	LMS	2MT	2-6-2T	1951
—	41313	LMS	2MT	2-6-2T	1952
—	46447	LMS	2MT	2-6-0	1950
—	D2298	BR	04	0-6-0DM	1960
—	3405*	SAR	25NC	4-8-4	1958
—	51886	BR	115	DMBS	1960
—	51899	BR	115	DMBS	1960
—	59761	BR	115	TCL	1960

*3ft 6in gauge

Industrial locomotives

Name	No	Builder	Type	Built
Sir Vincent	—	A/Porter (8800)	0-4-0WT	1917
Blue Circle	—	A/Porter (9449)	2-2-0TG	1926
Scott	—	Bagnall (2469)	0-4-0ST	1932
—	—	Baguley (2161)	0-4-0DM	1941
Swanscombe	—	Barclay (699)	0-4-0ST	1891
—	—	GF3 Barclay (1477)	0-4-0F	1916
—	—	Barclay (2243)	0-4-0F	1948
Osram	—	Fowler (20067)	0-4-0DM	1933
—	3	H/Leslie (3717)	0-4-0ST	1928
Sir Thomas	—	H/Clarke (1334)	0-6-0T	1918
—	—	H/Clarke (1742)	0-4-0ST	1946
—	—	Hunslet (2067)	0-4-0DM	1940
Arthur	—	Hunslet (3782)	0-6-0ST	1953
Juno	—	Hunslet (3850)	0-6-0ST	1958
—	65	Hunslet (3889)	0-6-0ST	1964
—	66	Hunslet (3890)	0-6-0ST	1964
—	26	Hunslet (7016)	0-6-0DH	1971
Redland	—	K/Stuart (K4428)	0-4-0DM	1929
—	14	M/Wardle (1795)	0-4-0ST	1912
Coventry No 1	—	NBL (24564)	0-6-0ST	1939
—	—	Peckett (1900)	0-4-0T	1936
Gibraltar	—	Peckett (2087)	0-4-0ST	1948
—	—	Peckett (2104)	0-4-0ST	1948
—	—	Peckett (2105)	0-4-0ST	1948
—	T1	Hibberd (2102)	4wD	1937
Tarmac	—	Hibberd (3765)	0-4-0DM	1955
—	—	Sentinel (6515)	4wVBTG	1926
—	11	Sentinel (9366)	4wVBTG	1945

England

Special notes: One of the largest collection of standard gauge locomotives, together with a most interesting collection of vintage coaching stock, much of which was built in the last century
General: The public area of the centre covers some 25 acres of land with views across the Buckinghamshire countryside. A picnic area is available at the miniature railway

Name	No	Builder	Type	Built
—	7	Sentinel (9376)	4wVBTG	1947
—	—	Sentinel (9537)	4wVBTG	1947
Chislet	9	Yorkshire (2498)	0-6-0ST	1951

Stock: *Coaches* —
1 LCDR 1st Class 4-wheeler; 1 MSLR 3rd Class 6-wheeler; 4 LNWR coach bodies; 2 GNR 6-wheelers; 3 LNWR; 3 LMSR; 1 BR(W) Hawksworth brake 3rd; 2 BR Mk 1; 1 BR Mk 2; 1 BR Suburban brake; 3 LNER; 1 LNWR full brake 6-wheeler; 1 LMSR passenger brake van; 1 GWR passenger brake van; 1 GCR Robinson brake third; 1 LNWR tri-compo lavatory coach
Wagons —
A large and varied collection including 1 LNWR combination truck; 1 LSWR ventilated fruit van; 1 SR PMV; 1 BR(W) 'Siphon G'; 1 BR horse box; 1 BR CCT
3 ex-London Underground coaches
1 2ft gauge post office mailbag car 803
Sentinel/Cammell 3-car steam railcar unit 5208 (ex-Egyptian National)
Numerous goods vehicles/wagons/vans

Owners
41298, 41313, 46447 and *Juno* the Ivatt Locomotive Trust
9466 the 9466 Group
Blue Circle on long-term loan from the Bluebell Railway

Timetable Service | Bure Valley Railway | Norfolk

Member: HRA, TT
Opened in 1990 the BVR runs over the old Great Eastern Wroxham-Aylsham line. It is paralleled throughout the entire 9 miles by the Bure Valley Walk which offers excellent photographic opportunities
Headquarters: Bure Valley Railway (1991) Ltd, Aylsham Station, Norwich Road, Aylsham, Norfolk NR11 6BW
Managing Director: Paul Conibeare
Telephone: (01263) 733858
Fax: (01263) 733814
Main public station: Aylsham (Norwich Road); Wroxham (Coltishall Road)
Other public stations: Coltishall, Brampton and Buxton
Car and coach parks: Aylsham and Wroxham
OS reference:
Aylsham — TG 195264;
Wroxham — TG 303186
Access by public transport: By rail – Wroxham station is adjacent to main line Hoveton & Wroxham station (Norwich-Cromer/

Locomotives

Name	No	Builder	Type	Built
Wroxham Broad	1	G&S/Winson	2-6-4T	1992
Volunteer†	2	H/Hunslet	0-4-0DH	1996
2nd Air Division				
USAAF	3	BVR	4w-4wDH	1989
—	5	Lister	4wDM	
Blickling Hall	6	Winson*	2-6-2	1994
Spitfire	7	Winson*	2-6-2	1994
Thunderer	8	BVR/Winson*	2-6-2T	1997
Little Titan	9	Cheeseman	Steam crane	1975
—	10	BVR/Winson**	4-6-4T	1999
—	11	T. Turner††	2-8-0	—

*based on Indian Railways 2ft 6in gauge 'ZB' class
†rebuilt by EAGIT
**under construction
††under construction, based on Great Central Railway locomotive

Stock
20 fully enclosed saloons, 1 fully enclosed brake saloon, 2 enclosed saloons designed to carry wheelchairs, 2 guard's vans, generator car, miscellaneous wagons

Sheringham line). By bus – Eastern Counties buses run between Norwich and Aylsham
Refreshment facilities: Restaurant at Aylsham, with picnic area and light refreshments at Wroxham
Souvenir shops: Aylsham and Wroxham
Journey time: Approximately 45min each way plus turnround time
Length of line: 9 miles; 15in gauge
Passenger trains: Frequency depends on time of year, maximum

frequency one per hour
Period of public operation: Open from Easter to end of October – trains run most days, telephone for details
Facilities for disabled: Toilets at Aylsham and Wroxham, special rolling stock to carry wheelchairs, advance notice would be appreciated
Special events: Please contact for details. Friends of Thomas the Tank 30-31 May & 25/26 September
Special notes: Steam locomotive driving courses. Party discounts available. Private charters by arrangement. Special combined train and Broads boat excursions run most days during the summer
Membership details: Friends of the Bure Valley Railway, Membership Secretary, c/o above address

---

Steam Centre — Cadeby Light Railway — Leicestershire

Members: HRA, TT

A new museum was opened in 1990, the 'Boston Collection', encompassing the lifetime collection of Teddy Boston and his family. The narrow gauge railway running in the grounds of the old rectory has been saved by Teddy Boston's enterprising widow and a small band of dedicated supporters in the face of considerable odds. Echoes of the *Titfield Thunderbolt* and Ancient and Modern. Their endeavours deserve your support

Location: 5.75 miles north of Hinckley on A447
OS reference: SK 426024
Operating society/organisation: Mrs J. A. Boston, The Old Rectory, Cadeby, Nuneaton CV13 0AS
Telephone: Market Bosworth (01455) 290462
Car park: Available
Access by public transport: Midland Fox/Stevenson 178 from Hinckley. 153 Arriva Fox from Leicester to Market Bosworth (1.25 miles away)
On site facilities: 2ft gauge railway, also traction engine and steam rollers, model railway, and a museum housing the 'Boston Collection'. Brass rubbing centre in church with over 70 replica brasses
Refreshment facilities: Light refreshments available
Public opening: 2nd Saturday of selected months in the year from 13.30. Please ring for further details. Admission free (donations requested)
Special events: Please contact for details
Special notes: Party bookings by prior arrangement

Narrow gauge locomotives

Name	No	Builder	Type	Built
Pixie	—	Bagnall (2090)	0-4-0ST	1919
—	—	Baguley (1695)	0-4-0PM	1928
—	—	Lister (4088)	4wPM	1931
—	—	O&K (4588)	4wPM	1932
—	—	Thakeham (4th)	4wPM	c1946
—	—	Deutz (10050)	0-4-0DM	1930
—	—	H/Clarke (D558)	4wDM	1930
—	—	M/Rail & T (1320)	4wDM	1918
—	87004	M/Rail & T (2197)	4wDM	1922
—	87009	M/Rail & T (4572)	4wDM	1929
—	—	M/Rail & T (5038)	4wPM	1930
—	—	M/Rail (5853)	4wDM	1934
—	—	M/Rail (7512)	4wDM	1938
—	42	M/Rail (7710)	4wDM	1939
—	20	M/Rail (8748)	4wDM	1942
—	87008	R/Hornsby (179870)	4wDM	1936
—	87051	R/Hornsby (404967)	4wDM	1957
—	—	SMH(104063G)	4wDM	1976

Standard gauge

—	V47	Peckett (2012)	0-4-0ST	1941

Stock
Penrhyn Quarryman's 'O'coach; Hudson open wagons, skip wagons, Cravens van fron RNAD Dean Hill, 2 slate wagons from Dinorwic Slate Quarries, flat trucks; brickcars and two vehicles from John Knowles (Wooden Box) Ltd

Also on site are two Aveling & Porter 10-ton steam rollers (5163/03 and 7856/12) and a Foster traction engine (14593/27)

Above right: **South Eastern & Chatham Railway Nos 65 and 592 leave Bluebell Railway's Sheffield Park station on 5 August 1999 whilst taking part in SE&CER Weekend** *Alan P. Barnes*

Right: **Great Western Railway No 4866 in action on the demonstration line at the Didcot Railway Centre, 4 August 1999.** *Alan P. Barnes*

England

Cambrian Railways Society

The Gobowen to Blodwell line is some 8.25 miles long and the Cambrian Railways Trust has been set up to negotiate with Railtrack to purchase this section of line. A series of meetings have been held at Gobowen station to progress this proposal. These have been chaired by Councillor David Lloyd with the aim of running trains initially between Gobowen and Oswestry and eventually in stages to Llynclys, Porthywaen and Blodwell. A price has been suggested for the purchase of the line with Railtrack and the Cambrian Railways Society has already done a considerable amount of work in clearing weeds, bushes and trees from the track up to the boundary.

It is hoped that trains may run between Oswestry and Gobowen by late summer, but there is a considerable amount of work and negotiation to be done in the meantime for this to become a reality.

Location: Oswestry station yard, Oswald Road, Oswestry, Shropshire SY11 1RE
OS reference: SJ 294297
Operating society/organisation: Cambrian Railways Society Ltd, C. W. Mottram, 'Delamere', Old Chirk Road, Gobowen, Oswestry, Shropshire SY11 3LH
Telephone: (01691) 671749

Locomotives and multiple-units

Name	No	Origin	Class	Type	Built
Cogan Hall	5952	GWR	'Hall'	4-6-0	1937
Ditcheat Manor	7821	GWR	'Manor'	4-6-0	1950

Industrial locomotives

Name	No	Builder	Type	Built
—	1	H/Clarke (D843)	0-4-0DM	1954
Adam	1	Peckett (1430)	0-4-0ST	1916
—	3	Hunslet (D3526)	0-6-0DM	1954
Oliver Velton	6	Peckett (2131)	0-4-0ST	1951
—	8	Barclay (885)	0-6-0ST	1900
—	322	Planet (3541)	4wDM	1952
Norma	3770	Hunslet (3770)	0-6-0ST	1952
—	No 3	Sentinel	0-4-0D	?
—*	—	Hibberd (3057)	4wDM	1946
—	—	Planet	4wDM	1960

*mobile compressor

Stock
1 GWR auto-trailer; 1 GWR brake van; 1 LMS brakevan; 2 tank wagons; 1 open wagon, 1 box van, 1 tank wagon (No 5), 2 tank wagon 4-wheel chassis (tanks removed) ex-Machynlleth Refuelling Depot, 1 GWR Syphon, Mess & Sleeping coach dating from 1911, 27-ton former TPO (now tool van), 4-wheel van, 12-ton box van, Warflat, bogie bolster, ex-S&M 10-ton box van

Car park: In Society's depot
Length of line: 400yd, opened 7 December 1996, the Light Railway Order having been granted
Public opening: Daily 10.00-16.00
On site facilities: Refreshment room — the 'Whistle Stop' (open on special days in former Llansantffraid signalbox) and picnic area

Special notes: Railwayana, artefacts and 20 bicycles, 17 motor cycles and 7 auto-cycles/mopeds on display. Normally Cogan Hall, Peckett 2131 and Hunslet 3770 are on display inside the building. Group discount available. Also known as Oswestry Transport Museum

Chasewater Railway

Member: HRA, TT
Founded in 1959 as the Railway Preservation Society (West Midlands District), the Chasewater Railway was re-formed in 1985 as a Registered Charity. The railway operates as 'The Colliery Line' to reflect its origins and location in the heart of the Cannock Chase coalfield. The railway runs a regular timetabled service between Brownhills West station and Norton Lakeside station (which adjoins

Chasewater's Wildfowl Reserve). An extension to a new station at Chasewater Heath is expected to open during 2000.
Location: Chasewater Park, Brownhills (off A5 southbound, nr jct A452 Chester Road)
OS Reference: SK 034070
Operating society/organisation: Chasewater Light Railway & Museum Co
Telephone: (01543) 452623
Car park: Within Chasewater Park

Access by public transport:
Nearest railway stations – Walsall and Birmingham New Street.
Bus services from Walsall (Bridge Street) — 362 (Sundays) and 396 (weekdays and Saturdays) to Brownhills West (Rising Sun Inn).
Bus services from Birmingham (Priory Queensway), bus stop Na; Carrs Lane, bus stop Ef —Midland red service 156 to Brownhills West (Rising Sun Inn).
Brownhills West station is approx

10min walk from the Rising Sun Inn.

For timetable information and details of services, contact Centro Hotline (0121) 200 2700

On site facilities: Refreshments, shop, lakeside walks and large grassed areas

Catering facilities: Hot and cold buffet

Length of line: 1.25 miles

Public opening: Sundays and Bank Holiday Mondays from Easter to end of October. Trains run at 45 min intervals from 12.00 until 17.15pm

Special events: Transport Festival — 17/18 June; Military Heritage Weekend — 12/13 August; Vintage Vehicle Rally — 7/8 October; Santa Specials 10, 17 December

Facilities for disabled: Disabled access to stations, trains and buffet

Membership details: Membership Secretary, Brownhills West Station, Hednesford Road, Brownhills West, Walsall WS8 7LT

Diesel multiple-units

Name	No	Builder	Class	Type	Built
—	W51370	Pressed Steel	117	DMBS	1960
—	W51372	Pressed Steel	117	DMBS	1960
—	W51412	Pressed Steel	117	DMS	1960
—	W59444	BR Derby	116	TS	1958
—	W59603	Pressed Steel	127	TSL	1959

Industrial locomotives

Name	No	Builder	Type	Built
Alfred Paget	11	Neilson (2937)	0-4-0ST	1882
Sheepbridge No.15	—	H/Clarke (431)	0-6-0T	1895
	6	Peckett (917)	0-4-0ST	1902
Asbestos	4	H/Leslie (2780)	0-4-0ST	1909
Colin McAndrew	3	Barclay (1223)	0-4-0ST	1911
Whit No.4		H/Clarke (1822)	0-6-0T	1949
Sentinel	5	Sentinel (9632)	4wVBT	1957
	1	M/Rail (1947)	4wPM	1919
	21	Kent Constr (1612)	4wDM	1929
	—	Fowler (4100013)	0-4-0DM	1948
	—	R/Hornsby (305306)	0-4-0DM	1952
Toad	37	Fowler (4220015)	0-4-0DH	1962
Fleet	7	R/Hornsby (458641)	0-4-0DE	1963

Rolling stock

A variety of passenger and freight vehicles are housed on site, including a number of considerable historical importance

---

Chinnor & Princes Risborough Railway — 'The Icknield Line'

Steam Centre | Oxfordshire

Member: HRA

The Chinnor & Princes Risborough Railway Association was formed in 1989 with the aim of restoring the disused line from Princes Risborough to Chinnor, part of the former Watlington branch

Location: Chinnor, Oxon, 10 miles SW of Aylesbury. J6 on M40, station signposted from B4009, which passes through village

OS reference: TL 774362

Operating society/organisation: Chinnor & Princes Risborough Railway Co, Chinnor Station, Station Road, Chinnor, Oxon OX9 4ER

Access by public transport: Main line Princes Risborough then Wycombe Bus Nos 232/331/332 to Chinnor (Sats only)

Length of line: 4 miles. First 3.5 miles opened for 1995 season

Passenger trains: Chinnor-Thame Junction-Chinnor

Locomotives

Name	No	Origin	Class	Type	Built
Haversham	13018	BR	08	0-6-0DE	1953
—	D8568	BR	17	Bo-Bo	1963
—	55023	BR	121	DMBS	1958
—	4247	GWR	4200	2-8-0T	1916

Industrial locomotives

Name	No	Builder	Type	Built
Sir Robert Peel	8	Hunslet (3776)	0-6-0ST	1952
Iris	459515	R/Hornsby (459515)	0-6-0DH	1952
Phoenix*	70	H/Clarke (1464)	0-6-0T	1921

*on loan fron East Lancashire Railway.

Stock - coaches

1 ex-LNWR Mess coach, 1 ex-BR Mk 1 NDV, 1 ex-BR Mk 1 RMB, 1 ex-BR Mk 1 CK, 1 ex-BR Mk 1 BSK, 1 ex-BR Mk 2 FK, 12 various wagons, 1 Coles self-propelled crane

Public opening: Weekends from Easter-end October. Thomas visiting in May and August. Santa & Mince Pie Specials in December. Up-to-date information on Talking Timetable (01844) 353535

On site facilities: Souvenir shop, buffet plus on-train buffet. Toilets, free car park, picnic area

Special notes: Replica station building to be completed during 2000. Visiting locomotives during

the season, please phone for details or see railway press
Membership details: Mr Peter Harris, 12 Ann's Close, Aylesbury, Bucks

Membership journal: *The Watlington Flyer* — quarterly

Cholsey & Wallingford Railway

Timetable Service   **Oxfordshire**

Member: HRA
Location: Hithercroft Industrial Estate, St Johns Road, Wallingford, Oxfordshire
Sales & Marketing: Jo Clyde
Operating Society: Cholsey & Wallingford Railway Preservation Society, PO Box 16, Wallingford, Oxon OX10 0NF
Telephone: (01491) 835067 (24hr information line)
Access by public transport: Thames Transit (390) from Oxford-London, main line trains Cholsey
Public opening: Trains run between 11.30-16.30 (from Wallingford) and 12.00-17.00 (from Cholsey) at hourly intervals. 22-24, 30 April; 1, 28/29 May; 10/11, 25 June; 2, 15/16, 29/30 July; 26-28 August; 23/24 September; 28/29 October; 3, 10/11, 16/17, 23 December
Length of line: 2.5 miles from Wallingford
Journey time: Approximately 20min (one way), 45min (return)
On site facilities: Souvenir and

Locomotives

Name	No	Origin	Class	Type	Built
Unicorn	(08022)	BR	08	0-6-0	1953
Lion	(08060)	BR	08	0-6-0	1953
George Mason	08123	BR	08	0-6-0	1955

Industrial locomotives

Name	No	Builder	Type	Built
Carpenter	3271	Planet (3271)	0-4-0	1949

Rolling stock — coaches: 4 BR Mk 1 coaches, 1 BR Mk 2 brake coach

coffee shop, museum, model railway
Special events: Day Out With Thomas — 22-24 April; Cholsey May Day Event/Animal Crackers —30 April/1 May; Musical Day — 28/29 May; Cholsey Millennium Main Event Weekend — 10/11 June; Wallingford Carnival (NO trains) —24 June; Cholsey Open Gardens Day — 25 June; Railwayana Car Boot & Auction — 2 July; Wallingford Millenniun Event (siege) — 15/16 July; Cholsey Flower Show — 26 August; Guinness Weekend —

26-28 August; Teddy Bears' Picnic/Military Vehicles — 23/24 September; Halloween — 28/29 October; Santa Specials — 3, 10/11, 16/17, 23 December
Special notes: Light Railway Order now granted. Railway crosses new bypass (A4130) at a level crossing. The Society is running into Cholsey bay platform.
Membership details: Ian Bowyer, at above address
Membership journal: *The Bunk* — 3 issues/year

Churnet Valley Railway

Steam Centre   **Staffordshire**

Member: HRA
This heritage railway is situated deep in the heart of the Staffordshire moorlands. Begin your journey at Cheddleton, a Victorian country station set in picturesque countryside complete with riverside parking and picnic island. The 6.5-mile return journey takes you to the idyllic hamlet of Consall Forge where pleasant walks can be taken alongside the Caulden Canal and the River Churnet. Please ring to confirm timetable and events
Location: Cheddleton station, near Leek, Staffordshire

Locomotives and multiple-units

Name	No	Origin	Class	Type	Built
—	2	NSR	New L	0-6-2T	1923
—	1	NSR	—	04-40BE	1917
—	4422	LMS	4F	0-6-0	1927
—	80136	BR	4MT	2-6-4T	1956
—	D2070	BR	03	0-6-0DM	1959
—	D2334	BR	04	0-6-0DM	1961
—	D3420	BR	08	0-6-0DE	1957
—	20154	BR	20	Bo-Bo	1966
Tamworth Castle	D7672	BR	25	Bo-Bo	1967
—	33102	BR	33	Bo-Bo	1960
Burma Star	33056	BR	33	Bo-Bo	1961
—	53455	BRCW	104	DMBS	1957
—	53437	BRCW	104	DMBS	1957
—	53494	BRCW	104	DMCL	1957

28   **England**

OS reference: SJ 983519
Operating society/organisation: Churnet Valley Railway (1992) plc
Telephone: Churnetside (01538) 360522
Car park: Adjacent to Cheddleton station
Access by public transport: Main line Stoke-on-Trent (10 miles). A regular bus service operated by Proctors, PMT and Stevensons runs from Hanley, Longton and Leek to Cheddleton village
On site facilities: Cheddleton station contains a refreshment room, souvenir shop and small relics museum. On open days visitors are allowed to visit the yard and locomotive display hall
Length of line: 3.25 miles, standard gauge
Public opening: Steam trains Easter-September inclusive — Sundays and Bank Holiday Mondays, 11.00-17.15. Wednesdays in August and every Saturday in July and August
Special events: Station at war — 15/16 April
Facilities for disabled: Access to most of the site is possible by wheelchair. Train rides by arrangement
Membership details: North Staffordshire Railway Co, Membership Secretary, c/o above address

Name	No	Origin	Class	Type	Built
—	53517	BRCW	104	DMCL	1957
—	59137	BRCW	104	TSL	1957

Industrial locomotives

Name	No	Builder	Type	Built
Josiah Wedgwood	3777	Hunslet (3777)	0-6-0ST	1952
Cammell	—	YEC	0-4-0DH	1960
Brightside	—	YEC	0-4-0DH	1960

Locomotive notes: Locos expected to be in service: 3777, 80136, D2334, D3420, D7672 and 33102.

Owners
4422 the 4422 Locomotive Fund
80136 and 3777 the Standard Four Trust
D3420, 33056, 33102 and D7672 the NSR Diesel Group
NSR 1 and 2 the National Railway Museum
20154 the Churnet Traction & Rolling Stock Group

Stock
Ex-BR Mk 1 coaches: CK (2), BSK (2), SO (1), TSO (2), FK (2), RMB (1) and RBR (1); ex-BR Mk 2 coaches: BFK (1) and BSO (1); ex-BR suburban coaches: S (1), BS (2), SLO (1); 1 ex-NSR coach body; 1 ex-LMS 6-wheel full brake; 2 ex-LMS goods brake vans; 1 ex-LMS 6-wheel CCT; 2 ex-LMS box vans; 3 ex-BR box vans; 2 ex-LMS 5-plank wagons; 1 ex-LMS hopper wagon; 1 Esso tank wagon; 1 ex-BR standard 20-ton brake van; 1 ex-BR shark; 3 ex-BR General Utility Vans; 2 ex-BR medfits; 2 ex-BR catfish; 1 ex-GWR bogie bolster; 1 7-ton diesel rail-mounted crane; 75-ton rail-mounted diesel crane; 3 ex-BR QQX tool vans; 1 ex-BR QPX staff and dormitory

Special notes: Coach parties catered for by prior arrangement. Guided tours available for parties on request

---

Timetable Service	**Cleethorpes Coast Light Railway**	North East Lincolnshire

Member: HRA, Britain's Great Little Railways
One of the country's latest 15in gauge recruits. Previously a 14.25in gauge railway, it was converted to 15in in time for the 1994 Steam Gala. The railway is gaining a reputation for good events and galas, as well as now being the chosen site for a Museum of Seaside Miniature Railways. .

  2000 will again feature steam haulage on the line, with visiting locomotives planned for the main season to assist the resident stock. The railway operating company is lucky to be able to call upon the

Locomotives

Name	No	Built/rebuilt	Type	Date
Konigswinter	1	CCLR	2-8-0GH	1992
Arnold J Rimmer	2	Lister	4wDH Tram	—
The Cub	3	CCLR	4w4DM	1993
Haigh Hall/Katie†	5	Guest	2-4-2	1954
—	6	Stanhope/CCLR	0-4-0VBT	1995
—	24	Fairbourne	2-6-2	1989
Seabreeze	—	CCLR	4-6-2	Under construction

Rolling stock
4 Severn Lamb semi-open saloons (one converted to brake coach by CCLR); 5 Alan Keef toastracks (one includes guard's compartment); 1 JMA open coach; 2 4-wheel tub wagons; 14-wheel box van; 14-wheel five plank wagon; 1 4-wheel ballast hopper, 1 bogie passenger brake van;

Cleethorpes Coast Light Railway Supporters' Association to provide the majority of operating staff. This small group are always looking for new helpers, and membership is free. Details are available from the company
Operating society/organisation: Cleethorpes Coast Light Railway Ltd, Lakeside Station, Kings Road, Cleethorpes, Lincolnshire DN35 0AG
Telephone/Fax: (01472) 604657
Access by public transport: By rail to Cleethorpes, Stagecoach

Owners/notes
24 — the Sandy River Consortium
†on loan from Wigan Council

service 17 from Sea Road passes the line. By car, Kings Road is the main resort road. Follow Lakeside brown tourist signs
On site facilities: Large 500 space car park (pay & display). Station gift shop at Kingsway station. Teapot tearoom for refreshments at Lakeside station. Lakeside picnic area

Period of public opening: Daily 1 April-14 September. Railway open from 10.00. *Winter weekends* — November-Good Friday. Winter daily running schools half term weeks (except 25/26 December)
Special events: Please phone for special events leaflet

Steam Centre — Colne Valley Railway — Essex

Member: HRA, TT
A completely reconstructed country station and railway within sight of the 12th century castle and specialising in entertainment. A complimentary Farm Park provides interest for all the family
Location: Castle Hedingham Station, Yeldham Road, Castle Hedingham, Halstead, Essex CO9 3DZ
OS reference: TL 774362
Operating society/organisation: Colne Valley Railway Preservation Society Ltd
Telephone: Hedingham (01787) 461174
Internet address:
Web site: www.cvr.uk.com
Car park: At the site (access from A1017 road between Castle Hedingham and Great Yeldham)
Access by public transport: Eastern National bus services 88 Colchester-Halstead, 89 Halstead-Hedingham and Hedingham Omnibuses 4 Braintree-Hedingham, 5 Sudbury-Hedingham. Nearest main line station — Braintree (7 miles)
On site facilities: Depot, museum, souvenir shop, buffet, 4-acre riverside picnic area, toilets, video carriage, exhibition centre, 30 acre farm park
Catering facilities: Buffet carriage when trains operating. Pullman on-train service on selected days for Sunday lunch, private hire and evening wine and dine (pre-

Locomotives and multiple-units

Name	No	Origin	Class	Type	Built
Blue Star	35010	SR	MN	4-6-2	1942
—	45163	LMS	5	4-6-0	1935
—	45293	LMS	5	4-6-0	1936
—	D2041	BR	03	0-6-0DM	1959
—	D2184	BR	03	0-6-0DM	1962
—	D5634	BR	31	A1A-A1A	1960
—	31163*	BR	31	A1A-A1A	1960
—	31166*	BR	31	A1A-A1A	1960
—	31188*	BR	31	A1A-A1A	1960
—	31206*	BR	31	A1A-A1A	1960
—	51138	BR	116	DMBS	1958
—	59501	BR	117	TCL	1960
—	51151	BR	116	DMS	1958
—	55033	P/Steel	121	DTC	1960
—	W79976	AC Cars	—	Railbus	1958
—	E79978	AC Cars	—	Railbus	1958

*may be on loan to other railways

Industrial locomotives

Name	No	Builder	Type	Built
Victory	8	Barclay (2199)	0-4-0ST	1945
—	WD190	Hunslet (3790)	0-6-0ST	1952
—	68072	Vulcan (5309)	0-6-0ST	1945
Jupiter	60	RSH (7671)	0-6-0ST	1950
—	40	RSH (7765)	0-6-0T	1954
Castle Donnington	No 2	RSH (7818)	0-4-0ST	1954
Barrington	—	Avonside (1875)	0-4-0ST	1921
—	1	H/Leslie (3715)	0-4-0ST	1928
—	—	Barclay (349)	0-4-0DM	1941
—	YD43	R/Hornsby (221639)	4wDM	1943
—	—	Hibbard (3147)	4wDM	1947
—	—	Unilok (2109)	4wDM R/R	1982
—	—	Lake & Elliot (1)	4wPM	1924
—	—	R/Hornsby (281266)	4wDM	1950

Stock
2 ex-Pullman cars, *Aquila* and *Hermione;* 10 ex-BR Mk 1 coaches (2xTSO, SO, 3xCK, SK, 2xBSK); 1 ex-BR Mk 3 SLEP; 9 BR NPCCS, 2 ex-LNER — 1xBTO (16551) 1xTK (42240); 1 LMS BG, 1 GER BTK;

booking essential for all Pullman services)
Length of line: 1-mile
Public opening: Daily for static displays except 24 December to 31 January. Steam trains operate every Sunday from 26 March to 22 October, also Wednesdays and Thursdays during school summer holidays, every Bank Holiday (except Christmas & New Year), Wednesdays during other school holidays (except February). Heritage diesel trains operate Tuesdays and Fridays during school holidays, Sundays 5, 12, 19 March and 29 October
Special events: Model Engineering Exhibition, A Day Out With Thomas, Santa Specials
Educational events: Diesel trains available every day for school visits. Learning with Thomas in June. Victorian Special in October. All educational events must be pre-booked
Family tickets: Available — 2 adults and up to 4 children, giving unlimited train rides except on special events
Facilities for disabled: Access to most areas. Ramps to trains, staff will help. Disabled toilet

4 goods brake vans (GWR, LNER, SR & BR), 3 oil tank wagons, BR steam crane, LT ballast wagon, BE Sturgeon, BR Conflat, GER van, BR van, BR Medfit, BR tube wagon

Owners
35010 and 45293 the British Engineman's Steam Preservation Society
51138, 59501, 51151, and 55033 Pressed Steel Heritage Ltd
Class 31s the Colne Valley Diesel Group

Special notes: The railway has been completely rebuilt on part of the original Colne Valley & Halstead Railway trackbed. The railway offers much of educational value specialising in school party visits by appointment at any time of the year
Membership details: Membership Secretary, c/o Castle Hedingham

---

| Museum | Darlington Railway Centre & Museum | County Durham |

Located on the original 1825 route of the Stockton & Darlington Railway, the restored North Road station, dating from 1842, is now a museum which forms the centrepiece of an area devoted to railway history and preservation.

The Museum is administered by Darlington Borough Council. The collection includes locomotives, rolling stock and many small exhibits. A special display on the story of the Stockton & Darlington Railway will be running during 2000, marking the railway's 175th anniversary. A major celebration the 'Millennium Cavalcade of Steam' will be staged over the August Bank Holiday weekend. The site also includes two other historic buildings of the S&DR — the former Goods Shed and the Hopetown Carriage Works. Steam train rides over a short length of line are available on selected dates, and there are plans for future development of steam operation.

The Ken Hoole Study Centre houses a collection of reference material on the railways of north-east England including the library of the North Eastern Railway

Locomotives

Name	No	Origin	Class	Type	Built
Locomotion	1	S&DR	—	0-4-0	1825
Derwent	25	S&DR	—	0-6-0	1845
—	1463	NER	1463	2-4-0	1885
—	910	NER	901	2-4-0	1875

Industrial locomotives

Name	No	Builder		Type	Built
Met	—	H/Leslie (2800)		0-4-0ST	1909
—	17	Head Wrightson (33)		0-4-0VB	1873
—	—	Bagnall (2898)		0-4-0F	1948
—	39	RSH (6947)		0-6-0T	1938

Stock
1 Stockton & Darlington Rly passenger coach (1846)
1 North Eastern Railway coach body (c1860)
1 NER 20-ton mineral wagon
1 Chaldron wagon

Owners
Locomotion, Derwent, 1463 and 910 are all on loan from the National Railway Museum
Met is on loan from Messrs D. & R. Branch

Darlington Railway Preservation Society
Member: HRA

Locomotives

Name	No	Origin	Class	Type	Built
—	78018	BR	2MT	2-6-0	1954

Association (access by appointment).

Northern Spirit train services provide a link to Darlington's main line station and to Shildon, for the Timothy Hackworth Museum

Museum Curator: Vacant

Location: North Road Station, Darlington, County Durham DL3 6ST. Approximately three-quarters of a mile north of town centre, off North Road (A167)

OS reference: NZ 289157

Telephone: (01325) 460532

Car park: At museum site

Access by public transport: Rail services to Darlington North Road station. Local bus services along North Road

Catering facilities: Refreshment area open during summer season. Confectionery and drinks at other times

On site facilities: Souvenir and book shop, toilets, meeting room

Public opening: Daily February to December 10.00-17.00 (except Christmas holidays). Days and times may be subject to amendment

Special events: Railway Carnival — September; steam days; Santa Specials — December (contact for details)

Facilities for disabled: Access to main museum building for wheelchairs. Disabled persons'

toilet. Parking spaces for disabled in forecourt

Membership details: Friends of Darlington Railway Museum, Darlington Railway Preservation Society, A1 Steam Locomotive Trust and North Eastern Railway Association all c/o above address

Note: Some locomotives are located in the former goods shed, where restoration work is being

undertaken by the Darlington Railway Preservation Society (limited opening to visitors — times vary; groups by arrangement). Part of the former carriage works has been renovated and is now used by the A1 Steam Locomotive Trust for assembly of the new Peppercorn Pacific *Tornado* (usually open to visitors on Saturdays, please enquire)

Industrial locomotives

Name	No	Builder	Type	Built
—	2	RSH (7925)	0-4-0DM	1959
—	1	Peckett (2142)	0-4-0ST	1953
David Payne	185	Fowler (4110006)	0-4-0DM	1950
Smiths Dock Co Ltd	—	Fowler (4200018)	0-4-0DM	1947
—	—	GEC	4wE	1928
—	—	R/Hornsby (279591)	0-4-0DM	1949
—	—	R/Hornsby*	4wDM	—
—	—	R/Hornsby*	4wDM	—
—	—	R/Hornsby*	4wDM	—

*1ft 6in gauge

Stock

Various wagons, steam and diesel cranes

A1 Steam Locomotive Trust

Member: HRA

Locomotives

Name	No	Origin	Class	Type	Built
Tornado	60163	A1SLT	8P6F	4-6-2	Under construction

Timetable Service	**Dean Forest Railway**	Glos

Member: HRA, TT

Passenger services operate between Norchard and Lydney Junction (Severn & Wye Joint), with an extension to Parkend planned to open in summer 2000. The current line boasts five level crossings, three of which are manually operated

Location: Norchard Railway Centre on the B4234. Signposted off the A48 Lydney bypass to town centre whence B4234 commences

OS reference: SO 629044

Operations Manager: Keith Johnson

Operating society/organisation: Dean Forest Railway Society in conjunction with owning company,

Locomotives and mutliple-units

Name	No	Origin	Class	Type	Built
—	28	TVR	O1	0-6-2T	1897
—	5541	GWR	4575	2-6-2T	1928
—	9642	GWR	5700	0-6-0PT	1949
—	9681	GWR	5700	0-6-0PT	1949
—	08238	BR	08	0-6-0DE	1956
—	50619	BR	108	DMBS	1958
—	51914	BR	108	DMS	1960
—	56492	BR	108	DTC	1960
—	56495	BR	108	DTC	1960

Industrial locomotives

Name	No	Builder	Type	Built
—	—	Barclay (2221)	0-4-0ST	1946
Uskmouth No 1	—	Peckett (2147)	0-4-0ST	1952
Wilbert	—	Hunslet (3806)	0-6-0ST	1953
Warrior	—	Hunslet (3823)	0-6-0ST	1954
—	—	Hunslet (2145)	0-4-0DM	1940

England

Forest of Dean Railway Ltd
Telephone: (01594) 843423
information line; (01594) 845840
(daytime); (01452) 840625
(general info and evenings)
Car park: Adequate for cars and
coaches — no charge
Access by public transport: Main
line station at Lydney
On site facilities: Shop available
at Norchard along with a museum,
riverside walk, forest trail and
picnic area (cafeteria at Norchard
on operating days)
Catering facilities: Hot and cold
snacks on steam days. Parties
catered for by appointment
Length of line: 2 miles
Public opening: Daily for static
display — shop and museum, open
every Saturday and Sunday 11.00-
17.00 and weekdays April to
December. Steam train rides: Good
Friday, Easter Saturday and all
Bank Holiday Sundays and
Mondays (Christmas/New Year
excepted). All Sundays April-
October. Wednesdays in June and

Name	No	Builder	Type	Built
—	—	Fowler (4210127)	0-4-0DM	1957
—	—	Hibberd (3947)	4wPM	1960

Owners
28 the National Railway Museum, on loan from the Museum of Wales
9642 the South Wales Pannier Group

Stock
4 ex-GWR coaches; 12 ex-BR coaches; 1 DFR constructed Cafeteria coach
(static at Norchard), 3 Wickham trolleys; 1 steam crane Thos Smith
(Rodley) TS 5027 (10-ton); Booth 15-24 tonne diesel-hydraulic crane
No 81548 built 1958, 100+ wagons

July. Wednesdays, Thursdays and
Saturdays in August. Heritage
DMU service operates on
Saturdays 10, 17, 24 June, 1, 8, 15,
22, 29 July; 1, 8, 15, 22, 29 August
Tuesday and Thursday 24, 26 and
October. Steam on Wednesday 25
October
Special events: Day Out with
Thomas the Tank Engine — 30/31
May, 1-4 June, 1-3 September;
Lydney Road & Rail Show — 15
October; Santa Specials — 3, 9/10,

16/17, 23/24 December; Mince Pie
Specials — 30/31 December 2000
and 1 January 2001
Facilities for disabled: Access to
museum, shop, toilets and train
rides
Membership details: Mr R.
Bramwell, 4 Poole Ground,
Highnam, Gloucester GL2 8NA
Membership journal: *Forest
Venturer* — half yearly
Marketing name: The Friendly
Forest Line

Museum — Derby Industrial Museum — Derbyshire

Member: TT
As would be expected of a railway
town, the museum has an extensive
collection of railway material
including locomotives and rolling
stock (most on display at the
Midland Railway Centre). The
railway gallery tells the stories of
railway industries in Derby,
especially as they relate to the
Midland Railway and its
successors. Replica Midland
Railway signalbox and model
railway (under construction). The
story is brought up to date by the
Railway Research Gallery which
looks at the role of the Railway
Technical Centre and includes a
replica of an InterCity 225 driving
cab

Industrial locomotives

Name	No	Builder	Type	Built
Victory	—	Peckett (1547)	0-4-0ST	1919
—	—	Motor Rail (6155)	4wPM	1919

Location: Silk Mill Lane, Derby
Operating society/organisation:
Derby Industrial Museum, Silk Mill
Lane, off Full Street, Derby
DE1 3AR
Telephone: (01332) 255308
Fax: (01332) 716670
Car park: Local car parks around
city
Access by public transport: Bus
station quarter mile, railway station
three-quarter mile.
On site facilities: Shop, baby
changing facilities

Opening times: Admission free.
Mondays 11.00-17.00, Tuesdays to
Saturdays 10.00-17.00, Bank
Holidays 14.00-17.00.
Sundays14.00-17.00
Facilities for disabled: Parking by
arrangement. Level access to
building, lifts and ramps to all
gallery areas, toilets, sign language
and subtitles in Rolls-Royce gallery

Steam Centre — Derwent Valley Light Railway — North Yorkshire

Member: TT

The Society has completed the rebuilding of Weldrake station at Murton

Location: Murton Park, Murton Lane, Murton, Nr York YO19 5UF

Operating society/organisation: Great Yorkshire Railway Preservation Society

Telephone: (01904) 489966

OS reference: SE 651537

On site facilities: Refreshments, souvenir shop (Yorkshire Museum of Farming)

Car park: Free, on site

Length of line: Half-mile

Access by public transport: York-Stamford Bridge bus service from main line York station

Facilities for disabled: Toilets, ramped ways etc

Public opening: Open daily mid-February-end October, for the Yorkshire Museum of Farming, Danelaw (Viking) Village and the

Locomotives and multiple-units

Name	No	Origin	Class	Type	Built
—	03079	BR	03	0-6-0DM	1960

Industrial locomotives

Name	No	Builder	Type	Built
—	8	A/Barclay (2369)	0-4-0ST	1955
—	—	H/Clarke (1631)	0-6-0T	1929
—	—	Fowler (22077)	0-4-0DM	1937
—	ED6	Fowler (4200022)	0-4-0DM	1948
Churchill	—	Fowler (410005)	0-4-0DM	1947
Jim	—	R/Hornsby (417892)	4wDM	1959
Octavius Atkinson	—	R/Hornsby (466630)	4wDM	1962
—	—	R/Hornsby (327964)	4wDM	1953

Rolling stock

1 NER coach, 1 NER coach body, 10 various freight wagons, and 1 rail crane

Derwent Valley Light Railway. Trains operate Sundays and Bank Holidays Easter-end September and for Santa Specials

Membership details: Andy Bell, 45 Maryland Avenue, Willerby Road, Hull HU5 5JA

Society journal: *DVLR News* (quarterly)

Railway Centre — Devon Railway Centre — Devon

The Devon Railway Centre features a lovingly restored Victorian Great Western Railway station together with historic locomotives, carriages and wagons as featured on TV. Unlimited passenger rides can be taken on the 2ft gauge railway and there is a large permanent model railway on exhibition. All-inclusive admission price

Location: Alongside Bickleigh Bridge over the River Exe on the A396, four miles south of Tiverton and 10 miles north of Exeter

General Manager: Matthew Gicquel

Contact address: Devon Railway Centre, Bickleigh, Nr Tiverton, Devon EX16 8RG

Telephone: (01884) 855671

OS reference: SS 938074

Car park: On site

Access by public transport: Regular bus service from Tiverton and Exeter, routes 55 and 55A

Industrial locomotives (2ft gauge)

Name	No	Builder	Type	Built
Merlin	—	Hudson (LX1001)	4wDH	1968
Pen-yr-Orsedd	—	R/Hornsby (235711)	4wDM	1945
Ruston	—	R/Hornsby (418770)	4wDM	1957
Planet	—	Planet (2201)	4wDM	1939
Lister	—	Lister (6299)	4wPM	1935
—	—	Planet (2025)	4wDM	1937
—	—	Kent (1747)	4wPM	1931
Ivor	—	Motor Rail (8877)	4wDM	1944
—	—*	Motor Rail (105H006)	4wDM	1919

*3ft gauge

Industrial locomotives (standard gauge)

Name	No	Builder	Type	Built
Boris	1	Baguley (3357)	0-4-0DM	1952

Locomotive notes: All locomotives are expected to be be working in 2000, except for Kent and Planet 2025

Rolling stock: All 2ft gauge unless indicated. Hudson bogie passenger coach, Dinorwic Yellow Coach, 2 slate slab wagons, GWR slate wagon, 5 skip wagons, Lochaber incline wagon (3ft gauge), Ravenglass & Eskdale wagon (15in gauge), copper mine tub (20in gauge), Cattybrook brickworks wagon (2ft 10in gauge), asssorted works wagons.
2 ex-BR Mk 1 coaches (standard gauge)

On site facilities: Passenger-carrying line, large model railway exhibition, restored GWR station, standard gauge static display, historic narrow gauge collection, refreshments and souvenirs

Length of line: Half mile, 2ft gauge
Opening times: Easter-31 October — Sundays, Bank Holidays and daily (except Saturdays) during most school holidays. November

and December open Sundays. Phone for details of extra midweek openings in spring and autumn, plus Santa Specials
Special events: Phone for details

| Steam Centre | Didcot Railway Centre | Oxfordshire |

Member: HRA, TT

Based around the GWR engine shed and depot, the Centre now has a typical GWR small country station with signalboxes (from Radstock and Frome), re-creation of Brunel's broad gauge railway, two demonstration lines, and a small relics museum

General Manager: Michael Dean
Location: Adjacent to BR station, Didcot, Oxfordshire. Access via station subway
OS reference: SU 525907
Operating society/organisation: Great Western Society Ltd, Didcot Railway Centre, Didcot, Oxon OX11 7NJ
Telephone: Didcot (01235) 817200
Internet address: Website: www.didcotrailwaycentre.org.uk
Car park: Didcot station
Access by public transport: Didcot Parkway BR station
Refreshment facilities: Refreshment room open all days centre is open (lunches, snacks). Picnic area
On site facilities: GWR locomotive depot, replica GWR station, museum and broad gauge demonstration. Souvenir sales. Rides are available on the demonstration lines on Steamdays. Admission price on Steamdays includes train rides
Length of line: 1,000yd
Public opening: Saturdays and Sundays all year. Daily 1 April-1 October, 21-29 October, 27 December to 3 January. Steamdays first and last Sunday each month from March, Bank Holidays, all Sundays July-August, all Wednesdays 12 July to 30 August. Open 10.00-17.00 (November/December 10.00-16.00)
Train rides: On Steam days there is normally continuous operation of

Locomotives

Name	No	Origin	Class/Builder	Type	Built
—	22	GWR	Diesel Railcar	1A-A1	1940
—	1338	GWR	Kitson (3799) (Cardiff Rly)	0-4-0ST	1898
Trojan	1340	GWR	Avonside (1380)	0-4-0ST	1897
—	1363	GWR	1361	0-6-0ST	1910
—	3650	GWR	5700	0-6-0PT	1939
—	3738	GWR	5700	0-6-0PT	1937
—	3822	GWR	2884	2-8-0	1940
Pendennis Castle*	4079	GWR	'Castle'	4-6-0	1924
—	4144	GWR	5101	2-6-2T	1946
Maindy Hall	4942	GWR	'Hall'	4-6-0	1929
—	4866	GWR	4800	0-4-2T	1936
Earl Bathurst	5051	GWR	'Castle'	4-6-0	1936
—	5322	GWR	4300	2-6-0	1917
—	5572	GWR	4575	2-6-2T	1927
Hinderton Hall	5900	GWR	'Hall'	4-6-0	1931
King Edward II	6023	GWR	'King'	4-6-0	1930
—	6106	GWR	6100	2-6-2T	1931
—	6697	GWR	5600	0-6-2T	1928
Burton Agnes Hall	6998	GWR	'Hall'	4-6-0	1949
—	7202	GWR	7200	2-8-2T	1934
Cookham Manor	7808	GWR	'Manor'	4-6-0	1938
—	D3771	BR	08	0-6-0DE	1959
Pontyberem	2	Burry Port & Gwendraeth Valley Rly		0-6-0ST	1900
Shannon	5	Wantage Tramway		0-4-0WT	1857

*expected to be repatriated from Australia during spring 2000

Industrial locomotives

Name	No	Builder	Type	Built
Bonnie Prince Charlie	1	RSH (7544)	0-4-0ST	1949
—	26	Hunslet (5238)	0-6-0DH	1962

Locomotive notes: Locomotives available in 2000 should be: 22, 1388, 3738, 4144, 4866, 5051. Locomotives under restoration include: 1340, 3650, 3822, 5322, 6023, 7202. Construction of the Firefly Trust's reproduction broad gauge locomotive *Firefly* is being undertaken

Stock
Over 40 ex-GWR coaches are preserved along with numerous ex-GWR freight wagons

Owners
5 on loan from the National Railway Museum

the passenger train, interrupted by Travelling Post Office demonstrations and turning of the locomotives on some days
Special events: Day Out with Thomas the Tank Engine — 3-5 March, 6-8 October; Didcot Steam 2000 (visiting locomotives & up to 2,000 models) — 27 May-4 June;

Photographers' Evening (to 9pm) — 27/28 October; Thomas Santa Special — 15-17, 23/24 December; New Year Steamings — 31 December-1 January 2001
Facilities for disabled: Steps at access from station subway may cause problems, but assistance can normally be provided (advance

notification is useful)
Membership details: Charles Roberts, at above address
Membership journals: *Great Western Echo* — quarterly; *National Newsletter* — seven times annually

---

| Operating Museum | East Anglia Transport Museum | Suffolk |

Member: HRA, TT

The East Suffolk Light Railway is the title given to the 2ft gauge railway, which winds its way some 300yd or so along the northern perimeter of the museum site, between the stations of Chapel Road and Woodside. The railway commenced operation in 1973 and aims to re-create a typical passenger-carrying light railway of years gone by. Many aspects of railway interest can be found along its length. The track came from Leziate sand quarry and Canvey Island, as well as from the Southwold Railway. There is also a signalbox from the Lowestoft-Great Yarmouth line, and signals from various local locations; all of which help to set the overall scene. Please note that the signalbox is being relocated during 2000 and might not be available for viewing
Location: Carlton Colville, three miles south-west of Lowestoft in Suffolk
OS reference: TM 505903
Operating society/organisation:

Industrial locomotives

Name	No	Builder	Type	Built
—	2	M/Rail (5912)	4wDM	1934
—	4	R/Hornsby (177604)	4wDM	1936
Thorpeness	5	M/Rail (22209)	4wDM	1964
Orfordness	6	M/Rail (22211)	4wDM	1964

Stock

Locally designed and built covered coach and brake van, suitable for wheelchairs. Small selection of wagons. Van body ex-Southwold Railway

East Anglia Transport Museum Society Ltd, Chapel Road, Carlton Colville, Lowestoft, Suffolk NR33 8BL
Telephone: (01502) 518459
Car park: Adjacent
Access by public transport: Eastern Counties L11, L12 & 171 (Monday-Saturday); Blue Bus 171 and Eastern Counties L18 & L19 (Sundays and Bank Holidays) from Lowestoft. Main line rail, Oulton Broad South (1.5 miles)
On site facilities: Refreshments, picnic area, souvenir and bookshop, toilets, working transport museum, including trams, narrow gauge railway, trolleybuses, steamrollers

and other commercial and public transport vehicles. Unlimited free rides
Public opening: Easter weekend, and then Sundays and Bank Holiday Mondays from 30 April to 24 September. Wednesdays and Saturdays June to September inclusive. Midsummer opening, daily 15 July to 3 September. Open from 14.00.
Special events: Please phone for details
Special notes: Limited facilities for the disabled. Pre-booked party rates
Membership details: From the above address

| Steam Centre | East Anglian Railway Museum | Essex |

Member: HRA, TT, RM, MLOA, AIM, EATB, EETB

Adjacent to Chappel Viaduct which is the most spectacular railway structure in East Anglia
Location: Chappel & Wakes Colne Station, near Colchester CO6 2DS
OS reference: TL 898289
Chairman: Gordon V. Adams
Operating society/organisation: East Anglian Railway Museum,

Chappel & Wakes Colne Station, Station Road, Wakes Colne, Essex CO6 2DS. Registered charity No 1001579
Telephone: Colchester (01206) 242524
Fax: (01206) 242524
Internet address: e-mail — earm@btinternet.com
Car park: On site
Access by public transport: Great

Eastern Chappel & Wakes Colne station. Also Eastern National/Hedingham Omnibus service No 88 Colchester-Halstead. Sundays Eastern National No 88C Colchester-Halstead
On site facilities: Refreshments, comprehensive bookshop, museum, signalboxes, souvenir shop, picnic area, miniature railway, heritage centre and toilets

England

Public opening: Daily 10.00-16.30
Special events: Not advised; please contact for details
Family tickets: Available on all days (unlimited rides on steam days)
Special notes: Special steam days are held first Sunday of month March-August inclusive and October, plus Bank Holidays, Wednesdays and Sundays in August. Three restored signalboxes, large goods shed and restoration shed. Original Victorian country junction station. Schools days and Santa steamings. Disabled visitors welcome — prior advice appreciated. Guided tours by prior arrangement. Buffet open daily May-October
Membership details: Membership Secretary, 50 Ayr Way, Rise Park, Romford, Essex RM1 4UH
Membership journal: *Stour Valley Steam* — 3 times/year

Locomotives and multiple-units

Name	No	Origin	Class	Type	Built
A. J. Hill	69621	GER	N7	0-6-2T	1924
—	D2279	BR	04	0-6-0DM	1960
—	D3940	BR	08	0-6-0DE	1960
—	50599	BR	108	DMBS	1958
—	56491	BR	108	DTC	1960
—	51568	BR	108	DMCL	1959
—	52053	BR	108	DMCL	1960

Industrial locomotives

Name	No	Builder	Type	Built
Jubilee	—	Bagnall (2542)	0-4-0ST	1936
—	1074	Barclay (1047)	0-4-0ST	1905
Belvoir	—	Barclay (2350)	0-6-0ST	1954
—	2	M/Vick	0-4-0E	1912
Jeffery	2039	Peckett (2039)	0-4-0ST	1943
Penn Green	54	RSH (7031)	0-6-0ST	1941
—	AMW144	Barclay (333)	0-4-0DM	1938
—	23	Fowler (4220039)	0-4-0DH	1965
—	2029	Simplex (2029)	0-4-0PM	1920

Locomotive notes: 69621 is operational, 80151 approaching completion

Stock
4 ex-BR Mk 1s; 1 ex-BR sleeping coach; 1 ex-BR Mk 1 full brake; 1 ex-LNER Buffet car; 1 ex-LNER pigeon van; 1 ex-LNER TSO coach; 1 fully restored GER 6-wheel full brake; 1 GER 6-wheel family saloon; 1 GER fully restored 4-wheel coach; 1 ex-GER bogie coach; 1 MSL 6-wheel coach; 1 SR PMV; 1 ex-BR CCT; 1 ex-BR 13-ton open wagon; 2 ex-BR 16-ton mineral wagons; 1 Lomac wagon; 1 ex-LMS 12-ton open wagon; 3 Wickham trolleys; 1 GWR Toad Brakevan; 1 ex-BR brake van; Somersham 'pump' trolley, 1 Grafton steam crane

---

Timetable Service	East Kent Railway	Kent

Member: HRA
The East Kent Light Railway Society was formed in 1985 with the aim of preserving the remaining 3-mile section of the Colonel Stephens light railway which originally ran from Shepherdswell to Wingham. Passenger-carrying operations between Shepherdswell and Eythorne started during 1995, and 1996 saw the first steam on the line for over 30 years. A future extension to Tilmanstone is planned
Location: Shepherdswell (EKLR) Station, Shepherdswell, Dover, Kent
OS reference: TR 258483
Operating society/organisation: East Kent Light Railway Society
Car park: Shepherdswell and Eythorne stations
Access by public transport: Connex South Eastern trains to

Multiple-units

Name	No	Origin	Class	Type	Built
—	65373*	BR	2EPB/416	DMBS	1953
—	68001	BR	MLV/419	MLV	1959
—	77558*	BR	2EPB/416	DTS	1953

*unit No 5759

Industrial locomotives

Name	No	Builder	Type	Built
Spitfire	—	Barclay (1964)	0-4-0ST	1929
—	—	Barclay (2248)	0-4-0ST	1948
Richborough Castle	—	E/Electric (D1197)	0-6-0D	1967
The Buffs	—	R/Hornsby (466616)	0-6-0DH	1961
Snowdon	—	Fowler (416002)	0-4-0DM	1952
Chislet	—	R/Hornsby (294268)	4wDM	1951
St Dunstan	—	Avonside (2004)	0-6-0ST	1927

Rolling stock
Leyland Experimental coach, LMS brake third, 2 x LMS full brake (BG), BR Mk 1 2 TSOs, BSK, FK, BR Mk 2A first brake, BR Mk 2 TSO and a selection of freight vehicles.

England

Shepherdswell station (adjacent).
Bus — Stagecoach East Kent
(limited service, not Sundays), Tel:
(01227) 472082
On site facilities: Light
refreshments, book and souvenir
shop, plus 3.5/5in gauge steam
railway. Picnic area and toilets.
Signalbox and small shop opening
at Eythorne during 2000
Public opening: Weekends and
Thursdays for static displays and
site facilities throughout the year.
Passenger trains — Easter-
Christmas
Special events: Easter Bunny
Specials — 21-24 April; Teddy

Owners
St Dunstan on long-term loan from British Coal
LMS BG the 33046 Fund
Leyland Experimental Coach the Nene Valley Railway
Multiple-units the EPB Preservation Group

Bears' Picnic — 28/29 May;
Father's Day Specials — 18 June;
Gala Weekend — 15/16 July;
Minis Transport Gala — 5/6
August; Know Your Railway
Weekend — 2/3 September; Ghost
Trains — 28/29 October; Santa
Specials — 26 November, and
weekends 2 to 24 December.
Events & site answerphone:

(01304) 832042
Facilities for disabled: Limited
access to buffet, and platforms at
both stations
Membership details: Mr
B. Hancock, 33 Beaufield,
Whitfield, Dover, Kent CT16 3JW
Membership journal: *East Kent
Railway News,* 4 times a year

East Lancashire Railway

Timetable Service

Lancashire

Member: HRA, TT
A very popular railway run by the
East Lancs Railway Society in
close co-operation with local
authorities, the line won the 1987
ARPS award. Visit the line to find
out the cause of the line's
popularity and success
Location: Bolton Street Station,
Bury, Lancashire BL9 0EY
OS reference: SD 803109
Publicity Director: Graham
Vevers
Operating society/organisation:
East Lancashire Railway
Preservation Society
Telephone: (0161) 764 7790
Access by public transport: Main
line services to Manchester, Bolton,
Rochdale and Burnley. Metrolink
from central Manchester to Bury
Interchange. Various bus services
also operate to Bury, Ramsbottom
or Rawtenstall from the main line
stations listed
On site facilities: Refreshments
normally available when trains are
running. Buffet car service on most
trains. Souvenir shop, transport
museum
Length of line: Approximately 8
miles
Public opening: Steam and diesel-
hauled services operate on
Saturdays, Sundays and Bank
Holidays throughout the year. Santa
Specials (advanced booking only)
in December
Special events: August — Teddy
Bears' Picnic; Santa Specials —

Locomotives and multiple-units

Name	No	Origin	Class	Type	Built
—	5029	GWR	'Castle'	4-6-0	1934
—	7229	GWR	7200	2-8-2T	1935
—	52322	L&Y	27	0-6-0	1896
—	42765	LMS	5P4F	2-6-0	1927
—	45337	LMS	5MT	4-6-0	1937
—	45407	LMS	5MT	4-6-0	1937
Leander	5690	LMS	'Jubilee'	4-6-0	1936
—	46441	LMS	2MT	2-6-0	1950
—	46428	LMS	2MT	2-6-0	1948
—	47324	LMS	3F	0-6-0T	1926
Taw Valley†	34027	SR	BB	4-6-2	1946
Tangmere	34067	SR	BB	4-6-2	1947
Duke of Gloucester	71000	BR	8P	4-6-2	1954
—	73156	BR	5MT	4-6-0	1956
—	75014	BR	4MT	4-6-0	1951
—	76079	BR	4MT	2-6-0	1957
—	80097	BR	4MT	2-6-4T	1954
Morning Star	92207	BR	9F	2-10-0	1959
—	388	USATC	S160	2-8-0	1942
—	D335	BR	40	1Co-Co1	1961
—	D345	BR	40	1Co-Co1	1961
3rd Carabinier	D99	BR	45	1Co-Co1	1961
Valiant	50015	BR	50	Co-Co	1967
Onslaught	D832	BR	42	B-B	1961
Western Prince	D1041	BR	52	C-C	1962
—	D2767	BR	—	0-4-0DH	1960
—	D2774	BR	—	0-4-0DH	1960
—	11506	BR	01	0-4-0DM	1956
—	D2062	BR	03	0-6-0DM	1959
—	20087	BR	20	Bo-Bo	1961
—	D5054	BR	24	Bo-Bo	1960
—	D5705	BR	28	Co-Bo	1958
Royal Highland Fusilier	D9019	BR	55	Co-Co	1961
—	37197	BR	37	Co-Co	1964
—	D7076	BR	35	B-B	1963
—	33117	BR	33	Bo-Bo	1960
—	D9531	BR	14	0-6-0DH	1965

England

weekends in December; Diesel Enthusiasts' Weekend and Friends of Thomas the Tank Engine Days — please apply for details; Irwell Valley Diner, Wine & Dine Trains (advance booking only — please apply for details)

Special notes: The Society re-opened the Bury-Summerseat-Ramsbottom section in 1987 and the Ramsbottom-Irwell-Rawtenstall section in 1991

Membership details: D. Flood

Membership journal: *The East Lancashire Railway News* — twice yearly

Marketing name: East Lancs

Owners
D345 the Class 40 Preservation Society
D5705 and 45135 the Pioneer Diesel Group
75014 the 75014 Locomotive Operators Group
73156 the Bolton Steam Locomotive Co

Gateshead	D1501	BR	47	Co-Co	1962
—	D3232	BR	08	0-6-0DE	1956
—	08479	BR	08	0-6-0DE	1958
—	7069	LMS	—	0-6-0DE	1936
—	51285	Cravens	105	DMBC	1958
—	51813	BRCW	110	DMBC	1961
—	51842	BRCW	110	DMCL	1961
—	56121	Cravens	105	DTC	1956
—	59701	BRCW	110	DMCL	1961
—	65451	BR	504	DMBS	1958
—	77172	BR	504	DTS	1958
—	79998*	BR	—	DMBS	1958
—	79999*	BR	—	DTCL	1958

*battery-electric Wickham Railcar multiple-unit
†at Riley & Sons Ltd for restoration

Industrial locomotives

Name	No	Builder	Type	Built
Gothenburg	32	H/Clarke (680)	0-6-0T	1903
Phoenix*	70	H/Clarke (1464)	0-6-0T	1921
—	1	Barclay (1927)	0-4-0ST	1927
—	DH16	Sentinel (10175)	4wDH	1964
—	—	Sentinel (10204)	4wDH	1964
MR Mercury	1	Hibberd (3438)	4wDM	1950
Winfield	—	M/Rail (9009)	4wDM	1948
—	4002	H/Clarke (D1076)	6wDM	1959

*on loan to Chinnor & Princes Risborough Railway

Stock
44 BR Mk 1 coaches; 1 GWR coach; 1 Bogie Guards coach; Cravens 50-ton steam crane RS1013/50 (1930), NER 5-ton hand crane DB915390 (1880) and Smiths 5-ton diesel crane (1939) plus over 80 goods vehicles

---

Timetable Service	(**East Somerset Railway**)	Somerset

Member: HRA, TT

Set up by the artist, David Shepherd, 'the man who loves giants', the railway line is 'home' to *Black Prince* and *The Green Knight* housed in their 'traditional' shed. As one might expect, Cranmore station is well laid out and aesthetically pleasing. An art gallery is situated at Cranmore station where prints of his, and other artists', paintings can be bought. One of only two remaining all-steam railways in the country

General Manager: Peter Chandler

Headquarters: East Somerset Railway, (Cranmore Railway Station) Shepton Mallet, Somerset BA4 4QP

OS reference: ST 664429

Telephone: Cranmore (01749) 880417

Locomotives

Name	No	Origin	Class	Type	Built
—	6634	GWR	5600	0-6-2T	1928
—	B110	LBSCR	E1	0-6-0T	1877
—	47493	LMS	3F	0-6-0T	1927
—	68846	GNR	J52	0-6-0ST	1899
The Green Knight**	75029	BR	4MT	4-6-0	1954
Black Prince†	92203	BR	9F	2-10-0	1959
—*	390	ZSR	7	4-8-0	1896

*3ft 6in gauge, on loan to Bristol Museum
†on loan to Gloucestershire Warwickshire Railway
**on loan to North Yorkshire Moors Railway

Industrial locomotives

Name	No	Builder	Type	Built
Lord Fisher	1398	Barclay (1398)	0-4-0ST	1915
—	705	Barclay (2047)	0-4-0ST	1937
Lady Nan	1719	Barclay (1719)	0-4-0ST	1920

Stock
10 ex-BR Mk 1 coaches; 25 assorted wagons, mostly LMS and SR; Rhodesian Railways sleeping car 1808. Home to the 'Riviera' main line vehicles. Frequent main line visitors

Fax: (01749) 880764
Main station: Cranmore
Car park: Cranmore — free
Refreshment facilities: Restaurant 'Whistle Stop' situated in car park offering lunches, snacks, teas, etc. Group catering by arrangement. Picnic areas at Cranmore, Merryfield Lane stations and depot. On-train catering by arrangement. Private saloon trips
Souvenir shop: Cranmore
On site facilities: Museum, Victorian style engine shed and workshops, children's play area. Railway and wildlife prints for sale in art gallery
Depot: Cranmore West
Length of line: 2.75 miles
Passenger trains: Cranmore to Mendip Vale. Stations at Cranmore

West, Merryfield Lane and Mendip Vale, unlimited train travel
Period of public operation: 2, 9, 16, 21-24, 29/30 April, 1, 7, 14, 21, 27/29, 31 May, 3/4, 7, 10/11, 14, 17/18, 21, 24/25, 28 June, 1/2, 5/6, 8/9, 10/11, 15/16, 19/20, 22/23, 26/27, 29/30 July, 2-6, 9-13, 16-20, 23-28, 30/31 August, 1-3, 6, 9/10, 13, 29/30 September, 7/8, 14/15, 21/22, 25, 28/29 October, 5, 12, 19, 26 November, Santa Specials 2/3, 9/10, 12, 16/17, 21-23 December. 2001 dates: 1, 7, 14, 21, 28 January, 4, 11, 18, 25 February
  Last admission 30min before closing time. Each day ticket allows unlimited travel on all timetabled trains
Special Mother's Day Wine & Dine — 2 April; Murder Mystery

— 6 May; Day Out with Thomas — 27-29 May; Father's Day Wine & Dine — 18 June; Transport Through the Ages — 2 July; Jazz Night — 22 July; Day Out with Thomas — 12/13 August; 60s Evening — 26 August; All Steamed Up — 26-28 August; Santa Specials — 2/3, 10/17, 13, 16/17, 21-23 December; Christmas Wine & Dine — 15 December
Facilities for disabled: Yes
Special notes: Footplate experiences courses available
Membership details: Please apply to above address, SAE for brochure
Membership journal: *East Somerset Railway Journal* — quarterly
Marketing name: The Strawberry Line

Steam Centre — Elsecar Heritage Centre — South Yorkshire

The Elsecar Railway runs between Elsecar Heritage Centre and the canal basin at Hemingfield, through a scenic conservation area alongside the Elsecar branch of the Dearne & Dove Canal
Location/headquarters: Elsecar Heritage Centre, Wath Road, Elsecar, Barnsley, South Yorkshire S74 8HJ
Telephone: (01226) 740203
Fax: (01226) 350239
Main station: Elsecar
Length of line: 1-mile, 20min journey
Car park location: On site
Access by public transport: Main line Elsecar from Sheffield, Huddersfield, Leeds
Refreshment facilities: On site
Souvenir shops: On site
On site facilities: Refreshments, souvenir shop, toilets

Industrial locomotives

Name	No	Builder	Type	Built
Countess Fitzwilliam	544996	R/Hornsby(382808)	4wDM	1968
Earl Fitzwilliam	1917	Avonside (1917)	0-6-0ST	1923
Earl of Stafford	2895	YEC (2895)	0-6-0DH	1963

Stock
3 ex-BR Mk 1 coaches

Museum: Attractions include 'The Power House' science centre, Science Track, Educational Workshops, 'Living History' centre, Bottle Collection, Hot Metal Press, Newcomen Beam Engine, working crafts people, various special events
Facilities for disabled: There are four disabled persons' toilets at different locations on the site. All buildings are fully wheelchair accessible at ground floor level
Public opening: Daily (except

25 December-1 January) 10.00-17.00
Special events: Include Friends of Thomas the Tank Engine and Victorian Christmas Fayre — contact for details. Halloween Steamings — 29 October 2000
Special notes: Entrance to site is free. Charges made for some attractions ('passport' and family tickets available). Santa specials run during December

---

Timetable Service — Embsay & Bolton Abbey Steam Railway — North Yorkshire

Member: HRA, TT
Yorkshire's 'Friendly Line' operates from Embsay station built in 1888. The railway is very

family-orientated with many events for children. The enthusiast is not forgotten, with one of the finest collections of ex-industrial tank

engines in Britain. The railway is currently constructing a new museum and workshop complex, and the line's extension to Bolton

Abbey opened in 1997. Bolton Abbey station has been built to the original Midland Railway style. An atmosphere of the rural branch line prevails, which is operated by ex-industrial locomotives

Operating Committee: Peter Burke

Business & Marketing Manager: Stephen Walker. Tel: (01756) 710614 (ext 3). Fax: (01756) 710720

Location: Bolton Abbey Station, Bolton Abbey, Skipton, Yorkshire BD23 6AF

OS reference: SE 007533

Operating society/organisation: Yorkshire Dales Railway Museum Trust

Telephone: Skipton(01756) 710614, 24hr Talking Timetable (01756) 795189

Car parks: Embsay and Bolton Abbey

Access by public transport: Pennine bus from Skipton, National Park bus from Ilkley summer Sundays

On site facilities: Souvenir shop at Bolton Abbey and Embsay — transport and industrial archaeological bookshop at Embsay

Catering facilities: Buffet and bar on most trains. Buffet at both Bolton Abbey and Embsay stations. Special charters; meals for parties can be arranged on normal service trains, subject to advance booking. Please write for further details

Length of line: 4.5 miles

Public opening: Steam trains run every Sunday throughout the year, weekends from April to October. Tuesdays in May, June and early July, daily (except for Monday and Friday) from mid July until the end of August. Trains run regularly between 10.45 and late afternoon

Special events: Friends of Thomas the Tank Engine at Easter, Spring and August Bank Holidays and Santa Trains from mid-November until December.
Certain summer Sundays will be designated Vintage Train days when in addition to a normal passenger train service a vintage train will operate using historic coaches

Special notes: Steam rides are on

Locomotives and multiple-units

Name	No	Origin	Class	Type	Built
—	D2203	BR	04	0-6-0DM	1952
—	NCB 38 (D9513)	BR	14	0-6-0DH	1964
—	LEV2	Derby	—	Railbus	1984
—	52006	BR	107	DMBS	1960
—	52031	BR	107	DMBL	1960

Industrial locomotives

Name	No	Builder	Type	Built
Annie	9	Peckett (1159)	0-4-0ST	1908
Gladiator	8	H/Clarke (1450)	0-6-0ST	1922
Slough Estates No 5	—	H/Clarke (1709)	0-6-0ST	1939
Primrose No 2	S121	Hunslet (3715)	0-6-0ST	1952
Ann	—	Sentinel (7232)	4wVB	1927
Beatrice	7	Hunslet (2705)	0-6-0ST	1945
Airedale	3	Hunslet (1440)	0-6-0ST	1923
York No 1	—	Yorkshire (2474)	0-4-0ST	1949
—	140	H/Clarke (1821)	0-6-0T	1948
Illingworth	—	H/Clarke	0-6-0ST	—
Spitfire	S112	Hunslet (2414)	0-6-0ST	1942
Wheldale	S134	Hunslet (3168)	0-6-0ST	1944
—	69	Hunslet (3785)	0-6-0ST	1953
Monkton No 1	—	Hunslet (3788)	0-6-0ST	1953
—	22	Barclay (2320)	0-4-0ST	1952
—	68005	RSH (7169)	0-6-0ST	1945
Thomas	4	RSH (7661)	0-4-0ST	1950
H. W. Robinson	—	Fowler (4100003)	0-4-0DM	1946
—	MDE15	Baguley/Drewry (2136)	4wDM	1938
—	887	R/Hornsby (394009)	4wDM	1955
—	—	Wickham (7610)	2w-2PMR	1957
—	—	Lister (9993)*	4wPM	1938
—	—	Lister (10225)*	4wPM	1938
—	—	R/Hornsby (175418)*	4wDM	1936
—	—	R/Hornsby*	4wDM	—
—	—	M/Rail (8979)*	4wDM	1946
—	—	M/Rail (5213)*	4wDM	1930
—	—	R/Hornsby	4wDM	1957
Meaford	—	Barclay (440)	0-4-0DH	1958
—	36	H/Clarke (D1037)	0-6-0DM	1958

*2ft gauge

Stock
18 ex-BR Mk 1 coaches (SK, CK, 2xBCK, 5xTSO, 2xRMB, 1xBSO(T), 1xRBR and 1xSLS), 4 ex-LNER coaches; 2 SR parcels vans; Freight stock and service vehicles, SR and GW brakes

Owners
52006/31 the Class 107 Ltd

4.5-mile line to the new station and picnic area at Bolton Abbey. Old Midland Railway buildings, fine collection of industrial locomotives

Membership details: Membership Secretary at above address

Membership journal: *Dale Steam, YDR News* — 4 times/year

Exmoor Steam Railway

First opened to the public in 1990 the Exmoor Steam Railway has been continually developed, the latest being the opening of a new terminus named Cape of Good Hope Farm reached via a spiral section from Exmoor Town which is adjacent to the main building

Location: Cape of Good Hope Farm alongside the B3230 to the north of South Molton in North Devon

Contact address: Exmoor Steam Railway, Cape of Good Hope Farm, Bratton Fleming, Devon EX32 7SN

Telephone/fax: (01598) 710711

OS reference: SS 661382

Car park: On site

Access by public transport: Bus service No 310 (Barnstaple-Lynton)

Locomotives (12.25in gauge)

Name	No	Builder	Type	Built
Denzil	—	ESR	0-4-2T	1995
Charlie	—	ESR	2-4-2	1998

Locomotives (2ft gauge)

Name	No	Builder	Type	Built
—	87	B/Peacock	2-6-2+2-6-2	1958
—	109	B/Peacock	2-6-2+2-6-2	1958
—	115	B/Peacock	2-6-2+2-6-2	1958
—	130	B/Peacock	2-6-2+2-6-2	1958

All former South African Railways Class NGG16, and on static display

On site facilities: 12.25in gauge passenger-carrying line giving 2-mile return journey, gift shop, refreshments (light lunches, cream teas etc)

Opening times: March, April and October — Sundays and Wednesdays only; May — Sundays, Tuesdays and Wednesdays; June and July — Sundays, Tuesdays, Wednesdays and Thursdays; August — daily (except Saturdays); September — Sundays, Tuesdays, Wednesdays and Thursdays

---

Foxfield Steam Railway

Member: HRA

The railway, built in 1893 to connect a colliery to the national system, closed in 1965, has been re-opened.

Chairman: Ian A. Rutherford

Headquarters: Foxfield Steam Railway, Blythe Bridge, Stoke-on-Trent

Telephone: (01782) 396210 (weekends), (01270) 874959 (weekdays)

Fax: (01270) 874959

Main station: Blythe Bridge (Caverswall Road)

OS reference: SJ 957421

Car park: Blythe Bridge

Access by public transport: Main line railway Blythe Bridge (400yd). PMT bus service to Blythe Bridge

Refreshment facilities: Blythe Bridge

Souvenir shop: Blythe Bridge

Passenger trains: Steam-hauled trains operate from Blythe Bridge (Caverswall Road) to Dilhorne Park and return

Family ticket: Available (2 adults

Industrial locomotives

Name	No	Builder	Type	Built
Whiston	—	Hunslet (3694)	0-6-0ST	1950
Wimblebury	—	Hunslet (3839)	0-6-0ST	1956
Roker	—	RSH (7006)	0-4-0CT	1940
Meaford No 2	2	RSH	0-6-0T	1951
Millom	—	Avonside (1563)	0-4-0ST	1908
Cranford	—	Avonside (1919)	0-6-0ST	1924
Lewisham	—	Bagnall (2221)	0-6-0ST	1927
Hawarden	—	Bagnall (2623)	0-4-0ST	1940
Florence	2	Bagnall (3059)	0-6-0ST	1953
Wolstanton No 3	—	Bagnall (3150)	0-6-0DM	1960
Bagnall	—	Bagnall (3207)	0-4-0DH	1961
—	—	B/Peacock (1827)	0-4-0ST	1879
—	4101	Dubs (4101)	0-4-0CT	1901
—	—	E/Electric (788)	4wBE	1930
Spondon No 2	—	E/Electric (1130)	4wBE	1939
—	6	R/Heath	0-4-0ST	1886
Henry Cort	—	Peckett (933)	0-4-0ST	1903
Lion	—	Peckett (1351)	0-4-0ST	1914
Ironbridge No 1	—	Peckett (1803)	0-4-0ST	1933
—	11	Peckett (2081)	0-4-0ST	1947
Moss Bay	—	K/Stuart (4167)	0-4-0ST	1920
—	—	K/Stuart (4388)	0-4-0ST	1926
Rom River	—	K/Stuart (4421)	6wDM	1929
—	1	Barclay (1984)	0-4-0F	1930
Meaford No 4	—	Barclay (486)	0-6-0DH	1964
Helen	—	Simplex (2262)	4wDM	1924

England

+ 2 children or 1 adult + 4 children)
Length of line: 2.75 miles
Period of public operation: Steam trains operate Sundays and Bank Holiday Mondays only, April-September inclusive between Blythe Bridge and Dilhorne Park.
Special events: Please contact for details. Santa Specials, weekends in December (advanced booking essential)
Facilities for disabled: Access to majority of facilities is on the level. For special requirements, prior notice is desirable
Membership journal: *Foxfield News* — quarterly

Name	No	Builder	Type	Built
—	820	Drewry (2157)	4wDM	1941
Amoco	—	R/Hornsby (395305)	0-4-0DM	1956
Gas-oil	—	R/Hornsby (408496)	0-4-0DM	1957
Hercules	—	Ruston (242915)	4wDM	1946
—	—	R/Hornsby	0-4-0DE	—
Megan	—	Thomas Hill (103C)	0-4-0DH	1957
Marston	3	H/Leslie (3581)	0-6-0ST	1924
Thorntwaite & Everard				

Stock
5 coaches; 4 scenery vans (some converted for other uses); 29 assorted wagons, 16-ton mineral wagons; 1 rail-mounted self-propelled diesel-electric crane

Timetable Service	**Gartell Light Railway**	Somerset

Owned and operated by three generations of the Gartell family, the Gartell Light Railway offers visitors the chance to travel by train along the route of the old Somerset & Dorset Joint Railway. From Pinesway Junction to Park Lane the line runs along a half-mile section of the S&D trackbed. Work has started on an extension northwards from Pinesway Junction along the S&D formation towards Templecombe. A flyover has already been constructed to carry the extension over the existing line and track has been laid as far as the old S&D level crossing keeper's cottage. The level crossing itself is to be reinstated in the spring of 2000. The GLR's first steam locomotive, a locally-built 0-4-2T, specially designed to cope with the steep gradients and sharp curves of the quarter-mile section from Common Lane up to Pinesway Junction, entered service in 1998 and has proved a great success. On most open days a three-train service is operated, with departures every 15min and trains crossing at Pinesway Junction. The GLR is fully signalled using a variety of upper and lower quadrant, colour-light and shunt signals controlled by two full size signalboxes
Location/headquarters: Gartell Light Railway, Common Lane, Yenston, Nr Templecombe,

Industrial locomotives
2ft gauge:

Name	No	Builder	Type	Built
Andrew	2	R/Hornsby	4wDH	1964/5
Alison	5	A. Keef (10)	4wDH	1983
Mr G	6	N. Dorset Loco Wks	0-4-2T	1998

0-4-0 steam locomotive and Bo-Bo diesel-hydraulic currently under construction

Rolling stock — coaches: 6 enclosed bogie coaches, 3 covered open-sided bogie coaches

Rolling stock — wagons: bogie PW gang/tool, goods guard's van, tool van, open wagon, bogie hopper, bogie open, bogie well, 2 bogie flats

Somerset BA8 0NB
Telephone: (01963) 370752
General Manager: John Gartell
Main station: Common Lane
Other stations: Pinesway Junction, Park Lane (southern terminus)
Car park: Large free car park at Common Lane
OS reference: ST 718218
Access by public transport: 1.5 miles south-east of Templecombe railway station
Refreshment facilities: Trackside refreshment room at Common Lane serving a range of hot and cold snacks and drinks. Lakeside picnic area at Pinesway Junction
Visitor Centre: Common Lane
Souvenir shop: Common Lane
Museum: Common Lane —

Templecombe Railway Museum (collection of artefacts, photographs, documents, models, etc recording the history of Templecombe station)
Depot: Common Lane (not open to public)
Length of line: 3/4-mile
Facilities for disabled: Enclosed passenger coach with accommodation for one wheelchair. Wheelchair access to refreshment room via ramp
Period of public operation: 1, 29 May; 25 June; 30 July; 27/28 August; 24 September, 29 October. 10.30-16.30
Special events: Traction engine display — 25 June; Santa Specials — 10, 17 December

Gloucestershire Warwickshire Railway

Member: HRA

Part of an ambitious project to link Cheltenham with Stratford, much has been done to re-create the railway and buildings that made up this cross-country route. The railway is home to many owners of private locomotives and rolling stock, so from time to time the items on display may vary. The extension from Gotherington to Cheltenham Racecourse is now under way

Location: Toddington station, Toddington

OS reference: SO 050322

Operating society/organisation: Gloucestershire Warwickshire Steam Railway plc, The Station, Toddington, Cheltenham, Glos GL54 5DT

Telephone: Toddington (01242) 621405

Main station: Toddington

Other public stations: Winchcombe

Access by public transport: Hourly service from Cheltenham to Greet for Winchcombe station. Local bus service Castleways will answer timetable queries on (01242) 602949

Car park: On site

On site facilities: Sales, catering, narrow gauge rides, toilets

Length of line: 6.5 miles

Public opening: On non-operating days the station is unmanned but visitors are welcome. Public services weekends, Bank Holiday Mondays, between March and October. Some summer weekdays and Sundays throughout the year

Special events: Diesel Gala — 24-26 March; Day Out with Thomas — 15/16 April, 12/13 August; Famous Named Trains Weekend — 28/29 May; Steam & Vintage Gala — 14/15 October; Model Railway Exhibition — 18 November; Santa & Mince Pie Specials — December/New Year

Special notes: The site is being developed as the headquarters of the railway between Cheltenham and Stratford. The GWR owns the railway land between Cheltenham

Locomotives and multiple-units

Name	No	Origin	Class	Type	Built
—	1450	GWR	1400	0-4-2T	1935
—	2807	GWR	2800	2-8-0	1905
Raveningham Hall	6960	GWR	6959	4-6-0	1944
Owsden Hall	6984	GWR	6959	4-6-0	1948
—	7069	LMS	—	0-6-0DE	1939
Peninsular & Oriental SNCo	35006	SR	MN	4-6-2	1941
—	45160	WD/TCCD	8F	2-8-0	1941
—	76077	BR	4MT	2-6-0	1956
Black Prince	92203	BR	9F	2-10-0	1959
—	03069	BR	03	0-6-0DM	1959
—	D2182	BR	03	0-6-0DM	1952
—	D9537	BR	14	0-6-0DH	1965
—	D9539	BR	14	0-6-0DH	1965
—	D9553	BR	14	0-6-0DH	1965
—	D8137	BR	20	Bo-Bo	1966
—	24081	BR	24	Bo-Bo	1960
—	26043	BR	26	Bo-Bo	1959
—	D5541	BR	31	A1A-A1A	1959
—	37099	BR	37	Co-Co	1962
—	37215	BR	37	Co-Co	1964
—	45149	BR	45	1Co-Co1	1961
—	47105	BR	47	Co-Co	1963
—	51134	BR	116	DMBS	1958
—	51147	BR	116	DMS	1958
—	51950	BR	108	DMBS	1960
—	52062	BR	108	DMC	1960

Industrial locomotives

Name	No	Builder	Type	Built
Byfield No 2	—	Bagnall (2655)	0-6-0ST	1941
—	19	Fowler (4240016)	0-6-0DH	1964
—	21	Fowler (4210130)	0-4-0DM	1957
—	—	H/Clarke (D615)	0-6-0DM	1938
John	—	Peckett (1976)	0-4-0ST	1939
King George	—	Hunslet (2409)	0-6-0ST	1942

Stock

4 ex-GWR coaches; 55 ex-BR coaches; 4 ex-LMS coach; Baguley-Drewry inspection vehicle; 2 Wickham trolleys; plus numerous wagons (including 10 brake vans, 45-ton steam crane, 18-ton diesel crane)

Owners

2807 the Cotswold Steam Preservation Ltd
35006 the P & O Locomotive Society
45160 and 7069 the Churchill (8F) Locomotive Co
92203 on long-term loan from East Somerset Railway
26043 and 45149 the Cotswold Mainline Diesel Group
D9537, D9539 and D9553 the Cotswold Diesel Preservation Group
37215 the Growler Group
47105 the Brush Type 4 Fund
51134 and 51147 the Llanelli Railway Society

and Broadway and operates over 6.5 miles from Toddington to Gotherington with an intermediate station at Winchcombe. The line is currently being extended towards Cheltenham

Guest locomotives will be operating during the year.

Family tickets available

Membership details: From above address

Membership journal: *The Cornishman* — quarterly

North Gloucestershire Railway
Industrial narrow gauge locomotives (2ft gauge)

Name	No	Builder	Type	Built
Isibutu	5	Bagnall (2820)	4-4-0T	1946
George B	—	Hunslet (680)	0-4-0ST	1898
Chaka	—	Hunslet (2075)	0-4-2T	1940
Justine	—	Jung (939)	0-4-0WT	1906
Brigadelok	—	Henschel (15968)	0-8-0T	1918
—	2	Lister (34523)	4wDM	1949
—	3	M/Rail (4565)	4wPM	1928
Spitfire	—	M/Rail (7053)	4wPM	1937
—	1	R/Hornsby (166010)	4wDM	1932
—	L5	R/Hornsby (181820)	4wDM	1936
—	—	R/Hornsby (354028)	4wDM	1953

Stock
3 coaches; 11 wagons

Timetable Service — Great Central Railway — Leicestershire

Member: HRA, TT

The original Great Central Railway's extension to London in 1899 was the last main line to be built in this country, most of which was closed in the 1960s. Steam-hauled services operate through attractive rolling Leicestershire countryside, crossing the picturesque Swithland reservoir. The railway's aim is to re-create the experience of British main line railway operation in the days of steam. The images of a main line are backed up by a double track line with long trains hauled by large locomotives

Headquarters: Great Central Railway plc, Loughborough Central Station, Great Central Road, Loughborough, Leicestershire LE11 1RW

Telephone: Loughborough (01509) 230726

Internet address: Website: www.gcrailway.co.uk
e-mail:
booking–office@gcrailway.co.uk

Main stations: Loughborough Central, Leicester North

Other public stations: Quorn & Woodhouse, Rothley

OS reference: SK 543194

Car park: Quorn, Rothley

Access by public transport: Loughborough main line station

Locomotives and multiple-units

Name	No	Origin	Class	Type	Built
Witherslack Hall	6990	GWR	'Hall'	4-6-0	1948
—	45231	LMS	5MT	4-6-0	1936
—	5305	LMS	5MT	4-6-0	1936
—	47406	LMS	3F	0-6-0T	1926
—	48305	LMS	8F	2-8-0	1943
—	1264	LNER	B1	4-6-0	1947
—	69523	LNER	N2	0-6-2T	1921
—	63601	GCR	8K	2-8-0	1919
Boscastle	34039	SR	WC	4-6-2	1946
Sir Lamiel	30777	SR	N15	4-6-0	1925
Brocklebank Line	35025	SR	MN	4-6-2	1948
—	78019	BR	2MT	2-6-0	1954
—	92212	BR	9F	2-10-0	1959
—	D3101	BR	08	0-6-0DE	1955
—	D4067	BR	10	0-6-0DE	1961
—	D8098	BR	20	Bo-Bo	1961
Harlech Castle	25265	BR	25	Bo-Bo	1963
—	31418	BR	31	A1A-A1A	1959
—	D5830	BR	31	A1A-A1A	1962
—	D123	BR	45	1Co-Co1	1961
—	D1705	BR	47	Co-Co	1965
—	51616	BR	127	DMBS	1959
—	51622	BR	127	DMBS	1959
—	59276	BR	120	TS	1958

Industrial locomotives

Name	No	Builder	Type	Built
Arthur Wright	D4279	Fowler (4210079)	0-4-0DE	1952
—	28	A/Barclay (400)	0-4-0DM	1956

Owners
69523 the Gresley Society
5305 the 5305 Locomotive Association
6990 the Witherslack Hall Locomotive Society

(0.75-mile). Trent, South Notts, and Arriva bus services to Loughborough bus station (0.75-mile). Some Arriva services pass bottom Great Central Road, 300yd.

Refreshment facilities: Licensed buffet car and light refreshments on all trains and at all stations. Saturday and Sunday lunches on 13.15 train; evening dining trains on most Saturday nights and Wednesday nights May-September; please contact railway for dates and reservations (advance booking recommended). Picnic areas at Quorn and Rothley stations. Most trains carry griddle car serving all-day Great Central breakfast and other hot food. Private charter trains available on request
Souvenir shop: Loughborough
Museum: Loughborough
Depot: Loughborough
Length of line: 8 miles
Passenger trains: Loughborough-Leicester North
Period of public operation:

1264 the Thompson B1 Locomotive Society
92212 the 92212 Holdings Ltd
63601 on loan from the National Railway Museum
30777 on loan from the National Railway Museum (under custody of the 5305 Locomotive Association)
D5830, D8098, 31418 and D1705 the Type 1 Locomotive Association

Weekends throughout the year and Bank Holiday Mondays. Daily Easter week, and mid May -late September.

Guided tours available by prior arrangement. School/party visits a speciality — Tel: (01509) 230726 for details
Special events: 1960s Gala — 25/26 March; 1940s Experience — 30 April/1 May; Adventures with Thomas — 6/7 May; Spring Gala — 27-29 May; Operation Sledgehammer (Wartime Weekend) — 17/18 June; Mails on Rails Gala — 24/25 June; *Steam Railway* Gala — 22/23 July; Adventures with Thomas — 17-28 August; Diesel Gala — 22-24 September; Autumn Gala — 7/8 October; Adventures

with Thomas — 14/15 October; Santa Specials — 25 November-24 December
Facilities for disabled: Special carriage for wheelchair/disabled persons (advance notice required). Wheelchair access good at Quorn and Rothley, can be arranged at Loughborough with advance notification. Boarding ramps at all stations
Membership & share details: Share enquiries: Company Secretary, Great Central Railway plc
Membership: Membership Secretary, Main Line Steam Trust Ltd. Both c/o above address

---

(Steam Centre) **Great Northern & East Lincolnshire Railway** (North East Lincolnshire)

Member: HRA
Headquarters: The Railway Station, Ludborough, Grimsby, NE Lincs DN36 5QS
Telephone: (01507) 363881
Contacts: David Ambler / Frank Street
Main station: Ludborough
Car park: Opposite station site
Access by public transport: No access by rail, very limited Grimsby-Louth bus service
Refreshment facilities: Light refreshments available in buffet car in bay platform
Souvenir shop: On site
Museum: On site
Depot: On site
Length of line: 500yd at present. Hoping to open extension to North Thornsby during 2000, giving a run of c2 miles
Period of public operation: Site open for static viewing all weekends except Christmas
Special events: Mother's Day — 2 April; Easter Special — 23/24 April; Teddy Bears' Picnic — 7

Locomotives and multiple-units

Name	No	Origin	Class	Type	Built
—	D3167	BR	08	0-6-0DE	1955

Industrial locomotives

Name	No	Builder	Type	Built
Lion	—	Peckett (1657)	0-6-0ST	1920
Fulstow No 2	—	Peckett (1749)	0-4-0ST	1928
Moorside	47	RSH (7849)	0-6-0ST	1955
M. F. P. No 1	—	Fowler (4210131)	0-4-0DM	1957
M. O. P. No 8	—	Fowler (4210145)	0-4-0DM	1958
—	4	R/Hornsby (375713)	0-4-0DM	1954
—	6	R/Hornsby (414303)	0-4-0DM	1957
—	7	R/Hornsby (421418)	0-4-0DM	1958

Stock
2 ex-BR coaches, several wagons

Owners
D3167 on loan from Lincoln City Council

May; Spring Bank Holiday — 28/29 May; Father's Day/Classic Cars — 18 June; Charity Day with stalls — 9 July; Family Fun Day — 30 July; Teddy Bears' Picnic — 13 August; August Bank Holiday — 28 August; Military Weekend/ 40s

Dance (Saturday evening) — 16/17September; Santa Specials — 10, 17 December
Membership journal: *On the Line* — 4 times/year

Great Whipsnade Railway

Location: Whipsnade Wild Animal Park, Dunstable, Bedfordshire LU6 2LF
Telephone: (01582) 872171 (extension 2270)
Fax: (01582) 872649
General Manager: Ian Gordon
Main station: Whipsnade Central
On site facilities: Car park (100yd), Souvenir shop, refreshments (30yd)
Period of public operation: January — no trains; February — half term; March — weekends only; April to July — daily (Weekdays diesels only/steam at weekends); August daily steam trains; September/October — daily (Weekdays diesels only/steam at

Locomotives

Name	No	Builder	Type	Built
Chevalier	1	M/Wardle (1877)	0-6-2T	1915
Excelsior	2	K/Stuart (1049)	0-4-2T	1908
Superior	4	K/Stuart (4034)	0-6-2T	1920
Victor	—	Fowler (4160004)	0-6-0DM	1951
Hector	—	Fowler (4160005)	0-6-0DM	1951
Mr Bill	10	R/Hornsby (221625)	0-4-0DM	1944
—	—*	Buch	0-6-0DM	—

*Polish State Railways Class LYD2

Rolling stock: 10 carriages, 9 wagons

weekends); November — no trains; December — steam, weekends & school holidays
Special events: Steam Weekend 2000 — 29/30 April, 1 May (two

engines in steam, traction engines, steam lorries, vintage cars and fire engines)
Facilities for disabled: Carriage designed for wheelchairs

Hollycombe Steam Collection

Member: TT
An extensive collection of working steam, including railways, traction engines, fairground rides, Bioscope, organs, the oldest Burrell Showman's engine *Emperor*, sawmill and engine from the paddle steamer *Caledonia*, set in woodlands and gardens
Location: Iron Hill, Hollycombe, Nr Liphook, Hants
OS reference: SU 852295
Operating society/organisation: Hollycombe Steam & Woodland Garden Society, Iron Hill, Midhurst Road, Liphook, Hants GU30 7LP
Telephone: Liphook (01428) 724900 (24hr answerphone)
Fax: (01428) 723682

Industrial locomotives

Name	No	Builder	Type	Built
Caledonia	70	Barclay (1995)	0-4-0WT	1931*
Jerry M	38	Hunslet (638)	0-4-0ST	1895*
Commander B	50	H/Leslie (2450)	0-4-0ST	1899
—	16	R/Hornsby	4wDM	1941*

*2ft gauge

Car park: On site
Access by public transport: Liphook main line station (1.5 miles)
On site facilities: Shop and refreshments, toilets, car park, *dogs allowed in car park only*
Length of lines: Standard gauge – quarter mile
2ft gauge 'Quarry Railway' – 1.5

miles
7.25in gauge – quarter mile
Public opening: All Easter weekend. Sundays and Bank Holidays 2 April-8 October. Daily 23 June-28 August. 13.00-17.00. Further open days/special events planned. Please phone for details

Irchester Narrow Gauge Railway Museum

Member: HRA
The aims of the controlling trust are to acquire and preserve narrow gauge railway locomotives, rolling stock and exhibits associated with

Northamptonshire and the East Midlands, to display the collection for the benefit of the public and to restore exhibits to working order so they may be demonstrated in a

proper manner
Location: Within Irchester Country Park, 2 miles south of Wellingborough
Operating society/organisation:

The Irchester Narrow Gauge Railway Trust, 71 Bedford Road, Cranfield, Bedford MK43 0EX

On site facilities: Shop, museum, demonstration line, picnic area

Access by public transport: Main line Wellingborough (Midland Road) station, buses to Irchester and Little Irchester

Car parks: Main park car parks

Toilets: Main park complex

Public opening: Every Sunday (summer 10.00-17.30, winter 10.00-16.00), at other times by arrangement. Steam and demonstration weekends are held on last full weekend of the month — March-October

Facilities for disabled: Museum and site on level, staff available if required

Industrial locomotives

Name	No	Builder	Type	Built
—	85*	Peckett (1870	0-6-0ST	1934
—	86*	Peckett (1871)	0-6-0ST	1934
—	87*	Peckett (2029)	0-6-0ST	1942
Cambrai	—*	Corpet (493)	0-6-0T	1888
—	ND3645*	R/Hornsby (211679)	4wDM	1941
—	—†	R/Hornsby (281290)	0-6-0DM	1949
—	ED10*	R/Hornsby (411322)	4wDM	1958
—	—†	M/Rail (1363)	4wPM	1918
The Rock	—*	Hunslet (2419)	0-4-0DM	1941

* metre gauge
† 3ft gauge

Membership details: Membership Secretary, 1 Wilby Street, Northampton NN1 5JX

Museum	**Ironbridge Gorge Museum**	Shropshire

The railway items form only a small part of the displays on two of the museum's main sites: Blists Hill and Coalbrookdale. The Blists Hill site offers an opportunity to see a number of industrial and other activities being operated in meticulously reconstructed period buildings. A working foundry is just one of the exciting exhibits. A full size working replica of Richard Trevithick's 1802 steam locomotive built by the Coalbrookdale Company can also be seen operating at certain times at the Blists Hill site. The Ironbridge Gorge was designated a World Heritage Site in 1987

Location: Ironbridge, Shropshire

OS reference: SJ 694033

Operating society/organisation: Ironbridge Gorge Museum Trust, Ironbridge, Telford, Shropshire TF8 7AW

Industrial locomotives

Name	No	Builder	Type	Built
—	—	Sentinel/Coalbrookdale (6185)	0-4-0VBT	1925
—	—	Sentinel/M/Wardle (6155)	0-4-0VBT	1925
—	5	Coalbrookdale	0-4-0ST	1865
—	—	A/Barclay	0-6-0ST	1896

All locomotives are at the Museum of Iron site. Coalbrookdale No 5 and Andrew Barclay are viewable only by appointment. Phone (01952) 433418 for details

Telephone: Telford (01952) 433522

Car park: At the sites

Access by public transport: Various private bus companies, including Midland Red, Williamson's Shearings, Elcocks, Boultons. Please telephone (01952) 433522 for further details

Catering facilities: Licensed Victorian pub, sweet shop and tea rooms at the Blists Hill site, serving drinks and mainly cold snacks. Tea, coffee and light refreshments at the Museum of Iron, Coalbrookdale and Coalport China Museum

Public opening: Main sites, including Museum of Iron and on Blists Hill, daily (except Christmas Eve and Christmas Day) 10.00-17.00, 10.00-18.00 during British Summer Time

Special notes: Tickets for all the sites or just for single sites available

---

Timetable Service	**Isle of Wight Steam Railway**	Isle of Wight

Member: HRA, TT

Separated from the mainland by the Solent, the line's isolation encouraged the maintenance and retention of Victorian locomotives and coaching stock which still operate the line today. Its rural charm enhances its attraction for the island's holidaymakers during the summer season

Commercial Director: Jim Loe

Headquarters: Isle of Wight

Steam Railway, Haven Street
Station, Ryde, Isle of Wight PO33
4DS
Telephone: Station: Isle of Wight
(01983) 882204
Main station: Haven Street
OS reference: SZ 556898
Other public stations: Wootton,
Ashey and Smallbrook Junction
Car park: Haven Street
Access by public transport:
'Island Line' service from Ryde or
Shanklin to Smallbrook Jct
Refreshment facilities: Light
refreshments available (licensed)
Souvenir shop: Haven Street
Museum: Small exhibits museum
at Haven Street
Depot: Haven Street
Length of line: 5 miles
Passenger trains: Wootton-
Smallbrook Jct
Period of public operation: Daily
— June to September. Selected
days — March to May and October
Special events: Steam
Extravaganza — 25-28 August.
Santa Specials, in December until
Xmas (please write for details)
Facilities for disabled: Limited
facilities, but can be catered for
individually, or in groups (by prior

arrangement), toilets available
Membership details: Membership
Secretary at above address
Membership journal: *Island Rail
News* — quarterly

Locomotives

Name	No	Origin	Class	Type	Built
Freshwater	W8 (32646)	LBSCR	A1X	0-6-0T	1876
Newport	W11 (32640)	LBSCR	A1X	0-6-0T	1878
Calbourne	W24	LSWR	O2	0-4-4T	1891
—	D2554	BR	05	0-6-0DM	1956
—	D2059	BR	03	0-6-0DM	1959

Industrial locomotives

Name	No	Builder	Type	Built
Invincible	37	H/Leslie (3135)	0-4-0ST	1915
Ajax	38	Barclay (1605)	0-6-0T	1918
Royal Engineer	198	Hunslet (3798)	0-6-0ST	1953

Locomotive notes: *Ajax* is not on public display.

Owners
Royal Engineer on loan from Royal Corps of Transport Museum Trust

Stock
1 IWR coach; 4 LBSCR coaches; 3 SECR coaches; 2 LCDR coaches; 5
IWR coaches (bodies only); 5 LCDR coaches (bodies only); 1 LBSCR
coach (body only); 1 crane; 1 ex-BR ballast tamper; 1 Wickham trolley; 30
wagons; 6 parcels vans; 2 ex-LT hoppers; 1 ex-BR Lowmac; 1 LSWR Road
van; 1 cattle van (on loan from the National Railway Museum)

Timetable Service	**Keighley & Worth Valley Railway**	West Yorkshire

1968 saw the reopening of the
Worth Valley branch following the
first sale of a standard gauge
railway to a preservation society.
Qualified volunteers have now
managed and operated the KWVR
every weekend, summer and winter
for three decades. The KWVR is
justifiably proud of having led the
British independent railway
movement in establishing the now
ubiquitous late 1950s/early 1960s
house style. Many have copied, but
few succeed so well as the Worth
Valley with totems, A5 handbills,
period posters, red uniform ties,
hanging baskets, gas lights and coal
fires. One of the most community-
orientated independent railways,
being the first to create a
'Resident's Railcard' discount fares
scheme since copied by Northern
Spirit plc!
**Chairman, Joint Management
Committee:** Brian A. Baker

Locomotives and multiple-units

Name	No	Origin	Class	Type	Built
—	41241	LMS	2MT	2-6-2T	1949
—	43924	MR	4F	0-6-0	1920
—	45212	LMS	5MT	4-6-0	1935
Bahamas	45596	LMS	'Jubilee'	4-6-0	1935
—	48431	LMS	8F	2-8-0	1944
—	47279	LMS	3F	0-6-0T	1925
—	1054	LNWR	—	0-6-2T	1888
City of Wells	34092	SR	WC	4-6-2	1949
—	80002	BR	4MT	2-6-4T	1952
—	75078	BR	4MT	4-6-0	1956
—	78022	BR	2MT	2-6-0	1953
—	30072	SR	USA	0-6-0T	1943
—	5775	GWR	5700	0-6-0PT	1929
—	52044	L&Y	2F	0-6-0	1887
—	19*	L&Y	Pug	0-4-0ST	1910
—	51218	L&Y	Pug	0-4-0ST	1901
—	752	L&Y	—	0-6-0ST	1881
—	85	TVR	O2	0-6-2T	1899
—	5820	USA TC	S160	2-8-0	1945
—	90733	MoS	WD	2-8-0	1945
—	68077	LNER	J94	0-6-0ST	1947
—	D226	BR	—	0-6-0DE	1956

Headquarters: Haworth Station, Keighley, West Yorkshire, BD22 8NJ
Telephone: Haworth (01535) 647777 24hr recorded timetable and information service; Haworth (01535) 645214 (other calls)
Main stations: Keighley, Ingrow West, Haworth, Oxenhope
Other public stations: Damems, Oakworth
OS reference: SE 034371
Car parks: Free at Keighley, Ingrow West, Oakworth, Oxenhope. Limited parking at Haworth (pay). Coaches at Ingrow West and Oxenhope only
Access by public transport: Fast and frequent electric Metro trains from Leeds, Bradford and Skipton to Keighley (joint station with KWVR). GNER direct service from King's Cross at 17.50 Monday-Friday. Northern Spirit through services from Glasgow, Carlisle, Morecambe, Lancaster to Keighley station. Through bookings to 'Oxenhope KWVR' are available from any travel centre throughout Britain and allow one day's unlimited travel on KWVR. Northern Spirit from Blackpool, Preston, Blackburn, Accrington, Burnley, Manchester to Hebden Bridge for connection via bus service 500 to Oxenhope (tel 01535 603284 for days of operation and timings)
Refreshment facilities: Buffet restaurant at Oxenhope. Buffet bar at Keighley (open when train service in operation). The only CAMRA-approved 'Real Ale' Bar operates on most steam trains (March-October). Wine and Dine by prior booking only — the 'White Rose Pullman' and 'West Riding Ltd'
Picnic areas: Keighley Station, Haworth Locomotive Depot, Oxenhope Station
Viewing areas: Keighley (Garsdale) Turntable, Haworth Locomotive Depot
Souvenir shops: Keighley, Haworth and Oxenhope stations; Ingrow Vintage Carriage Museum
Museums: Vintage Carriage Trust's carriage and locomotive museum at Ingrow Railway Centre. Open daily 11.00-16.30
Depots: Carriage and wagon —

Name	No	Origin	Class	Type	Built
—	D2511	BR	—	0-6-0DM	1961
—	D3336	BR	08	0-6-0DE	1954
—	D5209	BR	25/1	Bo-Bo	1963
—	D8031	BR	20	Bo-Bo	1960
—	50928	BR	108	DMBS	1959
—	51565	BR	108	DMC	1959
—	79962	W&M	—	Railbus	1958
—	79964	W&M	—	Railbus	1958

Industrial locomotives

Name	No	Builder	Type	Built
Hamburg	31	H/Clarke (697)	0-6-0T	1903
Nunlow	—	H/Clarke (1704)	0-6-0T	1938
Brussels	118	H/Clarke (1782)	0-6-0ST	1945
Southwick	—	RSH (7069)	0-4-0CT	1942
Fred	—	RSH (7289)	0-6-0ST	1945
Tiny	—	Barclay (2258)	0-4-0ST	1949
Merlin	231	H/Clarke (D761)	0-6-0DM	1951
—	1999*	Peckett (1999)	0-4-0	1941
Austins No1	—	Peckett (5003)	0-4-0DM	1961
—	MDHB No 32	Hunslet (2699)	0-6-0DM	1944

*away on loan

Stock
30 coaches including examples of pre-Grouping types; BR Mk 1 stock including the oldest vehicle in existence, part of the prototype batch; a Pullman car, NER and L&Y observation cars

Owners
19, 752 and 51218 the L&YRPS Trust
75078 and 78022 the Standard 4 Preservation Society
Bahamas, Nunlow, Tiny the Bahamas Locomotive Society
1054 the National Trust
52044 the Bowers 957 Trust
34092 the *City of Wells* Syndicate

Oxenhope; Motive power/loco works — Haworth, 'Bahamas Locomotive Society' workshops at Ingrow Railway Centre
Length of line: 4.75 miles
Passenger trains: Early morning local shoppers' services worked by diesel railbus/diesel multiple-unit, otherwise all steam-hauled
Frequent bus service between Haworth station and Haworth village top on Sundays (May-September) and Bank Holidays, 11.20-17.20
Period of public operation: Steam-hauled passenger services every weekend and Bank Holiday throughout the year (in December diesel-hauled). Daily from mid-June to early September
Special events: Vintage Trains — 16 April, 7, 13/14, 21 May, 8 October; Enthusiasts' Weekends — 13/14 May, 21/22 October; Friends of Thomas the Tank Engine — 3/4 June, 23/24 September; Diesel Weekend— 22/23 July; Heritage Diesel Service — 23-27 October; Santa Specials — 2/3, 9/10, 16/17, 22/23 December
Facilities for disabled: Wheelchairs accommodated in guard's compartments on trains. Please advise before visit to the Advanced Bookings Officer, c/o Haworth station
Special notes: Accompanied children under 5 years of age free. Children 5-15 and senior citizens at 50% discount. Family ticket available (2 adults + 3 children/senior citizen)
Membership details: Membership Secretary c/o above address
Membership journal: *Push & Pull* — quarterly
Marketing name: Worth Valley

Kent & East Sussex Railway

Member: HRA, TT

The Kent & East Sussex Railway owes much of its charm to its origin as the world's first light railway. The tightly-curved line with steep gradients is typical of those country railways that were developed on shoestring budgets to bring the 'iron horse' to sparsely populated areas. Services operate over 10.5 miles of line from the picturesque town of Tenterden to Bodiam.

  Pride of the line's coach fleet is the magnificently restored train of Victorian carriages built between 1860 and 1901

Company Secretary: Cathy Roberts

Headquarters: Tenterden Railway Co Ltd, Tenterden Town Station, Tenterden, Kent TN30 6HE

Telephone: Tenterden (01580) 762943 (24 hour talking timetable); Tenterden (01580) 765155 (office)

Main station: Tenterden Town

Other public stations: Rolvenden, Wittersham Road, Northiam, Bodiam

Car parks: Tenterden, Northiam

OS reference:
Tenterden TQ 882336,
Northiam TQ 834266

Access by public transport:
Maidstone & District bus service No 400 from Ashford (Kent) main line station

Refreshment facilities: Tenterden Town and Northiam. Also on many trains. Lunch and afternoon teas on many trains (advanced booking essential). Picnic areas at Tenterden, Wittersham Road and Northiam

Souvenir shop: Tenterden Town Station

Museum: Colonel Stephens' Railway Museum

Depot: Rolvenden

Length of line: 7 miles

Passenger trains: Tenterden-Bodiam. Daily April to September; Sundays only October to March

Special events: Centenary Week (featuring the reopening of Bodiam station — 2-9 April; Bank Holiday Steam Ups — 21-24, 30 April, 1 May; Victorian Days — 27/29 May; Steam Gala & Historic

Locomotives and multiple-units

Name	No	Origin	Class	Type	Built
Bodiam	3	LBSCR	A1X	0-6-0T	1872
Sutton	32650	LBSCR	A1X	0-6-0T	1876
Knowle	2678	LBSCR	A1X	0-6-0T	1880*
—	1556	SECR	P	0-6-0T	1909
Wainwright	DS238	SR	USA	0-6-0T	1943*
Maunsell	65	SR	USA	0-6-0T	1943*
—	1638	GWR	1600	0-6-0PT	1951
—	20	GWR	AEC	diesel railcar	1940
Norwegian	376	NSB	21c	2-6-0	1919*
—	D2023	BR	03	0-6-0DM	1958◊
—	D2024	BR	03	0-6-0DM	1958
—	11223	BR	04	0-6-0DM	1957
—	08108	BR	08	0-6-0DE	1955◊
—	48 (D9504)	BR	14	0-6-0DH	1964◊
—	D9525	BR	14	0-6-0DH	1965◊
—	14029 (D9529)	BR	14	0-6-0DH	1965◊
Ashford	D6570	BR	33	Bo-Bo	1961◊
—	51571	BR	108	DMC	1959
—	53971	BR	108	DMBS	1959

Industrial locomotives

Name	No	Builder	Type	Built
Marcia	12	Peckett (1631)	0-4-0T	1923
Charwelton	14	M/Wardle (1955)	0-6-0ST	1917*
Holman F. Stephens	23	Hunslet (3791)	0-6-0ST	1952*
Rolvenden	24	Hunslet (3800)	0-6-0ST	1953*
Northiam	25	Hunslet (3797)	0-6-0ST	1953*
—	40	BTH	Bo-Bo	1932
—	42	Hunslet (4208)	0-6-0DM	1948
Titan	—	R/Hornsby (423661)	0-4-0DM	1958

*in passenger traffic
◊in use for shunting/engineering trains

Passenger stock in service
SECR family saloon; LNWR 6-wheel director's saloon; SECR 4-wheel full third; SR Maunsell CK; GER 6-wheel composite; District Railway 4-wheel full first; SR Maunsell nondescript brake-open; BR Mk 1 RU and 5 other BR Mk 1 coaches; 1926 Pullman Parlour Car *Barbara*

Stock
2 ex-SECR 'Birdcage' coaches; 2 ex-LSWR coaches; 1 GER observation car; 2 Pullman cars; 5 ex-SR Maunsell coaches; 3 steam cranes; large interesting collection of freight vehicles, totalling 51 vehicles

Vehicle Gathering — 8/9 July; Steam Back to the Sixties — 27/28 August; Day Out with Thomas— 16/17 September; Austin Counties Car Rally — 14/15 October; Delivering the Goods Weekend — 21/22 October

Facilities for disabled: A special coach for disabled people, 'Petros', is conveyed in many trains (telephone for confirmation of

availability), reserved parking at Northiam.
Toilets with disabled access at Tenterden and Northiam, and in 'Petros'

Special notes: The Wealden Belle luxury dining car service operates on most Saturday evenings April to October and selected Wednesdays in the summer. Roast lunch served most Sundays. Advance booking is essential for these trains. Santa Special services operate on each Saturday and Sunday in December. Advanced booking recommended **Membership details:** New

Members Secretary, c/o above address
Membership journal: *The Tenterden Terrier* — 3 times/year

Steam Centre — Kew Bridge Steam Museum — London

The museum is housed in a magnificent 19th century Pumping Station and centres around the station's five world famous Cornish Beam Engines, two of which can be seen in steam every weekend. Originally used to pump West London's water supply for more than a century, one of them, the 'Grand Junction 90,' is the world's largest working beam engine. In surrounding buildings other large engines also work at weekends, demonstrating more modern steam and diesel pumping machinery.

A new gallery, opened in September 1997, reveals the fascinating history of London's water supply from Roman toilet spoons to the massive 'high-tec' London ring main.

Many Victorian waterworks had their own railway. At Kew Bridge this is demonstrated by a short line, operated by the Hampshire Narrow Gauge Railway Society. 1998 saw the return to steam of *Cloister* for the first time in 22 years

Location: 100yd from the north side of Kew Bridge, next to the tall Victorian tower

Operating group: Kew Bridge Engines Trust, Green Dragon Lane, Brentford, Middx TW8 0EN

Telephone: (020) 8568 4757 (information line)

Internet address: http://www.cre.canon.co.uk/~davide/kbsm

Industrial locomotives

2ft gauge:

Name	No	Builder	Type	Built
Cloister	—	Hunslet (542)	0-4-0ST	1891
Wendy	1	Bagnall (2091)	0-4-0ST	1919
Alister	2	Lister (44052)	4wDM	1958

Car park: Free on site

Access by public transport: *Rail*: South West Trains, Kew Bridge (from Waterloo via Clapham Junction); *Bus:* Nos 65, 237, 267, 391; *Tube:* Gunnersbury (District Line, then 237 or 267 bus), Kew Gardens (District Line, then 391 bus)

Length of line/gauge: About 100yd, 2ft gauge

Public opening: Museum: Daily 11.00-17.00. Railway: see below

Special events: Exhibitions: Loos Change 'Green Sanitation' in the 21st Century — 22 April-30 June and Robert Stirling and the Hot Air Engine 21 July-8 October; The Magic of Meccano — 8/9 April; Historic Fire Engine Rally — 21 May; Tower Open Day —3 June; Mineral & Fossil Show — 10 June; Tower Open Day — 2 September; Festival of Steam — 7/8 October; Live Steam Model Railway Show — 18/19 November.

The railway is scheduled to operate on: 8/9, 22/23, 29/30 April; 1, 27-29 May; 10/11, 24/25 June; 8/9, 28/29 July; 12/13, 26-28 August; 9/10, 28/29 September; 7/8, 28/29 October; 18/19, 25/26 November

On site facilities: Bookshop/toilets/car park. Refreshments available at weekends only

Facilities for disabled: Access to most of museum, including lower floor. Access via ramps and lift. Large print guide available and guide dogs welcome. Wheelchair loan service

Special notes: Groups of 10 or more can be given guided tours and a 10% discount on admission charges. Special steaming can be arranged and touch tours are available for partially sighted groups. All groups must be pre-booked

Museum contact: Kew Bridge Engine Trust, c/o above address

Railway contact: HNGRS, 44 St Thomas' Avenue, Hayling Island, Hants PO11 0EX

Other attractions: Museum displays a selection of stationary steam engines and associated water supply displays

Museum — Kidderminster Railway Museum — Worcestershire

Established in an 1878 GWR warehouse, the museum houses an enormous collection of railway relics, photographs and documents, with a number of 'hands-on' exhibits.

Contact address: Station Approach, Comberton Hill, Kidderminster, Worcestershire DY10 1QX

General Manager: David Postle

Telephone: Kidderminster (01562) 825316

Internet address: *E-mail:* krm@krm.org.uk *Web site:* www.krm.org.uk

OS reference: SO 837763

Location: Adjacent to SVR station

Car park: SVR car park
Access by public transport:
Kidderminster main line station, Midland Red bus service X92 to Kidderminster
Facilities for disabled: Ramp
access for wheelchairs to ground level
Special events: Practical signalling courses using Museum and SVR resources. Filmshows, model railway exhibitions, railway art
exhibitions, postcard/photograph fairs,
On site facilities: Souvenirs, refreshments
Public opening: Open on SVR operating days

Member: HRA
Location/headquarters: Clayton West, A636 Wakefield-Denby Dale road
Operating society/organisation: Kirklees Light Railway, Park Mill Way, Clayton West, Nr Huddersfield HP8 9XJ
Telephone: (01484) 865727
Main station: Clayton West
Other station: Cuckoos Nest, Skelmanthorpe, Shelley
Length of line: 4 miles, 15in gauge (extension now open)
Car park: Clayton West — free
Access by public transport: Bus No 235 from Huddersfield & Barnsley; 240 from Huddersfield/Scissett; 484 from Wakefield. Rail to Huddersfield, Wakefield or Denby Dale stations
Refreshment facilities: Clayton West, new Visitor Centre and Café now open

Locomotives

Name	No	Builder	Type	Built
Fox	—	Taylor	2-6-2T	1987
Badger	—	Taylor	0-6-4T	1991
Toby the Tram Engine	7	Taylor	0-4-0	1995
Jay	—	Taylor	4wD	1992
Hawk	—	Taylor	0-4-4-0*	1998

*articulated

Rolling stock
2 rakes of five, heated carriages, 4-wheel tool van, 4-wheel ballast/stone wagon, heavy bogie flat car for rail carrying

Souvenir shop: Clayton West
On site facilities: Toilets, swings, half-scale roundabouts, lake. HQ of Barnsley Society of Model Engineers
Facilities for disabled: Yes
Period of public operation:
Winter— weekends & most school holidays. Summer — daily from Spring Bank Holiday to end August

Special events: Easter Eggspress — 21-25 April; Wild West Weekend — 13/14 May; Friends of Thomas the Tank Engine —24/25 June, 29/30 July; Teddy Bears' Picnic — 12/13 August; Halloween Ghost Trains — 28/29 October; Santa Specials every weekend in December. Please phone or write for details

---

Member: HRA, TT
Originally this Furness Railway branch line carried passengers and freight from Ulverston to Lakeside but now the only part remaining is the 3.5-mile section from Haverthwaite to the terminus at Lakeside where connections are made with the lakeside steamers which ply the 10-mile length of Windermere
General Manager: M. A. Maher
Headquarters: Lakeside & Haverthwaite Railway Co Ltd, Haverthwaite Station, Nr Ulverston, Cumbria LA12 8AL
Telephone: Newby Bridge (015395) 31594
Main station: Haverthwaite

Locomotives and multiple-units

Name	No	Origin	Class	Type	Built
—	20	FR	A5	0-4-0	1863
—	42073	LMS	4MT	2-6-4T	1950
—	42085	LMS	4MT	2-6-4T	1951
—	17(AD601)	LMS	—	0-6-0DE	1945
—	5643	GWR	5600	0-6-2T	1925
—	8(D2117)	BR	03	0-6-0DM	1959
—	D2072	BR	03	0-6-0DM	1959
—	20214	BR	20	Bo-Bo	1967
—	D5301	BR	26	Bo-Bo	1958
—	52029	BR	107	DMS	1960
—	52071	BRCW	110	DMBC	1961
—	52077	BRCW	110	DMBC	1961

Industrial locomotives

Name	No	Builder	Type	Built
Caliban*	1	Peckett (1925)	0-4-0ST	1937
Rachel	9	M/Rail (2098)	4wDM	1924

Other public stations:
Intermediate station at Newby
Bridge. Terminus at Lakeside
OS reference: SD 349843
Car parks: Haverthwaite, Lakeside
Access by public transport:
Lakeside steamers on Windermere
call at Lakeside. CMS bus to
Haverthwaite
Refreshment facilities:
Haverthwaite
Souvenir shop: Haverthwaite
On site facilities: Picnic area at
Haverthwaite
Depot: All rolling stock at
Haverthwaite
Length of line: 3.5 miles
Passenger trains: Steam-hauled
Haverthwaite-Lakeside
Period of public operation: Easter
then daily from early May to end of
October.
Special events: Santa Specials
(advance booking essential); please
contact for details

Name	No	Builder	Type	Built
Repulse	11	Hunslet (3698)	0-6-0ST	1950
Princess	14	Bagnall (2682)	0-6-0ST	1942
Askam Hall	15	Avonside (1772)	0-4-0ST	1935
Alexandra	12	Barclay (929)	0-4-0ST	1902
David	13	Barclay (2333)	0-4-0ST	1953
Cumbria	10	Hunslet (3794)	0-6-0ST	1953
—	7	Fowler (22919)	0-4-0DM	1940
Fluff	16	Hunslet/Fowler	0-4-0DM	1937
—	20	Jones crane	0-4-0DM	1952
Sir James	21	Barclay (1550)	0-6-0F	1917
—	22	Fowler (4220045)	0-4-0DM	1967

*under restoration at Steamtown, Carnforth

Stock
10 ex-BR Mk 1 coaches; 1 ex-LNER BG; 1 ex-BR Mk 1 miniature buffet
coach, Royal saloon No 5 (built GER, Stratford 1898); Small selection of
freight vehicles

Special notes: Combined
railway/lake steamer tickets
available from the station at
Haverthwaite and Lakeside
steamers piers at Bowness and
Ambleside. Lakeside steamer is
operated by Windermere Lake
Cruises Ltd
Membership journal: *The Iron
Horse* — quarterly

Steam Centre — Lappa Valley Railway — Cornwall

Member: TT
Location/headquarters: Benny
Halt, St Newlyn East, Nr Newquay,
Cornwall TR8 5HZ
Telephone: (01872) 510317
General Manager: Miss Amanda
Booth
Main station: Benny Halt
Other station: East Wheal Rose,
Newlyn Downs Halt
Car park: Benny Halt
Access by public transport: Bus
service, Newquay to Truro and
return. Western National and The
Cornishman coaches to St Newlyn
East. Signposted, half-mile walk
from bus stop to railway. May to
September – bus from Newquay to
railway (3 times daily)
Refreshment facilities: Café at
East Wheal Rose serving hot and
cold food, snacks, hot & cold
drinks; licensed
Souvenir shop: East Wheal Rose
and Benny Halt

Locomotives

Name	No	Builder	Type	Built
Muffin	2	Berwyn	0-6-0	1967
		rebuilt Tambling		1991
Zebedee	1	S/Lamb	0-6-4T	1974
		rebuilt Tambling		1990
Gladiator	3	Minirail	4w-4wDH	c1960
Pooh	4	Lister (20698)	4wDM	1942

(all 15in gauge)
Also one 10.25in gauge diesel

Rolling stock
15in gauge — 10 passenger coaches
10.25in gauge — 4 passenger coaches, 2 wagons
7.25in gauge — 1 Mardyke APT set

On site facilities: 15in, 10.25in and
7.25in gauge railways. Canoes,
paddle boats, crazy golf, pedal cars,
electric motorbikes, children's play
area, brick path maze, listed engine
house, walks and a video
Depot: Benny Halt
Facilities for disabled: Yes

Public opning: Easter to end of
October, usually daily but ring for
early and late season opening days
Special notes: Entry by one all-in
price, except for motorbikes.
   Family tickets and reduced
afternoon saver fares are available
all days. Under 3s free

Launceston Steam Railway

Member: TT

The railway runs through the beautiful Kensey Valley on a track gauge of 1ft 11.5in, following the trackbed of the old North Cornwall line. The locomotives formerly worked on the Dinorwic and Penrhyn railways in North Wales. Launceston station contains a museum of vintage cars and motorcycles and a collection of stationary steam engines which are demonstrated at work. There are catering, gift shop and bookshop facilities. At the far end of the line there are pleasant riverside walks and a shaded picnic area, adjacent to Newmills Farm Park (a popular separate attraction). The covered rolling stock ensures an enjoyable visit whatever the weather

Location: Newport Industrial Estate, Launceston, Cornwall

OS reference: SX 328850

Operating society/organisation: The Spice Settlement Trust Co Ltd, trading as the Launceston Steam Railway, Newport, Launceston PL15 8DA

Telephone: (01566) 775665

Stations: Launceston-Hunts Crossing-New Mills

Car park: Newport Industrial Estate, Launceston

Length of line: 2.5 miles

Industrial locomotives

Name	No	Builder	Type	Built
Lilian	—	Hunslet (317)	0-4-0ST	1883
Velinheli	—	Hunslet (409)	0-4-0ST	1886
Covertcoat	—	Hunslet (679)	0-4-0ST	1898
Sybil	—	Bagnall (1760)	0-4-0ST	1906
Dorothea	—	Hunslet (763)	0-4-0ST	1901
—	—	M/Rail (5646)	4wDM	1933
—	—	M/Rail (9546)	4wDM	1950

Locomotive notes: Only the three Hunslet locomotives (317/409/679) are expected to be in use during 2000.

Stock
1 electric inspection trolley; 4 bogie carriages and 1 4-wheel carriage

Gauge: 1ft 11.5in

Access by public transport: Main line Gunnislake 13 miles, Plymouth or Bodmin 25 miles

On site facilities: Buffet, transport museum, workshop tours, gift and bookshop, all situated at Launceston

Period of public operation: Easter holiday, then Tuesdays and Sundays until Whitsun. Daily (not Saturdays) Whitsun until end of September. Tuesdays and Sundays in October. Santa Specials may run in December (contact Launceston Lions tel: [01566] 774303)

Public opening: Trains run from 11.00-16.30. Departures about every 40min and more frequently if required. Unlimited riding on date of issue of ticket

Family ticket: Available, 2 Adults and up to 4 children

Journey time: Return 30min

Facilities for disabled: Easy access to all areas except bookshop and motorcycle museum. No toilet facilities for disabled. However, public toilets are reasonably accessible

Special events: Double-headed trains on Wednesdays in July and August (whenever possible). Demonstration freight trains (contact for details)

Lavender Line

Member: HRA

The Lavender Line is centred around a typical country station, which, somewhat untypically is in the village it was built to serve. The image portrayed is of the transition steam-diesel era of the 1950s/1960s on the Southern Region of British Railways. An expanded museum and an extension of the running line should be opened during the 2000 operating season.

Location: Isfield Station, Isfield, Nr Uckfield, East Sussex TN22 5XB. Isfield village is off the A26 between Lewes and Uckfield

OS reference: TQ 452171

Operating society/organisation: The Lavender Line Preservation Society

Telephone/Fax: Information line: 0891 800645 Business/fax: (01825) 750515 (24hr answerphone when not manned)

Car park: On site, free to patrons

Access by public transport: Lewes station and 729 bus (Mon-Sat), 129 bus on summer Suns. Uckfield station and 729 bus (Mon-Sat), taxi on summer Suns. Tel: South Coast Buses before travelling on (01424) 433711 (Mon-Sat 09.00-17.00) for bus details. Tel: National Rail Enquiries on 0345 484950 (24hrs/7 days a week)

On site facilities: 'Cinders' buffet/restaurant, gift shop, goods shed museum, picnic area, access to signalbox. Children's parties arranged on operating days. Private functions, weddings and parties etc catered for

Length of line: 1-mile

Public opening: Steam or diesel trains. Sundays from 11.00 (midday in November/December) throughout the year. Saturdays in July, August and December from midday. Wednesdays and Thursdays in August from 11.00. Good Friday and Bank Holiday Mondays from 11.00. Closing times vary from 16.00 to 17.00 — call information line.

Please note that the the Isfield site is not normally open for viewing outside of operating dates.

Footplate courses: Full day steam or diesel courses are run on certain Saturdays January-June (inc) and September-November (inc). Please telephone or fax for a booking form

Facilities for disabled: Access to most facilities on site. No wheelchair access to toilets at present. Visitors must telephone to confirm that the carriage will be in the train. A ramp is available and help with access to the train will be given to infirm and disabled visitors

Special events: Vintage weekend and fireworks in September. Steam-

Locomotives

	Name	No	Origin	Class	Type	Built
	Sir Herbert Walker	73003	BR	72	Bo-Bo	1962
	—	73004*	BR	72	Bo-Bo	1962

*for spares only

Industrial locomotives

Name	No	Builder	Type	Built
Annie	945	Barclay (945)	0-4-0ST	1904
Blackie	68012	Hunslet (3193)	0-6-0ST	1944
—	15	Barclay	0-4-0DM	1945
—	16	Barclay	0-4-0DM	1945
—	ND 3827	Hibberd (SC2196/3857)	0-4-0DM	1957
—	ND 10022	Hibberd (SC3986/3968)	0-4-0DM	1960

Stock

3 ex-BR Mk 1 coaches
A variety of BR and pre-Nationalisation wagons are in service in a vintage goods train, or are under restoration. A GWR Toad brake van is used on most passenger trains, allowing visitors to ride on the verandah or inside by the stove. The engineering vehicle fleet includes examples from London Transport and pre-Grouping companies

hauled Santa Specials in December. Various events throughout the year — call information line. Please note that on special event days, prices may vary and that Site Entrance Only tickets may not be available.

Ticket price valid for unlimited rides on day of issue

Museum	**Leeds Industrial Museum**	Leeds

Location: The Leeds Industrial Museum, Armley Mills, Canal Road, Leeds LS12 2QF
OS reference: SE 275342
Operating society/organisation: Leeds City Council, Department of Leisure Services, The Town Hall, The Headrow, Leeds LS1 3AO
Curator: D. C. Rooke
Telephone: (0113) 263 7861
Car park: Cark park adjacent to the Museum
Access by public transport: Nos 5A, 14, 66 and 67 from City Square, Leeds (outside the railway station)
Public opening: April-September: Tuesdays-Saturdays 10.00-17.00, Sundays 13.00-17.00. October-March: Tuesdays-Saturdays 10.00-17.00, Sundays 13.00-17.00. Closed Mondays (except Bank Holidays). NB: last admission 16.00 on all days
Special events: Plant in Steam — Tuesdays 25 July-12 September
On site facilities: Museum shop, refreshments (vending machines), picnic area
Special notes: Facilities for the

Industrial locomotives

	Name	No	Builder	Type	Built
1ft 6in gauge					
	Jack	—	Hunslet 684)	0-4-0WT	1898
	Coffin	—*	G/Bat (1326)	0-4-0BE	1933
2ft gauge					
	Barber	—	T/Green (441)	0-6-2ST	1908
	Cheetal	—	Fowler (15991)	0-6-0WT	1923
	Simplex	—	M/Rail (1369	4wPM	1918
	Hudson Fordson	—	Hudson (36863)	4wDM	1928
	Layer	—*	Fowler (21294)	4wDM	1936
	Hudson Hunslet	—	Hunslet (2959)	4wDM	1944
	Resin	—	Hunslet (2008)	0-4-0DM	1939
	Nacob	—*	Hunslet (5340)	0-4-0DM	1957
	Sharlston	—†	H/Clarke (1164)	0-4-0DM	1959
	Demtox	—†*	Hunslet (6048)	0-4-0DM	1961
2ft 1in gauge					
	Fricl	—*	Hunslet (4019)	0-4-0DM	1948
	Pitpo	—*	Hunslet	0-4-0	1955
	Calverton	—*	H/Clarke (1368)	0-4-0DM	1965
2ft 6in gauge					
	Junin	—	H/Clarke (D557)	2-6-2DM	1930
	Fimyn	—†	Hunslet (3411)	0-4-0DM	1947
2ft 8in gauge					
	Ficol	—*	Hunslet (3200)	0-4-0DM	1945

England

disabled (toilets, etc), lifts. Museum can be viewed by visitors in wheelchairs (most areas are accessible)

Details of locomotive and rolling stock: Locomotive collection includes steam, diesel, mines locomotives and a narrow gauge railway and engines

Name	No	Builder	Type	Built
2ft 11in gauge				
Lurch	—	H/Clarke (D571)	4wDM	1932
3ft gauge				
Lord Granby	—*	H/Clarke (633)	0-4-0ST	1902
Cement	—*	Fowler (20685)	2-4-0DM	1935
Lofti	—*	Hunslet (4057)	0-6-0DM	1953
3ft 6in gauge				
Progress	—	H/Clarke (D634)	0-6-0DM	1946
Festival of Britain	—*	H/Clarke (D733)	0-6-0DM	1951
Standard gauge				
Hodbarrow	—*	Hunslet (299)	0-4-0ST	1882
Aldwyth	—	M/Wardle (865)	0-6-0ST	1882
Capper	—	Fowler (22060)	0-4-0DM	1938
Fort William	—*	Fowler (22893)	0-4-0DM	1940
Trecwn	—	Hunslet (2390)	0-4-0DM	1941
Elizabeth	—	H/Clarke (1888)	0-4-0ST	1958
Southam No 2	—*	H/Clarke (D625)	0-4-0DM	1942
Luton	—	G/Bat (1210)	0-4-0BE	1930
Smithy Wood	—*	G/Bat (2543)	0-4-0WE	1955

Notes
*not currently on public display
†on loan to Red Rose Steam Society/Astley Green Colliery Museum
Simplex is on loan to Moseley Industrial Railway Museum

Timetable Service	Leighton Buzzard Railway	Bedfordshire

Member: HRA, TT

The LBR enables visitors to take a 65min journey into the vanished world of the English light railway.. Sharp curves and steep gradients make the locomotives work hard and the railway is unique with its roadside running. The LBR possesses the largest collection of narrow gauge locomotives in Britain, together with a varied selection of coaches and wagons — an important part of the national railway heritage. Many items are on permanent display, and some can be seen in action at special events

General Manager: J. Horsley

Headquarters: Leighton Buzzard Railway, Page's Park Station, Billington Road, Leighton Buzzard, Bedfordshire LU7 8TN

OS reference: Page's Park SP 928242

Telephone: (01525) 373888, 24hr answerphone with service and event details

Fax: (01525) 377814

Internet address: *E-mail:* buzzrail@btinternet.com

Locomotives

Name	No	Builder	Type	Built
—	740	O&K	0-6-0T	1907
—	—	Baldwin (778)	4-6-0T	1917
Berlin	—	Freudenstein (73)	0-4-0WT	1901
Alice	—	Hunslet (780)	0-4-0ST	1902
Peter Pan	—	K/Stuart (4256)	0-4-0ST	1922
Chaloner	1	de Winton	0-4-0VBT	1877
Pixie	2	K/Stuart (4260)	0-4-0ST	1922
Rishra	3	Baguley (2007)	0-4-0T	1921
Doll	4	Barclay (1641)	0-6-0T	1919
Elf	5	O&K (12740)	0-6-0WT	1936
Falcon	7	O&K (8986)	4wDM	1939
—	8	Ruston (217999)	4wDM	1943
Madge	9	O&K (7600)	4wDM	1934
Haydn Taylor	10	Simplex (7956)	4wDM	1945
P. C. Allen	11	O&K (5834)	0-4-0WT	1912
Carbon	12	Simplex (6012)	4wPM	1930
Arkle	13	M/Rail (7108)	4wDM	1937
—	14	Hunslet (3646)	4wDM	1946
Tom Bombadil	15	Hibberd (2514)	4wDM	1941
Thorin Oakenshield	16	Lister (11221)	4wDM	1939
Damredub	17	Simplex (7036)	4wDM	1936
Feanor	18	M/Rail (11003)	4wDM	1956
—	19	M/Rail (11298)	4wDM	1965
—	20	M/Rail (60s317)	4wDM	1966
Festoon	21	Simplex (4570)	4wPM	1929
Fingolfin	22	under construction	—	
—	23	Ruston (164346)	4wDM	1932
—	25	Simplex (7214)	4wDM	1938

www.btinternet.com/~buzzrail
Main station: Page's Park. The station is on the A4146 to the east of Leighton Buzzard
Other public stations: Stonehenge Works
Car park: Page's Park, free
Access by public transport:
Leighton Buzzard main line station, Silverlink County services from London (Euston), Watford, Hemel Hempstead, Milton Keynes, Northampton and stations to Birmingham (Tel: 0345 484950). Nearest bus stops at Stanbridge Road (10min walk) and Leighton Buzzard town centre (25min walk). on summer Saturdays some services are routed to Page's Park. (Tel: 01234 228337 for details)
Refreshment facilities: Dobbers buffet at Page's Park. Picnic area by station. Cafe for hot & cold snacks, refreshments and ice creams
Souvenir shop: Page's Park
Depots: Page's Park and Stonehenge Works
Length of line: 3 miles, 2ft gauge
Journey time: Single 25min, return 65min
Passenger trains: Page's Park-Stonehenge Works
  Group discounts and packages such as Birthday Breaks, Schools Specials, Twilight Trains available
Period of public operation:
Sundays 19 March-29 October; Mondays 24 April, 1, 29 May, 28 August; Tuesdays 1-29 August; Wednesdays 26 April, 31 May-30 August, 25 October; Thursdays 3-31 August; Friday 1 September (morning only); Saturdays 22, 29 April, 27 May, 10, 17 June, 5 August-2 September
Special events: Mothering Sunday — 2 April; Easter Fun — 21-24 April; Teddy Bears' Weekend —

Name	No	Builder	Type	Built
Yimkin	26	Ruston (203026)	4wDM	1941
Poppy	27	Ruston (408430)	4wDM	1957
RAF Stanbridge	28	Ruston (200516)	4wDM	1940
Creepy	29	Hunslet (6008)	4wDM	1963
—	30	M/Rail (8695)	4wDM	1941
—	31	Lister (4228)	4wDM	1931
—	32	Ruston (172892)	4wDM	1934
Name	No	Builder	Type	Built
—	33	Hibberd (3582)	4wDM	1954
Red Rum	34	M/Rail (7105)	4wPM	1936
—	35	Hunslet (6619)	0-4-0DM	1966
Caravan	36	Simplex (7129)	4wDM	1938
—	37	Ruston (172901)	4wPM	1934
Harry Barnet	38	Lister (37170)	4wDM	1951
T. W. Lewis	39	Ruston (375316)	4wDM	1954
Trent	40	Ruston (283507)	4wDM	1949
—	41	Hunslet (2536)	4wDM	1941
—	42	Ruston (223692)	4wPM	1944
—	43	Simplex (10409)	4wDM	1954
Kestrel	44	Simplex (7933)	4wDM	1941
—	46	Ruston (209430)	4wPM	1942
—	47	Hudson (38384)	4wDM	1930
—	48	Hunslet (RFST2)	4wDM	1952
Beaudesert	80	A/Keef	4wHM	1999
—	2275	M/Rail (1377)	4wPM	1918
—	24	M/Rail (11297)	4wDM	1965

Stock
10 coaches and a wide selection of wagons

29 April-1 May; Museums & Galleries Month Open Day — 14 May; European Steam Weekend — 10/11 June; Beer Festival — 17/18 June; Vintage Vehicles Day — 25 June; Model Railways Day — 2 July; Sunday Best Anorak Day — 16 July; Family Fun Days — 6, 20 August; September Steam Up — 1-3 September; Mad Hats Day — 10 September; Halloween Haunting — 29 October.
Special Heritage Attractions:
Industry Trains Display — 23 April, 25 June, 16 July, 13 August, 3 September; Quarry Digger Demonstration — 24 April, 14, 29 May, 6 August, 2 September; Demonstration Freight Train — 22 April, 26 May, 26 August;

Christmas Specials 2-28 December
Facilities for disabled: Priority parking at Page's Park. Ramp access to all facilities including dedicated toilet at Page's Park. Wheelchairs are conveyed in a specially adapted coach. Advance notice appreciated
Special notes: Visiting steam locomotives expected during 2000
Membership details: The line is operated by unpaid volunteers. Membership secretary, c/o above address
Membership journal: *Chaloner* — quarterly
Marketing name: England's Friendly Little Line

```
 _____        _____         _____
(   Museum   )======( London Transport  )======(   London   )
 ‾‾‾‾‾‾‾‾‾‾‾‾        (     Museum         )       ‾‾‾‾‾‾‾‾‾‾‾‾
                     ‾‾‾‾‾‾‾‾‾‾‾‾‾‾‾‾‾‾‾‾
```

London Transport Museum

Member: HRA, TT
Spectacular displays of buses, trams and trains reveal a fascinating story of travel, people and the history of London itself. Special exhibitions, family activities, actors, videos and working models

all bring the story to life.
  Only a small proportion of the museum's collection is on display, a single custom built store will be completed in 1999. Once complete it will have regular open days please see press for details

Location: Covent Garden, London WC2E 7BB
OS reference: TQ 303809
Operating society/organisation: London Regional Transport
Telephone: (020) 7379 6344. (24hr [020] 7836 8557)

Access by public transport:
Underground to Covent Garden, Leicester Square or Charing Cross. Buses to Strand/Aldwych
On site facilities: Museum shop, lecture theatre, photo and research libraries (by appointment), resource centre and café
Public opening: Daily 10.00-18.00 (except Fridays 11.00-18.00) (last admissions 17.15). Closed 24-26 December. Reduced admission prices for children, students, senior citizens, registered disabled, UB40 holders and pre-booked parties. Family season ticket available
Facilities for disabled: Disabled toilets available, wheelchair access to all displays. Reduced admission for registered disabled visitors and person accompanying them. Please advise in advance if a party of disabled visitors would like to visit
Special notes: Visitors can put themselves in the driving seat of a bus, a tube simulator; there are also 'hands-on' demonstrations of signals and points. In addition to the vehicles and rolling stock there

Locomotives

Name	No	Origin	Class	Type	Built
—	23	Met Rly	A	4-4-0T	1866
John Hampden	5	Met Rly		Bo-Bo	1922

Industrial locomotives

Origin	Builder	Type	Built
Wotton Tramway	A/Porter (807)	0-4-0TG	1872

Electric stock
4248 District Rly Q23 stock driving motor coach 1923
11182 LPTB 1938 stock driving motor coach
400 Met Rly bogie stock coach 1899
30 City & South London Rly 'Padded Cell' coach 1890
Great Northern Piccadilly & Brompton Railway 'Gate stock' car 1906 (sectioned)

Stock
1 Met Rly milk van; 3 electric trams; 3 horse buses; 7 motorbuses; 1 trolleybus; 1 horse tram; 1 petrol-electric bus chassis; 1 tram/trolleybus tower wagon

are models, signs, posters, photographs, audio-visual displays and a 1906 Otis lift car. The museum runs a full programme of events and activities in addition to temporary exhibitions on a variety of topics. In addition to the vehicles on display there is a growing reserve collection
Membership details: Details from the Friends of the London Transport Museum

---

Mangapps Farm Railway Museum
Steam Centre — Essex

Member: HRA
Mangapps re-creates the atmosphere of a rural light railway. Featuring a large museum collection, strong in items of East Anglian interest, railway signalling and goods rolling stock. Other features include original station buildings from Mid-Suffolk Light, Great Eastern and Midland & Great Northern Railways.
Superintendent of the Line: John Jolly
Commercial Manager: June Jolly
Location: Mangapps Farm Railway Museum, Southminster Road, Burnham-on-Crouch, Essex CM0 8QQ. (Entrance on B1021, 1-mile north of Burnham)
Telephone: (01621) 784898
Fax: (01621) 783833
Internet address: Website: www.mangapps.co.uk
Access by public transport:
Burnham station approx 1 mile
On site facilities: Station, car park,

Locomotives and multiple-units

Name	No	Origin	Class	Type	Built
—	D2089	BR	03	0-6-0DM	1960
—	03399	BR	03	0-6-0DM	1961
—	D2325	BR	04	0-6-0DM	1961
—	11104	BR	04	0-6-0DM	1953
—	54287	BR	121	DTS	1960
—	59664	BR	115	TCL	1960
—	22624	LT	R38	DMS	1938

Industrial locomotives

Name	No	Builder	Type	Built
Minnie	—	F/Walker (358)	0-6-0ST	1878
Brookfield	—	Bagnal (2613)	0-6-0PT	1940
—	47	Barclay (2157)	0-4-0ST	1943
Empress	—	Bagnall (3061)	0-6-0ST	1954
Elland	No 1	H/Clarke (D1153)	0-4-0DM	1959
—	—	S/Henshaw (7502)	4wDM	1966

Rolling stock
Lynton & Barnstaple Railway coach No 7 (being rebuilt)

souvenir shop, toilets, amenity and picnic areas
Refreshment facilities: teas and light refreshments
Length of line: Three-quarter-mile
Public opening: Weekends & Bank Holidays all year (except 25/26 December, and daily during

Easter and summer school holidays. Closed January. Steam trains operate first Sunday of March to December, every Sunday during August & December and Bank

Holidays, diesels on other days
Opening times: 13.00-17.30 diesel days; 11.30-17.30 steam days
Special events: Friends of Thomas the Tank Engine; Transport Day;

Santa Specials — during December; Steam Special — 1 January 2001

Timetable Service — Mid-Hants Railway — Hampshire

Member: HRA

Originally built as the Winchester to Alton link, the Mid-Hants Railway became known as the Watercress Line through regularly carrying this local produce to London markets. Now restored, the line runs from its BR connection at Alton through rolling countryside to its terminus at Alresford. Large and powerful locomotives work impressively over the steeply inclined route, known to railwaymen as 'the Alps'. No 41312 entered service early 1999. No 34016 returns to service in summer 2000. Nos 35018 and 31806 are expected to be the next locomotives to enter service

Headquarters: Mid-Hants Railway plc, Alresford Station, Alresford, Hants SO24 9JG

Telephone: Alresford (01962) 733810

Fax: (01962) 735448

Talking timetable: (01962) 734866

Internet address: http://www.watercress.co.uk

Main station: Alresford

Other public stations: Ropley, Medstead & Four Marks, Alton

OS reference: Alresford SU 588325, Ropley SU 629324

Car park: Alresford-WCC, pay & display (free Sundays & Bank Holidays). Alton station pay & display

Access by public transport:

South West Train services — just over 1hr from London. Through ticketing arrangements available from Waterloo and all main line stations. Alternatively, travel to Winchester station and take the bus to Alresford from nearby City Road.

Bus services – operated by Stagecoach (01962) 846924

Refreshment facilities: Buffet service on most trains; 'West

Locomotives

Name	No	Origin	Class	Type	Built
—	30499	LSWR	S15	4-6-0	1920
—	30506	LSWR	S15	4-6-0	1920
—*	31625	SR	U	2-6-0	1929
—	31806	SR	U	2-6-0	1926
—	31874	SR	N	2-6-0	1925
Bodmin	34016	SR	WC	4-6-2	1945
249 Squadron	34073	SR	BB	4-6-2	1948
Swanage	34105	SR	WC	4-6-2	1950
Shaw Savill†	35009	SR	MN	4-6-2	1942
British India Line	35018	SR	MN	4-6-2	1945
—	41312	LMS	2MT	2-6-2T	1952
—	73096	BR	5MT	4-6-0	1956
—	76017	BR	4MT	2-6-0	1954
Franklin D. Roosevelt	701	USATC	S160	2-8-0	1944
—	D3358	BR	08	0-6-0DE	1957
—	12049	BR	11	0-6-0DE	1948
—	D5353	BR	27	Bo-Bo	1961
—	D6515§	BR	33	Bo-Bo	1960
Captain Bill Smith RNR	D6525	BR	33	Bo-Bo	1960
—	D6593	BR	33	Bo-Bo	1962
—	D6593	BR	33	Bo-Bo	1962
—	45132	BR	45	1Co-Co1	1961

*currently running as No 5 *James*
†currently under restoration at Swindon Railway Workshop
§on loan to Swanage Railway

Industrial locomotives

Name	No	Builder	Type	Built
—	4	Fowler (22889)	0-4-0DM	1939
Thomas	1	Hunslet (3781)	0-6-0T	1954
Barbara	—	Hunslet (2890)	0-6-0ST	1943

Stock

3 steam cranes; 1 Plasser & Theurer AL250 lining machine; 26 ex-BR Mk 1 coaches; 15 ex-BR Mk 2 coaches; 4 ex-SR coaches; 1 ex-LSWR coach; 2 ex-LMS coaches; Numerous goods vehicle

Owners

30499 and 30506 the Urie Locomotive Society
34105 the 34105 Light Pacific Group
76017 the Standard 4 Locomotive Group
Class 33s the 71A Locomotive Group

Country' buffet at Alresford; 'T-Junction' picnic/barbecue area at Ropley; tea/coffee available at Alton when information office open
Catering facilities: The 'Countryman' pre-booked Sunday

lunch trains and Christmas specials, and some evening trains. The 'Watercress Belle' operates on certain Saturday evenings April-October. Early booking is essential, please telephone to confirm seat

availability for both trains. Evening dinner in the West Country buffet, Friday and Saturday (booking essential). Real Ale trains — certain special events and Saturday evenings featuring beers from local breweries
Souvenir shops: Alresford, Alton and Ropley — which also specialises in secondhand books
On site facilities: Picnic area and viewing facilities at Ropley, including children's playground
Depot: Ropley. Locomotive yard open on operating days 10.30-16.30
Length of line: 10 miles
Passenger trains: Phone Talking Timetable (01962) 734866), or website to confirm details. Sundays February; Weekends and Bank Holidays March to end October; mid-week June/July; daily July to first week September. Santa Specials (bookings commence end of August)
Journey time: Round trip 1hr 40min max
Special events: Day out with Thomas — 21 April-1 May and 5-13 August inclusive; Open Weekend — 13/14 May and 23/24 September; Classic Motorcycles — 21 May; Model Railway Exhibition — 28/29 May; Jaguar Car Day — 11 June; War on the Line — 17/18 June; Alresford Millennium Day — 24 June; Morris Day — 2 July; Rolls-Royce Day — 9 July; Bus Rally — 16 July; Railway Enthusiasts' Event — 22/23 July and 28/29 October; Black Cabs Day — 30 July; Harley Davidson Weekend — 19/20 August; Craft Fayre — 3 September; South Hants Vehicle Preservation Day — 24 September; Santa Specials — 2/3, 9/10, 16/17, 20-24 December
Facilities for disabled: Toilets at Ropley and 100yd from Alresford station. Passengers in fixed wheelchairs can be carried in the brake compartment of all trains. Ramps are provided to ease entry to trains
Membership details: Membership Secretary, c/o above address

| Timetable Service (Diesel) | Mid-Norfolk Railway | Norfolk |

Member: HRA
A scheme to preserve part of the former Great Eastern line from Wymondham to Wells-next-the-Sea. The section from Wymondham to Dereham has been purchased and opened for passenger and freight traffic since May 1999. The Mid-Norfolk Railway Preservation Trust also operates County School station as a tearoom and visitor centre during the summer months
Headquarters: The Railway Station, Station Road, Dereham, Norfolk NR19 1DF
Main station: Dereham
Telephone: (01362) 690633 (answerphone)
Fax: (01362) 698487
Internet address: web site; http://www.horizonpress.commnr
Car park: At Dereham
Museum: Small relics museum at Dereham
Souvenir shop: Dereham
Refreshment facilities: Railway Buffet at Dereham (all year) and tearoom at County School station (summer only)
Access by public transport: Bus from Norwich and King's Lynn. Central Trains to Wymondham
Period of public operation:

Locomotives & multiple-units

Name	No	Origin	Class	Type	Built
—	20069	BR	20	Bo-Bo	1961
Ramillies	50019	BR	50	Co-Co	1968
—	51073	Gloucester	119	DMBC	1958
—	51360	BR	117	DMBS	1959
—	51572	BR	108	DMC	1959
—	54224	BR	108	DTC	1959
—	55006	Gloucester	122	DMBS	1958
—	55009	Gloucester	122	DMBS	1958
—	56301*	Gloucester	100	DTC	1957

*in use as static shop and tearoom at County School station

Industrial locomotives

Name	No	Builder	Type	Built
Little Barford*	—	Barclay (2069)	0-4-0ST	1939
—	—	R/Hornsby (497753)	0-4-0DE	1963

*on loan until June 2000

Locomotive notes: 20069, 50019 and DMUs 55006, 51572 & 54224 are in service.

Rolling stock 5 BR Mk 2 coaches. Ex-TPO BG and breakdown van (ex-Stewarts Lane). TSO 5536 to be used as bar coach. Selection of freight wagons

Regular trains from Dereham to Wymondham operate most of the year. Occasional working freight trains
Special events: Mid-Norfolk Festival of Classic Transport, May 2000. Santa and Mince Pie Specials in December

Membership details: Stuart Moye, 21 The Brambles, Ware, Herts SG12 0XU
Membership journal: *The Blastpipe* (four times a year)

Museum — Mid-Suffolk Light Railway — Suffolk

Location: Wetheringsett, Nr Stowmarket, Suffolk IP14 5PW
OS reference: TM 129659
Operating organisation: Mid-Suffolk Light Railway Company
Telephone: (01449) 766899
Car park: On site
Access by public transport: Main line Stowmarket (8 miles); by bus from Ipswich on summer Sundays
On site facilities: Souvenir shop, refreshments, railway walk, railwayana and photographic exhibition, toilets and picnic area
Period of public opening: Sundays and Bank Holidays, Easter to end September
Special events: Subject to confirmation, please enquire locally

Industrial locomotives

Name	No	Builder	Type	Built
—	1604	H/Clarke (1604)	0-6-0ST	1928
—	304470	R/Hornsby (304470)	0-4-0DM	1951

Rolling stock

2 GER ventilated vans, 1 GER non-ventilated van, Moy private owner coal wagon (conversion of BR open wagon), GER 5-compartment third, GER 2-compartment brake third, GER 3-compartment first, BR tube wagon, nondescript flat wagon, LNER brake van, 3 GER coach bodies, NER milk van body, LMS horse box body

Special notes: Museum dedicated to Mid-Suffolk Light Railway. Original MSLR restored buildings and artefacts. Reproduction MSLR ticket on entry. *Railway World* award winner

Membership details: Membership Secretary, 4 Felix Road, Stowupland, Stowmarket, Suffolk IP14 4DD
Society journal: *Making Tracks:* quarterly MSLRS newsletter

Steam Centre — Middleton Railway — Leeds

Members: HRA
This is a preserved section of 'the world's oldest working railway', authorised by the first railway Act of Parliament in 1758, and also the first standard gauge railway to be taken over by volunteers in 1960
Headquarters: Middleton Railway Trust Ltd, Moor Road, Leeds LS10 2JQ
Telephone: (0113) 271 0320
Internet addresses: web site: www.personal.leeds.ac.uk/mph6mi p/mrt/mrt.htm
e-mail: howill@globalnet.co.uk
Main station: Moor Road, Hunslet
OS reference: SE 302309
Car park: Moor Road (free)
Access by public transport: Nearest mainline station, Leeds City. Bus No 76 from City Square (opposite Leeds railway station) to Moor Road station (every 30min)
Souvenir shop: Moor Road
Museum: In preparation. Depot open weekends and Bank Holidays 10.00 to 17.00 in season
Length of line: 1.25 miles (extension pending)
Passenger trains: Sunday trains, Bank Holidays and special events

Locomotives

Name	No	Origin	Class	Type	Built
—	1310	NER	Y7	0-4-0T	1891
—	54	LNER	Y1	0-4-0VB	1933
—	385	DSB	HsII	0-4-0WT	1893
John Alcock	7051	LMS	—	0-6-0DM	1932
(Olive)	RDB998901	BR	—	4wDM	1950

Industrial locomotives

Name	No	Builder	Type	Built
John Blenkinsop	—	Peckett (2003)	0-4-0ST	1941
—	—	Peckett (2103)	0-4-0ST	1948
Henry de Lacy II	—	H/Clarke (1309)	0-4-0ST	1917
Mirvale	—	H/Clarke (1882)	0-4-0ST	1955
Brookes No 1	—	Hunslet (2387)	0-6-0T	1941
Windle	—	Borrows (53)	0-4-0WT	1909
Matthew Murray	—	Bagnall (2702)	0-4-0ST	1943
Lucy	—	Cockerill	0-4-0VBT	1890
Arthur	—	M/Wardle (1601)	0-6-0ST	1901
—*	—	Brush (91)	0-4-0DE	1958
—	No 6	H/Leslie (3860)	0-4-0ST	1935
Carroll	—	H/Clarke (D631)	0-4-0DM	1946
Mary	—	H/Clarke (D577)	0-4-0DM	1932
—	—	Fowler (3900002)	0-4-0DM	1945
—	—	Thomas Hill (138C)	0-4-0DH	1963
Rowntrees No 3†	—	R/Hornsby (441934)	4wDM	1960

*on loan from BSC Orb Works, Newport
†on loan from North Yorkshire Moors Railway

steam operated. Saturdays usually diesel hauled. Charter trains can be arranged

Period of public operation:
Saturdays, Sundays and Bank Holidays from Good Friday to December. Saturdays — 13.00-16.20. Other days — 11.00-16.20

Special events: A Day Out with Thomas — 25/26 March, 1/2 April; Easter Bunnies Weekend — 21-24 April; Postman Pat's Special — 13/14 May; Anniversary Gala — 17/18 June; Volunteers' and Members' Open Day — 9 July; Teddy Bears' Picnic — 6 August; Steam Extravaganza — 23/24 September; A Day Out with Thomas — 4/5, 11/12 November;

Stock
2 CCTs converted for passenger use Nos 1867 and 2048; CCT as stores van No 2073; Norwegian brake coach; Various goods vehicles; 5-ton Booth rail crane; 1 3-ton Smith steam crane; 1 3-ton Isles steam crane; 7.5 ton steam crane

Owners
1310, 385 the Steam Power Trust
RDB998901 the EM2 Locomotive Society

Santa Specials — 3, 9/10, 16/17, 23/24 December
Facilities for disabled: Good access with additional assistance by prior arrangement
Special notes: Never having closed since 1758 the railway still operates under its original Act of Parliament. The first railway to successfully use steam locomotives commercially

from 1812. The first standard gauge railway to be operated by volunteers from June 1960. Conveyed 10,000 tons of freight annually from BR to local works from 1960 to 1983. Part of Leeds Heritage Trail, highlighting former locomotive works in the area, etc

---

Timetable Service	**Midland Railway Centre**	Derbyshire

Member: HRA, TT

The Centre is a rapidly developing Preservation Scheme with a difference. The massive 57 acre Museum site and 35 acre Country Park enables the Centre to become 'More Than Just a Railway' as its publicity says. The seven-road Matthew Kirtley Museum allows much of the historic collection to be on display and most of the locomotives to be stored and displayed under cover. A miniature railway (3.5 and 5in gauge) and a 1-mile narrow gauge line (2ft gauge) carry passengers through the Country Park. A new development is the Brittain Pit Farm Park, with its wide variety of livestock. And of course there is a 3.5-mile standard gauge line complete with Midland signals, three restored signalboxes, Butterley station, the scenic delights of Butterley Reservoir and Golden Valley!

The Millennium year will see the restoration to main line working order of *Duchess of Sutherland* as well as continued development of a number of projects, particularly at the Swanwick Junction museum site. The first stage of the Diesel Depot will be approaching completion, the Stationary Power display will hopefully be open, and the National Headquarters of the

Locomotives and multiple-units

Name	No	Origin	Class	Type	Built
Princess Elizabeth	6201	LMS	8P	4-6-2	1933
Princess Margaret Rose	46203	LMS	8P	4-6-2	1935
Duchess of Sutherland	6233	LMS	8P	4-6-2	1938
—	44027	LMS	4F	0-6-0	1924
—	44932	LMS	5MT	4-6-0	1945
—	45491	LMS	5MT	4-6-0	1943
—	47564	LMS	3F	0-6-0T	1928
—	47327	LMS	3F	0-6-0T	1926
—	47357	LMS	3F	0-6-0T	1926
—	47445	LMS	3F	0-6-0T	1927
—	158A	MR	—	2-4-0	1866
—	53809	S&DJR	7F	2-8-0	1925
—	73129	BR	5MT	4-6-0	1956
—	80080	BR	4MT	2-6-4T	1954
—	80098	BR	4MT	2-6-4T	1955
—	92214	BR	9F	2-10-0	1959
—	92219	BR	9F	2-10-0	1959
—	D2138	BR	03	0-6-0DM	1960
—	08590	BR	08	0-6-0DE	1959
—	12077	BR	11	0-6-0DE	1950
—	D8001	BR	20	Bo-Bo	1957
—	20205	BR	20	Bo-Bo	1967
Traction	20227	BR	20	Bo-Bo	1967
—	D7671	BR	25	Bo-Bo	1967
—	31108	BR	31	A1A-A1A	1959
—	5580	BR	31	A1A-A1A	1960
—	31271	BR	31	A1A-A1A	1961
—	33201	BR	33	Bo-Bo	1962
—	37190	BR	37	Co-Co	1964
Aureol	40012	BR	40	1Co-Co1	1959
Andania	40013	BR	40	1Co-Co1	1959
Great Gable	D4	BR	44	1Co-Co1	1959
Royal Tank Regiment	45041	BR	45/1	1Co-Co1	1962
—	45133	BR	45/1	1Co-Co1	1961

Historical Model Railway Society should also see its first stage in use The Victorian Railwaymen's Church, the demonstration signalbox, and all the other many attractions that make up the Midland Railway Centre will be open throughout the year

Location: Midland Railway Centre, Butterley Station, Nr Ripley, Derbyshire DE5 3QZ
OS reference: SK 403520
General Manager: John Hett
Operating society/organisation: Midland Railway Trust Ltd
Telephone: Ripley (01773) 747674, Visitor Information Line (01773) 570140.
Fax: (01773) 570271
Car park: Butterley station on B6179 1-mile north of Ripley
On site facilities: Museum, award winning country park, Brittain Pit Farm Park, souvenir shops, miniature railway, narrow gauge railway, garden railway, model railways
Refreshment facilities: Butterley station buffet, Johnson Buffet (Swanwick), on-train bars and extensive 'Wine and Dine' trains. 'The Midlander' (details from above address)
Length of line: Standard gauge 3.5 miles, narrow gauge 0.8-mile
Public opening: Every Saturday, Sunday and Bank Holiday Monday from 22 January, every Wednesday from April to October and daily from 15 April to 1 May, 27 May to 4 June, 18 July to 4 September, 21-30 October.
On other dates the centre will be open for static display.
Golden Valley Light Railway: weekends, Bank Holiday Mondays April to October, Wednesdays June-October.
Butterley Park Miniature Railway: operates Sundays and Bank Holiday Mondays Easter to October.
Journey time: Approximately 1hr
Special events: Spring Diesel Gala— 25/26 March; Mother's Day Lunch Train — 2 April; Demonstration Goods Trains — 15 April, 20 May, 17 June, 15 July, 19 August, 23 September, 7 October; Easter Eggstravaganza — 15-28 April; Diesel & Steam Weekend — 15/16 April, 20/21 May, 17/18 June, 15/16 July, 19/20 August,

Name	No	Origin	Class	Type	Built
—	46045	BR	46	1Co-Co1	1963
—	47401	BR	47	Co-Co	1963
—	D1516	BR	47	Co-Co	1963
Sir Edward Elgar	50007	BR	50	Co-Co	1967
Tulyar	55015	BR	55	Co-Co	1961
Western Lady	D1048	BR	52	C-C	1962
Electra	27000	BR	EM2	Co+Co	1953
—	50019	BR	114	DMBS	1956
—	55966	BR	127	DPU	1959
—	55976	BR	127	DPU	1956
—	56006	BR	114	DTC	1956
—	59609	BR	127	TC	1959
—	79018	BR	—	MBS	19??
—	79612	BR	—	DTC	19??
—	29663	M/Cam	—	TC	1931
—	29666	M/Cam	—	TC	1931
—	29670	M/Cam	—	TC	1931
—	56171	Wickham	109	DMBS	1957
—	50416	Wickham	109	DMBS	1957

Locomotive notes: In service 80080, 80098, 47327, 47357, 20001, 20227, 33201, 46045, 08590, 5580, Class 114 DMU, D4, 47401, D2138, 40012, 12077, 45133, 55015 and D7671. Under restoration 6201, 6233, 44027, 53809, 73129, 92214, 45491, 44932, Wickham unit, 127 unit. Awaiting repairs or stored 31108, 47417, 47445, 92219. Boiler and frames only 47564. Static display 158A, 31271, 27000

Industrial locomotives

Name	No	Builder	Type	Built
Gladys	—	Markham (109)	0-4-0ST	1894
Stanton	24	Barclay (1875)	0-4-0CT	1925
Whitehead	—	Peckett (1163)	0-4-0ST	1908
Lytham St Annes	—	Peckett (2111)	0-4-0ST	1949
Brown Bailey	4	N/Wilson (454)	0-4-0ST	1894
Castle Donnington	1	RSH (7817)	0-4-0ST	1954
Neepsend	—	Sentinel (9370)	4wVBT	1947
Andy	2	Fowler (16038)	0-4-0DM	1923
—	RS9	M/Rail (2024)	0-4-0DM	1921
—	RS12	M/Rail (460)	0-4-0DM	1912
Boots	2	Barclay (2008)	0-4-0F	1935
Castle Donnington	2	Barclay (416)	0-4-0DM	1957
Boots	—	R/Hornsby (384139)	0-4-0DE	1955
Handyman*	—	H/Clarke (573)	0-4-0ST	1900
Rothwell Colliery*	—	H/Clarke (D718)	0-6-0DM	1950
—	—	H/Clarke (D1152)	0-6-0DM	1959
Albert Fields	—	H/Clarke (D1114)	0-6-0DM	1958
—†	—	Deutz (10249)	4wDM	1932
Campbell Brick Works†	—	M/Rail (60S364)	4wDM	1968
—†	—	Lister (3742)	4wDM	1931
—†	—	M/Rail (11246)	4wDM	1963
—†	2	O/Koppel (7529)	0-4-0WT	1914
—†	—	O/Koppel (5215)	4wDM	1936
Wheal Jayne†	19	BEV	4wBE	1985
—†	—	Ruston (7002/0567/6)	4wDM	1966
Berryhill†	—	Ruston (222068)	4wDM	1943
Hucknall Colliery†	3	Ruston (480678)	4wDM	1961
—†	—	Hunslet (7178)	4wDH	1971
Calverton Colliery†	22	H/Clarke (1117)	0-6-0DM	1958
Welbeck Colliery††	—	H/Clarke	0-6-0DM	—
Linby Colliery††	—	H/Clarke (DM647)	0-6-0DM	1954
—†	—	Lister (53726)	4wDM	1963

England

Pacific power on the Great Central Railway with No 60532 *Blue Peter* at the head of the 10.15 from Loughborough, whilst on loan on 25 March 1999. *Alan P. Barnes*

Another loan locomotive, this time *Dora* is seen in action on the Nothampton & Lamport Railway during a visit from the Rutland Railway Centre. *J. Pepper*

23/24 September, 7/8 October; Vintage Train Bank Holiday — 29 April-1 May, 26-28 August; Goods Gala 2000 — 13/14 May; Narrow Gauge Railway Event — 13/14 May; Days Out with Thomas — 27 May-4 June, 29 July-6 August; Model Railway Exhibition — 10/11 June; Father's Day Lunch Train — 18 June; Diesel Gala — 24/25 June; Teddy Bears' Picnic — 1/2 July; Road Rally — 9 July; Free for Registered Disabled — 22/23 July; Narrow Gauge Railway and Garden Festival Railway Festival — 12/13 August; Stationary Engine and Tractor Show — 30 September/1 October; Branch Line Weekend — 14/15 October; Oswald the Talking Engine's Birthday Party — 21-27 October; Halloween Fireworks Party — 28 October; Fireworks Night— 4 November; Santa Specials 25/26 November, 2/3, 9/10, 13, 16/17, 20-24, 26/27 December; Mince Pie Specials — 28 December-1 January 2001
Facilities for disabled: Toilets, special coach, access to shop and cafeteria, special weekend
Membership details: J. Hett, at above address
Membership journal: *The Wyvern* — quarterly
Marketing names: 'More than just a railway'; Golden Valley Light Railway (narrow gauge); Butterley Park Miniature Railway (miniature line)

Name	No	Builder	Type	Built
—†	—	SMH (40SD529)	4wDM	1983
—†	NG24	Baguley/Drewry (3703)	4wBE	1974
Claverton No 7†	7	Hunslet (8911)	4wDM	1980
—†	RS202	SMH (102T20)	4wDH	19xx
—§	—	Chrzanow (3226)	0-6-0T	1954
—§	—	Chrzanow (1983)	0-6-0T	1949
*Princess Elizabeth***	6201	H/Clarke (D611)	4-6-2DM	1938
*Princess Margaret Rose***	6203	H/Clarke (D612)	4-6-2DM	1938

*3ft gauge   †2ft gauge   ††2ft 4in gauge   §2ft 6in gauge   **21in gauge
Locomotive notes: In service: Boots, *Castle Donnington No 2*, NG24, Ruston 222068, SMH (40SD529 & 102T20), *Calverton Col No 22*, Lister, Deutz 10249, *Albert Fields*, M/Rail 60S364. Under restoration: *Andy* RS12, *Princess Margaret Rose*. Awaiting repairs or stored on display: Stanton, RS9, Hunslet 7178, M/Rails 5906/11246. Static display *Gladys*, 4, Boots No 2, *Handyman*, Sentinel 9370, both Chrzanows, *Lytham St Annes*

Stock
Numerous carriages, wagons and cranes. Museum display includes MR Royal saloon, MR 4-wheeled coach, MR brake third, LD&ECR all third, BR horsebox, LMS travelling Post Office, L&YR family saloon, MR motor carvan, MR bogie brake third, restored freight vehicles, LMS 50-ton steam crane, and much more

Owners
6201 the 6201 Princess Elizabeth Society Ltd
158A, 44027 on loan from the National Railway Museum
53809 the 13809 Preservation Group
47357, 47327, 47445, 47564, 73129 Derby City Council
6233, 46203, 80080, 80098 the Princess Royal Class Locomotive Trust
55015 the Deltic Preservation Society
D4, 45041 and 46045 the Peak Locomotive Preservation Co Ltd
D7671 Derby Industrial Museum

Museum	**Monkwearmouth Station Museum**	County Durham

The Museum is one of Britain's finest neo-classical stations and was built in 1848 to commemorate the election of George Hudson as MP for Sunderland. Restored features include the booking office, unchanged since it was installed in 1866, waiting shelter on the west platform and siding area
Location: North Bridge Street, Sunderland SR5 1AP
Telephone: (0191) 567 7075
OS reference: NZ 396576

Rolling stock
NER brake van 1915, LNER CCT van 1939

On site facilities: Car parking on museum forecourt, shop
Access by public transport: 10min walk from Sunderland Central station. Served by several bus routes from Sunderland city centre, Newcastle and South Shields
Public opening: Daily 1 January- 31 December (except New Year's Day, Good Friday, Christmas Day, Boxing Day). Monday-Friday 10.00-17.00. Saturday 10.00-16.30. Sunday 14.00-17.00. Free admission.
Access for disabled: Ramped access, suitable for wheelchair users

Museum of Army Transport

Museum | **East Yorkshire**

Member: TT

Operating a substantial network of railways in wartime, the Army is still responsible for railways feeding MoD depots in this country. Not only does the Museum hold extensive archives and display some fascinating maps, drawings and photographs, it contains some very interesting stock from the former military railways

Location: Museum of Army Transport, Flemingate, Beverley, East Yorkshire HU17 0NG

OS reference: TA 041392

Operated by: The Museum of Army Transport Ltd (Charitable Status Company)

Telephone: Hull (01482) 860445

Car park: Yes, 1.25 acres

Access by public transport: Rail: 10min walk from Beverley station. Bus: served by East Yorks Motor Service

On site facilities: Museum — The Royal Corps of Transport Collection of road, rail, sea, air and movement control artefacts. Licensed cafeteria. Shop in building. Lavatories, including special for disabled. Large car and bus park

Facilities for disabled: The Museum is on one floor. This allows viewing of all vehicles. Access is available by ramp into the Armoured Train. Access is not possible into the Beverley aircraft,

Locomotives

Name	No	Builder	Type	Built
Woolmer	—	Avonside (1572)	0-6-0ST	1910
Waggoner	92	Hunslet (3792)	0-6-0ST	1953
Rorke's Drift	—	Drewry (2047)	0-4-0DM	1934
Lyddia	AD41†	R/Hornsby (191646)	4WDM	1933
—	110	R/Hornsby (411319)	4wDM	1958
—	1035	Wickham Rail Car	4w	1958
—	3282*	Wickham Target Trolley	4w	1943
—	LOD 758009†[1]	M/Rail	4wDM	1941-3
—	LOD 758220†[2]	M/Rail	4wDM	1941-3
—	LOD 758228†	M/Rail (8667)	4wDM	1941
—	LOD 758028†	M/Rail (8855)	4wDM	1943
—	RTT 767182†	Wickham Target Trolley	4w	WW2

*2ft 6in gauge
†2ft gauge
[1] fitted with air-brake for use with passenger stock
[2] stored on site, may be moving

Rolling stock

Collection of various rolling stock items including Lord Kitchener's coach (c1885), a World War 1 Armoured Train gun truck and a World War 2 ramp wagon

A 2ft gauge system based on the ADLR of World War 1, some 200yd long, and worked by World War 2 Simplex rail tractors operated by volunteers, on Saturday and Sunday afternoons and at other times as advertised locally during the summer. Intending travellers should check the line is operating.

the railway locos and the signalbox frame

Public opening: 10.00-17.00 every day except 24-26 December. Group discount rate for parties of 20 or more

Special notes: Please bear in mind that while what is reported here deals with railways, other parts of this extensive museum cover movement by road, sea and air

Honorary Railway (and Port) Consultant: Major J. A. Robins (Retd)

The Museum of Science & Industry in Manchester

Museum | **Manchester**

Based in the buildings of the world's oldest passenger railway station (dating from 1830), the Museum has colourful 'hands-on' galleries that amuse, amaze and entertain. There are train rides on Sundays, commencing Easter 2000 (please ring for details) and visitors can find out about our industrial past, walk through a Victorian

Locomotives and multiple-units

Name	No	Origin	Class	Type	Built
Lion	57	L&MR	—	0-4-2	1838
Pender	3††	IoMR	—	2-4-0T	1873
Novelty	Replica of 1829 locomotive using some original parts				1986
—	3157†	PR	—	4-4-0	1911
—	2352§	SAR	GL	4-8-2+2-8-4	1929
Ariadne	1505 (27001)	BR	EM2 (77)	Co-Co	1954
Hector	26048	BR	EM1 (76)	Bo-Bo cab only	1952

sewer complete with sounds and smells, and hunt an alien!
Location: Liverpool Road, Castlefield, Manchester (off Deansgate near Granada studios)
OS reference: SJ 831987
Operating society/organisation: The Museum of Science and Industry in Manchester, Liverpool Road, Castlefield, Manchester M3 4FP
Telephone: (0161) 832 2244
Car parks: On site, plus parking in the area (Museum car park £1.50)
Access by public transport: Manchester Victoria, Piccadilly, Oxford Road and Deansgate main line stations. GM bus 33. G-Mex Metrolink station
On site facilities: Oldest passenger railway station, weekend train rides, listed buildings containing exhibitions about science, industry, aviation, space, water supply and sewage disposal, gas and electricity. Xperiment! the 'hands-on' science centre and the 'Out of this world' space gallery. World's largest collection of working steam mill engines in the Power Hall, demonstrated every afternoon. Kites Café and Mosaics gift shop with a restaurant that is scheduled to open in February 2000

Name	No	Origin	Class	Type	Built
Planet*	—	Replica	—	2-2-0	1992

Industrial locomotives

Name	No		Builder	Type	Built
Lord Ashfield	—		Barclay (1964)	0-4-0ST	1929
—	258		E/Electric (1378)	4wBE	1944

*replica of 1830-built locomotive
††ex-Isle of Man Railways, 3ft gauge, sectioned (B/Peacock 1255)
†ex-Pakistan Railways, 5ft 6in gauge (V/Foundry 3064)
§ex-South African Railways, 3ft 6in gauge (B/Peacock 6693)

Rolling stock
BR Mk 2 SO E5241, 1966
Replica M&BR 1st class carriage c1840 using original fragments
2 replica L&MR 2nd class carriages c1835
c1908 L&YR ambulance carriage re-built 1923 as Medical Examination Car, LMS No 10825 (under restoration)
B782903 4-wheeled covered goods van, BR (Wolverton), 1961
B783709 4-wheeled covered goods van, BR (Wolverton), 1962
3-plank loose coupled goods wagon, MSLR (Dukinfield)?, c1890
Manchester Ship Canal wagon, c1886 (in very poor condition)

Owners
Lion on loan from the National Museums & Galleries on Merseyside
Novelty on loan from the National Railway Museum, York
Industrial locomotives on loan from PowerGen

Public opening: Daily except 24-26 December, including Saturdays and Sundays, 10.00-17.00. Entrance in Lower Byrom Street. Admission charged

Special notes: Good wheelchair access, toilets for the disabled, lecture and conference facilities

Tram Service — National Tramway Museum — Derbyshire

Member: HRA, TT
An experience of living transport history with vintage horse-drawn, steam and electric trams running through a re-created townscape of authentic buildings, stone setts, iron railings and historic street furniture. The heart of the Museum is its collection of over 70 vintage trams and you can enjoy the thrill of travelling on the scenic mile-long track
Location: Crich, Nr Matlock, Derbyshire DE4 5DP
OS reference: SK 345549
Manager: Lesley Wyld
Operating society/organisation: Tramway Museum Society
Telephone: (01773) 852565
Car park: Site; coach parking also available
Access by public transport: Nearest stations: Cromford (main line) or Alfreton (main line) then by bus; or Whatstandwell (main line) and steep uphill walk
On site facilities: Souvenir shop, play areas, bookshop and picnic areas. 1-mile electric tramway. Tramway period street, depots, displays, exhibitions and video theatre. Large exhibition hall with new interpretive display depicting the history of the tram and Turn of the Century Trade Exhibition plus other exhibitions/displays
Refreshment facilities: Hot and cold snacks and meals
Public opening: January, February, March, November and December — Sundays and Mondays (10.30-16.00); April to October — daily (10.00-17.30) (18.30 weekends in June, July and August, plus all Bank Holidays)
Special events: A 'Mane' Event — 21 May; The Mighty Mini Meet — 4 June; Tram-jam-boree — 11 June; In Living Memory — 16 July; Festival of Transport — 27/28 August; Funtasia — 24 September; A Yorkshire Date — 1 October; Treasure Trail — 21-28 October
Family tickets: Available
Facilities for disabled: Access to all public facilities, Braille guide book available. Also 1969 Berlin tram specially adapted to lift and carry people in wheelchairs. Also a 'wheelway', a smooth path routeing around and through cobbled areas
Special notes: Crich houses the largest collection of preserved trams in Europe and has a 1-mile working tramway on which restored electric trams are regularly operated. Special events are arranged at weekends and Bank Holidays throughout the season. Part of tram line occupies route of narrow gauge mineral railway built by George Stephenson

Membership details: From above address
Membership journal: *The Journal* — quarterly

Locomotives

Name	No	Builder	Type	Built
—	—	B/Peacock (2464)	0-4-0VB tram loco	1885
—	—	E/Electric (717)	4wE	1927
*Rupert**	—	R/Hornsby (223741)	4wDM	1944
*GMJ**	—	R/Hornsby (326058)	4wDM	1952
—*	—	R/Hornsby (373363)	4wDM	1954

*not on display

Also some 70 trams (including examples from Czechoslovakia, Germany, The Netherlands, Portugal, USA and South Africa), about a third of which have been restored to working order

Museum	# National Railway Museum	North Yorkshire

Members: HRA, TT, MLSOG
Location: National Railway Museum, Leeman Road, York YO26 4XJ
OS reference: SE 594519
Operating society/organisation: Part of the National Museum of Science and Industry
Telephone: York (01904) 621261
Car park: Available on site, additional charge applies. Coach parking is available — pre-booking required
Access by public transport: The Museum is within a few minutes' walking distance of the railway and bus stations in York. The York City & District Bus Service operates to the door
On site facilities: Museum shop, restaurant and toilets. Reference library (free by appointment). Also model railway, miniature railway, baby changing facilities, indoor and outdoor play areas, children's interactive learning centre, conference centre
Public opening: Daily 10.00-18.00. Closed 24-26 December. Over 60s free from April 2000
Facilities for disabled: Most areas of the museum are accessible
Special notes: The Museum has been open since 1975 and has welcomed over 20 million visitors.

It offers the visitor three extensive exhibition halls, the Great Hall, the Station Hall and The Works, which house the world's premier collection of railway related material.

The Great Hall displays are on the theme of railway technology. There is a magnificent display of railway locomotive development round the turntable. Signalling, the permanent way, the modern railway and the Channel Tunnel are also represented. The displays reflect the present and the past and include a full-sized model of the nose cone of a state of the art Transmanche Super Train operating between England and the Continent. Displays on the operation of the railways, tape/slide presentations can be found on the Balcony Galleries.

'Stephenson's *Rocket* — the spark that started a revolution' was open during 1999; please contact the museum for details of this year's theme and other special events.

The Station Hall illustrates the concept of travel by train — for passengers and freight. Several trains are drawn up at platforms with a number of footplates and carriages open to visitors. The vehicles displayed range from the superb Royal carriages to humble freight wagons.

The Interactive Learning Centre provides visitors with 'hands-on' experience of various aspects of railway operation.

The Museum's extensive reference library (including the photographic and drawings collections) continues to be free to all booked enquirers every weekday from 10.30-17.00.

The tables which follow indicate the whereabouts (display, on loan, in store) of the National Railway Collection. It must be emphasised that the appearance of any particular item on public display cannot be guaranteed. If it is vital to discover the exact whereabouts of a specific item, enquirers should contact the Museum in York before the trip.

The National Railway Museum is open for evening hire for private viewings and celebrations; menus and details are available on request.

Details of membership of the Museum's support group, including free entry and a quarterly newsletter are available from: The Secretary, Friends of the National Railway Museum, c/o the above address.

Locomotives — Steam

Name	No	Origin	Builder	Class	Type	Built
Agenoria	—	Shutt End Colliery	Foster/Raistrick	—	0-4-0	1829
Coppernob	3	FR	Bury, Curtis & Kennedy	—	0-4-0	1846
Pet	—	LNWR	Crewe	—	0-4-0ST	1865
Aerolite	66	NER	Gateshead	X1(LNER)	2-2-4T	1869

Name	No	Origin	Builder	Class	Type	Built
—	1	GNR	Doncaster	—	4-2-2	1870
Bauxite	2	Hebburn Works	B/Hawthorn	—	0-4-0ST	1874
—	1275	NER	Gateshead	—	0-6-0	1874
Boxhill	82	LB&SCR	Brighton	A1	0-6-0T	1880
Gladstone	214	LB&SCR	Brighton	—	0-4-2	1882
Wren	—	LYR	B/Peacock	—	0-4-0ST	1887
—	1008	LYR	Horwich	—	2-4-2T	1889
Hardwicke	790	LNWR	Crewe	—	2-4-0	1892
—	563	LSWR	Nine Elms	T3	4-4-0	1893
—	1621	NER	Gateshead	M	4-4-0	1893
—	245	LSWR	Nine Elms	M7	0-4-4T	1897
—	673	MR	Derby	—	4-2-2	1899
—	737	SECR	Ashford	D	4-4-0	1901
—	251	GNR	Doncaster	C1	4-4-2	1902
—	1000	MR	Derby	4	4-4-0	1902
City of Truro	3440	GWR	Swindon	'City'	4-4-0	1903
—	87	GER	Stratford	J69	0-6-0T	1904
—	1217	GER	Stratford	J17	0-6-0	1905
—	2818	GWR	Swindon	2800	2-8-0	1905
Lode Star	4003	GWR	Swindon	'Star'	4-6-0	1907
Butler Henderson	506	GCR	Gorton	'Director'	4-4-0	1920
—	485	LNWR	Crewe	G2/Super D	0-8-0	1921
Cheltenham	925	SR	Eastleigh	V/Schools	4-4-0	1934
—	2500	LMS	Derby	4P	2-6-4T	1934
—	5000	LMS	Crewe	5MT	4-6-0	1935
—	KF7	Chinese Govt Rlys	Vulcan	KF	4-8-4	1935
Green Arrow	4771	LNER	Doncaster	V2	2-6-2	1936
Mallard	4468	LNER	Doncaster	A4	4-6-2	1938
Duchess of Hamilton	46229	LMS	Crewe	8P	4-6-2	1938
Eustace Forth	15	—	RSH (7063)	—	0-4-0ST	1942
Winston Churchill	34051	SR	Brighton	BB	4-6-2	1946
Ellerman Lines	35029	BR(SR)	Sectioned	MN	4-6-2	1949
—	—	Imperial Paper Mills	Barclay	—	0-4-0F	1956
Frank Galbraith	5	Tees-Side Bridge & Engineering Co	Sentinel	—	4wTG	1957
Evening Star	92220	BR	Swindon	9F	2-10-0	1960
Rocket (replica)	—	—	Loco Enterprises	—	0-2-2	1979
Iron Duke (broad gauge replica)	—	GWR	RESCO	—	4-2-2	1985

Locomotives — Electric

Name	No	Origin	Builder	Class	Type	Built
—	75S	W&CR	Siemens (6)	—	Bo electric	1898
—	1	NER	BTH	—	Bo-Bo electric	1904
—	809	GPO	Green Bat	—	2w-2E	1931
—	26020	BR	Gorton/Metrovick	76	Bo-Bo Electric	1951
—	E3036	BR	N/British	84	Bo-Bo	1960

Locomotives — Diesel

Name	No	Origin	Builder	Class	Type	Built
—	—	—	Simplex (4217)	—	4wPM	1925
Hexhamshire	15	CEGB	A/Whitworth (D21)		0-4-0DE	1933
—	08064	BR	Darlington	08	0-6-0 DE	1953
BEA Carrington Station	3	CEGB	RSH (7746)	—	0-6-0 DM	1954
—	D8000	BR	E/Electric	20	Bo-Bo	1957
Deltic	—	E/Electric	E/Electric	—	Co-Co	1955
—	5500	BR	Brush	31	A1A-A1A	1957

England

Name	No	Origin	Builder	Class	Type	Built
—	D200	BR	E/Electric	40	1Co-Co1	1958
—	03090	BR	—	03	0-6-0DM	1960
—	D2860	BR	YEC	02	0-4-0 DH	1960
Western Fusilier	D1023	BR	Swindon	52	C-C	1963
Glorious	50033	BR	E/Electric	50	Co-Co	1968
—*	41001	BR	Crewe	41	Bo-Bo	1972

*stored at MoD Kineton
†stored at MoD Kineton

Rolling Stock Powered Units— Gas Turbine
1972   BR Advanced Passenger Train

Rolling Stock Powered Units — Electric
1915	LNWR Motor Open Third Brake No 28249
1925	SR Motor Third Brake No S8143S
1937	SR Motor Third Open Brake No S11179S
1940	SR (W&C) Motor Driving Car No 61
1941†	LMS Class 502 BMS No 28361
1941†	LMS Class 502 DTC No 29896
1975†	BR Maglev prototype
1983†	BR APT protoype train

Rolling Stock Powered Units — Diesel
1959	BR DMU Class 108 Nos 51562 & 51922
1975	Leyland Motors LEV-1 experimental railbus

Rolling Stock — Departmental
1850	GNR 4-wheel hand crane No 112
1890	GNR Locomotive Tender No 1002
1891	NER Snow Plough No DE900566
1899	GWR Hand Crane No 537
1904	MR Officers' Saloon No 2234
1906	NER Dynamometer Car No 902502
1907	NER Steam Breakdown Crane No CME 13
1907	Match Truck No DE942114
1911	GWR Track Testing Coach
1926	LNER Match Truck No DE320952
1931/2	LNER Petrol-driven platelayers' trolley No 960209
1936	GWR Ballast Wagon No 80659
1938	LMS Mobile test unit No 1, No 45053
1949	BR Matisa tamping machine No 74007
1949†	GWR/BR Inspection Saloon No ADW80970
1955	GEC 12.5-ton Coles Crane
1957	BR Track recording trolley No DX 50002 Neptune
1969	BR Plasser Tamping & Liner No 73010

Rolling Stock — Passenger
1834	B&WR 1st & 2nd composite
1834	B&WR 2nd class
1834	B&WR 3rd class
1842	L&BR Queen Adelaide's Saloon
1845	S&DR 1st/3rd Composite No 59
1850	NER Brake End (body only)
1851	ECR 1st class No 1
1860	Cornwall Rly broad gauge coach (body only)
1861	NBR Port Carlisle branch 'dandy car'
1869	LNWR Queen Victoria's Saloon
1872	NLR Directors' Saloon No 1032
1885	MR 6-wheel composite brake No 901
1885	WCJS 8-wheel TPO No 186

1887	GNR Brake Van No 848
1887	GWR 6-wheel tricomposite No 820
1897	Lynton & Barnstaple Rly brake composite No 6992
1898	ECJS 3rd class No 12
1899	Privately owned Duke of Sutherland's Saloon No 57A
1900	LNWR (ex-WCJS) Dining Car LMS 76
1902	LNWR King Edward's Saloon No 800
1902	LNWR Queen Alexandra's Saloon No 801
1903	LSWR Tricomposite brake No 3598
1905†	LNWR Corridor 1st Brake 5154 (Royal Train)
1905†	LNWR Corridor 1st Brake 5154 (support vehicle)
1908†	ECJS Royal Saloon No 395
1913	Pullman Car Co 1st class parlour car Topaz
1914	MR Dining car No 3463
1920†	LNWR Royal Saloon No 45000
1925	LMS 3rd class vestibule No 7828
1928	LMS 3rd Sleeping Car No 14241
1930	L&MR 1st Huskinson (replica)
1930	L&MR 1st Traveller (replica)
1930	L&MR 2nd (replica)
1930	L&MR 2nd (replica)
1934	GWR Buffet Car No 9631
1936	CIWL Night Ferry sleeping car No 3792
1937	LNER Buffet Car No 9135
1938	GJR TPO (replica)
1941	LMS Royal Saloon 799 (armoured car)
1945†	GWR Royal Saloon No 9006
1955	BR Lavatory composite No E43046
1960†	BR Griddle car No Sc1100
1960	Pullman Car Co 1st class Parlour car No 326 Emerald
1962†	BR Prototype Mk II 1st class corridor No 13252
1962	BR Mk II 2nd brake corridor No 35468
1962†	BR Mk II 1st corridor No 21274
1969	BR Mk IIb 2nd open No 5455
1985	GWR 2nd (broad gauge replica)
1985	GWR 3rd (broad gauge replica)

Rolling Stock — Freight & Non Passenger Carrying
1815	Little Eaton (Derby Canal) Gangroad Wagon
1815	Peak Forest Canal Tramway Wagon No 174
1816	Grantham Canal Tramway Truck
1826	Cramlington Colliery Chaldron Wagon
1828	Dandy Cart
1840	Stratford & Moreton Tramway wagon
1850	South Hetton Colliery Chaldron Wagon No 1155
1870	Seaham Harbour Colliery Chaldron Wagon
1870	S&DR Chaldron Wagon (replica,)

1889	Shell-Mex oil tank wagon No 512		1938	LMS Single bolster wagon No 722702
1894	LSWR Brake van No 99		1940	WD Warflat No 161042
1895	LSWR Open carriage truck No 5830		1944	LMS Lowmac No M700728
1901	Shell/BP Tank Wagon No 3171		1944	GWR 13-ton open wagon No DW143698
1902	NER 20-ton wooden hopper wagon No 4551		1946	SNCF 16-ton mineral wagon No ADB192437
1907	NER 16ton bogie stores van No 041273		1946	LNER 20-ton hopper wagon No E270919
1908	LNWR Open Carriage Truck No 11275		1949	BR40-ton Flatrol No B900402912
1912	LB&SCR Open wagon No 27884		1949	BR Bogie bolster D No B941000
1912	LSWR Gunpowder van No KDS61209		1950	BR 24-ton iron ore hopper wagon No B436275
1912	NER Sand wagon No DE14974			
1912	GNR 8-ton van No E432764		1950	BR 20-ton Weltrol No B900805
1914	GWR Shunters' truck No W94988		1951	ICI Liquid chlorine tank wagon No 47484
1917	MR 8-ton open wagon		1951	BR(SR) Show cattle wagon No S3733S
1917	GCR Box Van		1951	BR 8-ton cattle wagon No B893343
1917	LNWR Box Van		1952	BR 30-ton bogie bolster wagon No B943139
1917	NER Box Van		1954	BR 27-ton Iron Ore Tippler No B383560
1920	GCR single bolster wagon		1954	National Benzole oil tank wagon No 2022
1920	GNR double bolster wagon		1955	BR china clay tip wagon No B743141
c1920	LSWR Lowmac NoDE563024		1957	BR Horse box No S96369
1924	LMSR Van		1959	BR Conflat No B737725
1926	GWR Fitted open wagon No 108246		1960	BR Banana Van No B882593
1927	LNER 40-ton flat wagon No DE633433		1960	BR 25-ton Weltrol WP No ADB 900916
1928	ICI Nitric acid tank wagon No 14		1961	BR Presflo cement wagon No B873368
1931	GWR Fruit Van No 112884		1961	BR 30ton bogie bolster No B923123
1931	Stanton Iron Works 12ton wagon		1962	BR Speedfreight container No BA 4324B
1933	LMSR 20-ton Goods Brake Van No 295987		1965	BR Boiler Wagon Nos DB902805, DB902806, DB902807, DB902808
1935	SR Bogie goods brake van No 56297			
1935	GWR Motor car van No 126438		1966	Milk Marketing Board 6-wheel tank No 42801
1935	PLM Train Ferry Van No 475014		1970	Phillips Petroleum 100-ton GLW tank wagon No PP85209
1936	LMSR 3 Plank Open Wagon No 472867			
1936	LMS Tube wagon No 499254		1970	BR 2,000gal Road/Rail Milk Tank No ADM707111
1937	GWR Siphon bogie milk van No 2775			
1937	LMSR Milk Tank Wagon No 44057		†Stored at MoD Kineton	
1938	GWR 20-ton Goods Brake Van No DW56518			

Items on Loan from the NRM
Locomotives

Original type/No/Name	Location	Builder	Built
Wylam Colliery	Science Mus	—	1813
Hetton Colliery 0-4-0	Beamish	G. Stephenson	1822
SDR 0-4-0 *Locomotion*	Darlington	R. Stephenson & Co	1825
L&MR 0-2-2 *Rocket*	Science Mus	R. Stephenson & Co	1829
L&MR 0-4-0 *Sans Pareil*	Science Mus	T. Hackworth	1829
L&MR 0-2-2 *Novelty*	Museum of Science & Technology (Manchester)	Braithwaite & Ericsson	1829
SDR 'Collier' class *Etherley* (tender only)	Shildon	—	1840
SDR 0-6-0 No 24 *Derwent*	Darlington Nth Rd Mus	A. Kitching	1845
LNWR 2-2-2 No 3020 *Cornwall*	Crewe	Crewe	1847
GJR 2-2-2 *Columbine*	Science Mus	Crewe	1845
Wantage Tramway 0-4-0WT No 5 *Shannon*	Didcot Rly Ctr	G. England	1857
LNWR 0-4-0ST 1439	East Lancs	Crewe	1865
MR 2-4-0 No 158A	Midland Rly Ctr	Derby	1866
South Devon Rly 0-4-0WT *Tiny*	South Devon Rly	Sara	1868
LSWR 2-4-0WT No 0298	South Devon Rly	B/Peacock	1874
NER 0-6-0 No 1275	Darlington	Duds & Co	1874
NER 2-4-0 No 910	Darlington Nth Rd Mus	Gateshead	1875
NER 2-4-0 No 1463	Darlington Nth Rd Mus	Gateshead	1885
C7SL No 1	LT Museum	B/Peacock	1890
S&MR 0-4-2WT *Gazelle*	Col Stephens Rly Mus	Dodman	1893
GER 2-4-0 No 490	Bressingham	Stratford	1894
GWR 0-6-0 No 2516	Steam, Swindon	Swindon	1897
TVR 0-6-2T No 28	Dean Forest	TVR	1897
GNR No 990 *Henry Oakley*	Bressingham	Doncaster	1989

72

Original type/No/Name	Location	Builder	Built
LSWR 4-4-0 No 120	Bluebell Rly	Nine Elms	1899
GNR 0-6-0ST No 1247	Bream (private workshop)	S/Stewart	1899
LT&SR 4-4-2T No 80 *Thundersley*	Bressingham	R. Stephenson	1909
GCR 2-8-0 No 102	Great Central	Gorton	1911
NSR 0-4-0wE No 1	Churnet Valley	Bolton	1917
WD No 1377 (2ft Gauge)	LBR	Simplex	1918
NER 0-8-0 No 901	North York Moors Rly	Darlington	1919
NSR No 2	Churnet Valley	Stoke	1922
GWR 4-6-0 No 4073 *Caerphilly Castle*	Steam, Swindon	Swindon	1923
LMS 0-6-0 No 4027	Midland Rly Ctr	Derby	1924
GWR 2-2-2 *North Star* (replica)	Steam, Swindon	R. Stephenson	1925
SR 4-6-0 No 777 *Sir Lamiel*	GCR	N/British	1925
SR 4-6-0 No 850 *Lord Nelson*	Eastleigh Works†	Eastleigh	1926
LMS 2-6-0 No 2700	East Lancs	Derby	1934
GWR No 6000 *King George V*	Steam, Swindon	Swindon	1927
SR 0-6-0 No C1	Bluebell Rly	Eastleigh	1942
GWR 0-6-0PT No 9400	Steam, Swindon	Swindon	1947
BR 4-6-2 No 70013 *Oliver Cromwell*	Bressingham	Crewe	1951
BR Bo-Bo No E5001	Crewe	Eastleigh	1958
BR Co-Co D9002 *King's Own Yorkshire Light Infantry*			
	Deltic9000	E/Electric	1961

†Private site

Powered Units

NER	electric parcels van No 3267, G. Stephenson Mus
SR	2BIL unit, No 2090, Hastings (private site)
GWR	diesel railcar No 4, Swindon GWR Mus

Departmental Stock

1907	LNWR match truck, No 284235, Churnet Valley
1908	LNWR steam crane, No 2987, Churnet Valley
1932	LMS Ballast plough brake van No 197266, Embsay
1949	BR(LMS) Dynamometer car No 3, No 45049, East Lancs

Passenger Stock

1846	SDR 1st & 2nd composite No 31, Darlington Nth Rd Mus
1850	SDR 3rd No 179, Timothy Hackworth Mus, Shildon
1850	NER 4-wheel coach body, Darlington
1908	ECJS Passenger Brake van LNER No 396, Bressingham
1910	GCR Open 3rd class No 666, Great Central Railway
1925	GWR 3rd class dining car No 9653, Severn Valley Rly
1925	GWR 3rd class dining car No 9654, Severn Valley Rly
1936	LNER 3rd Open, No 13254, Great Central
1937	LMS corridor 3rd class brake No 5987, Steamtown
1939	SR TPO No 4920, Nene Valley
1941	LMS Royal saloon No 798, Glasgow Museum of Transport
1945	GWR Royal Saloon No 9007, West Somerset
1950	BR (LMS) 3rd brake, No 27093, Midland Rly Ctr
1960	Pullman Car Co 1st class Kitchen car No 311 *Eagle*, NYMR

Freight & Non-Passenger-Carrying Stock

1909	GWR Girder Wagon Set (Pollen E) Nos DW84997, 84998, 84999, 85000, Didcot
1917	GWR Hydra-D No 42193, Didcot Railway Ctr
1920	LSWR Lowmac, No DE563024, NYMR
1922	LB&SCR cattle truck No 7116, Isle of Wight Steam Rly
1933	LMSR gunpowder van, No 288824, NYMR
1939	SR postal sorting van No 4920, Nene Valley Rly
1941	LNER 20-ton brake van, No 246710, NYMR
1945	GWR 25-ton machine truck, Embsay
1948	BR(SR) 12-ton shock absorbing wagon No 14036, NYMR
1949	BR 40-ton Gane-A No DB996724, Churnet Valley
1950	BR 12-wheel well wagon, No KDB901601, East Lancs
1955	BR 16-ton mineral wagon No B227009, Middleton
1959	BR Fish van No B87905, Hull
1970	S&D Chaldron wagon (replica), Shildon

Member: HRA

The museum has commenced a Lottery update of the galleries and site which should be completed by Easter 2000

Location: Gloucester Docks — signposted 'Historic Docks'

OS Reference: SO 826183

Operating society/organisation: National Waterways Museum, The Waterways Trust, Llanthony Warehouse, Gloucester Docks, Gloucester GL1 2EH.

Tel: (01452) 318054

Fax: (01452) 318066

Internet address: Website: www.nwm.org.uk

E-mail: info@nwm.org.uk

Keeper of Collections and Volunteer Co-ordinator: David McDougall

Car parks: Pay & Display outside museum. Free coach parking

Access by public transport: Main line Gloucester station, 1-mile

On site facilities: Tearoom, souvenir and specialist bookshop (canal-related with some railway literature). School room/children's holiday activities. Working demonstrations vary. Tug rides (summer weekends). Trip boats and other museums in docks

Facilities for disabled: Full facilities, lifts, ramps, toilets. All indoor displays, quaysides and tea room accessible. Floating exhibits not accessible

Public opening: Daily, 10.00-17.00, except 1/2 January and 25 December. Admission charged

Special events: Preservation, modellers' & craft events; leisure learning courses (send for further information)

Membership details: 'Friends' support organisation. Membership Secretary, c/o Museum address, Volunteers active in restoration/fundraising. Winter Meetings programme.

Membership journal: *Llanthony Log* — quarterly

Industrial locomotives

Name	No	Builder	Type	Built
—	1	A/Barclay (2126)	0-4-0F	1942

Ex-Gloucester Corporation, Castle Meads Power Station, Gloucester Docks. Under restoration for static display

Rolling stock

William Balmforth of Rodley crane, c1880. Small collection of GW, Midland, LMS and BR vans. Sharpness Docks open wagons and Gloucester-built flat wagon, Manchester Ship Canal (ex-GWR) Toad brake van

---

Member: HRA, TT

This unique railway's collection includes locomotives and coaches from 10 countries and two continents. It is a regular location for TV and film makers — from films like *Goldeneye* with Pierce Brosnan as 007 to ITV's *London's Burning*. The railway and the pleasant Cambridgeshire countryside have doubled for locations as diverse as Russia and Spain

General Manager: Mr M. A. Warrington

Headquarters: Nene Valley Railway, Wansford Station, Stibbington, Peterborough, Cambs PE8 6LR

Telephone: Stamford (01780) 784444; Talking Timetable (01780) 784404

Main station: Wansford

Locomotives

Name	No	Origin	Class	Type	Built
Mayflower	1306	LNER	B1	4-6-0	1948
92 Squadron	34081	SR	BB	4-6-2	1948
City of Peterborough	73050	BR	5MT	4-6-0	1954
—	D3871	BR	08	0-6-0DE	1960
—	D9516	BR	14	0-6-0DH	1964
—	D9523	BR	14	0-6-0DH	1964
Atlantic Conveyor	D306	BR	40	1Co-Co1	1960
—	64.305-6	DB	64	2-6-2T	1936
—	7173	DB	52	2-10-0	1943
—	656	DSB	F	0-6-0T	1949
—	101	SJ	B	4-6-0	1944
—	1178	SJ	S	2-6-2T	1914
—	3.628	Nord	3500	4-6-0	1911
—	51401	BR	117	DMS	1959
—	51347	BR	117	DMBS	1959
—	59508	BR	117	TCL	1959

Industrial locomotives

Name	No	Builder	Type	Built
—	—	Avonside (1945)	0-6-0ST	1926
Toby	—	Cockerill (1626)	0-4-0VBT	1890

Other public stations: Orton Mere, Ferry Meadows, Peterborough NVR (15min walk from city centre)
OS reference: TL 903979
Car park: Wansford, Orton Mere, Ferry Meadows, Peterborough NVR
Access by public transport: Buses from Peterborough to Orton Mere and Ferry Meadows
Refreshment facilities: Wansford, Orton Mere. Bar coach on most trains
Souvenir shops: Wansford, Orton Mere, Ferry Meadows, Peterborough
Museum: Wansford
Depot: Wansford
Length of line: 7.5 miles
Passenger trains: Yarwell Mill-Wansford-Orton Mere-Peterborough NVR
Period of public operation: Open all year at Wansford (loco yard). Services operate every Sunday January-end October; Weekends April-end October; Wednesdays May-end August; every day (except Mondays) mid July-end August
Special events: Easter Holiday Specials (with *Thomas* at Wansford) — 21-24 April; Thomas' Birthday Party Weekend — 23-25 June; Vintage Weekend

Name	No	Builder	Type	Built
Muriel	—	E/Electric (1123)	0-4-0DH	1966
Rhos	—	H/Clarke (1308)	0-6-0ST	1918
Derek Crouch	—	H/Clarke (1539)	0-6-0ST	1924
Thomas	—	H/Clarke (1800)	0-6-0T	1947
Jacks Green	—	Hunslet (1953)	0-6-0ST	1939
—	75006	Hunslet (2855)	0-6-0ST	1943
—	—	R/Hornsby (294268)	4wDM	1951
Doncaster	—	YEC (2654)	0-4-0DE	1957
—	11	Rebuilt Hill	4wD	1963
Stanton No 50	—	YEC (2670)	0-6-0DE	1958
—	DL83	R/Royce (10271)	0-6-0DH	1967

Stock
14 BR Mk 1 coaches; Wagons Lits sleeping car, Italian-built; Wagons Lits dining car, Belgian-built; 6 coaches from Denmark; 1 coach from France; 4 coaches from Belgium; 2 steam rail cranes; SR Travelling Post Office; TPO coach M30272M; 20 12-ton Vanfits plus items of freight stock

Owners
34081 the Battle of Britain Locomotive Preservation Society
73050 Peterborough City Council

— 8/9 July. *Thomas* will also be out and about at Bank Holidays and October half-term. Santa Specials in December (phone for details). Regular driver experience courses on Nos 101 and 34081
Facilities for disabled: Ramp access to all stations and shops. Full toilets in Wansford station, souvenir shop. Disabled persons and helpers are eligible for concessionary fares. Passengers can be assisted on and off trains
Membership details: Bill Foreman, c/o above address
Membership journal: *Nene Steam* — 3 times/year; *Nene Staff* (workers' newsletter) — 3 times/year
Marketing name: Britain's International Steam Railway

Timetable Service	North Norfolk Railway	Norfolk

Member: HRA, TT
Part of the former Midland & Great Northern Joint Railway, other elements of the LNER have crept in in the guise of the 'B12' and a Gresley buffet car. The GER 'J15' is being restored. Guest locomotives can be viewed at various times throughout the year. The line runs through beautiful coast, wood and heathland scenery with a nature trail running along its side between Weybourne and Kelling Heath
General Manager: Geoff Gowing
Headquarters: North Norfolk Railway, Sheringham Station,

Locomotives and multiple-units

Name	No	Origin	Class	Type	Built
—	564	GER	J15	0-6-0	1912
—	8572	LNER	B12	4-6-0	1928
—	D3935	BR	08	0-6-0DE	1961
—	12131	BR	11	0-6-0DE	1952
—	D5207	BR	25	Bo-Bo	1962
Holt Pioneer	D5386	BR	27	Bo-Bo	1962
Mirage	D6732	BR	37	Co-Co	1962
—	79960	W&M	—	Railbus	1958
—	79963	W&M	—	Railbus	1958
—	Car 87*	M/Cam	5BEL	TPS	1932
—	Car 91*	M/Cam	5BEL	DMPBS	1932
—	51346	P/Steel	117	DMBS	1959
—	51388	P/Steel	117	DMS	1959
—	59516	P/Steel	117	TCL	1960

*ex-'Brighton Belle' Pullman cars, converted to locomotive-hauled

England

Sheringham, Norfolk NR26 8RA
Telephone: Sheringham (01263) 822045. Talking timetable: (01263) 825449
Fax: (01263) 823794
Main station: Sheringham
Other public stations: Weybourne, Kelling Heath Park, Holt
OS reference: Sheringham TG 156430, Weybourne TG 118419
Car parks: Sheringham, Weybourne, Holt
Access by public transport: By train to Sheringham station (200 yd)
Refreshment facilities: Sheringham, Weybourne
Souvenir shops: Sheringham, Weybourne, Holt
Museum: Sheringham
Depot: Weybourne
Length of line: 5.25 miles
Passenger trains: Steeply graded, Sheringham-Weybourne-Holt
Period of public operation: Weekends in March, daily from mid-April to end September, certain dates through October and November. Santa Specials through December

Industrial locomotives

Name	No	Builder	Type	Built
Ring Haw	—	Hunslet (1982)	0-6-0ST	1940
—	3809	Hunslet (3809)	0-6-0ST	1954
—	68009	Hunslet (3825)	0-6-0ST	1953
—	10	E/Electric (C8431)	0-4-0DH	1963
Wissington	—	H/Clarke (1700)	0-6-0ST	1938
—	—	Bagnall (2370)	0-6-0F	1929

Stock
3 ex-LNER coaches, GNR quad set, 7 ex-BR coaches, 3 coach King's Cross suburban set; Small number of wagons and Southern Railway PMV

Owners
564 and 61572 the Midland & Great Northern Railway Society

Special events: Day out with Thomas — 29 April to 1 May; Beer Festival — 20/21 May; Open Day — 3 June; Model Railway Exhibition — 17/18 June; Vintage Transport Display — 8/9 July; Railway Gala — 8-10 September; 1940s Weekend — 23/24 September; Day out with Thomas — 21-23 October; Santa Specials — 2/3, 9/10, 16/17, 19-24 December
Facilities for disabled: Specially adapted Pullman Car available, advanced booking essential

Membership details: Midland & Great Northern Joint Railway Society, Mr R. Page, Church Farm House, Norwich Road, Strumpshaw, Norwich NR13 4NT
Membership journal: *Joint Line* — quarterly
Marketing name: The Poppy Line

Museum — North Woolwich Old Station Museum — London

No expense has been spared in the very imaginative restoration of this attractive Victorian terminus building overlooking the Thames. Railway artefacts, documents, drawings, etc, are well displayed in glass cases or on the walls, the stock being stabled in the platform area. Convenient for the new City airport and connections for the Docklands Light Railway
Location: North Woolwich Old Station Museum, Pier Road, North Woolwich, London E16 2JJ
OS reference: TQ 433798
Organisation: Newham Museum Service
Telephone: (020) 7474 7244
Car park: Only in adjoining streets
Public transport: Main line North

Locomotives

Name	No	Origin	Class	Type	Built
—	229	GER	209	0-4-0ST	1876

Industrial locomotives

Name	No	Builder	Type	Built
—	—	Hibberd (3294)	4wDM	1948
—	—	Peckett (2000)	0-6-0ST	1942

Stock
1 ex-LNER coach; 2 compartment sections of LTSR coach; NLR Luggage Van; 1 ex-Royal Arsenal Ammunition Van (18in gauge)

London Link. Buses: 101, 69 and 473
Facilities: Museum shop
Public opening: Open April to September, Saturdays 10.00-17.00, Sundays 10.00-17.00. Mondays to

Wednesdays (school summer holiday only) 13.00-15.00. Winter — closed
Admission: Free

North Yorkshire Moors Railway

Member: HRA, TT

This 18-mile line runs through the picturesque North York Moors National Park and is host to an extensive collection of main line locomotives

Financial & Commercial Director: Ken Kitching

Headquarters: Pickering Station, Pickering, North Yorkshire YO18 7AJ

Telephone: Pickering (01751) 472508 for passenger enquiries, charter and dinner bookings

Main station: Pickering

Other public stations: Grosmont, Goathland, Levisham

OS reference: Pickering NZ 797842, Levisham NZ 818909, Goathland NZ 836013, Grosmont NZ 828053

Car parks: Grosmont, Goathland, Levisham, Pickering

Access by public transport: Main line service to Grosmont from Whitby and Middlesbrough. Bus services Malton-Pickering, York or Scarborough-Pickering and Whitby-Goathland and Pickering

Refreshment facilities: Available on most trains and at Grosmont, Goathland and Pickering

Souvenir shops: Pickering, Goathland, Grosmont

Depot: Grosmont

Length of line: 18 miles

Passenger trains: Steam-hauled services Grosmont-Pickering. Pullman evening dining service and 'Moorlander' Sunday lunch service run regularly. GWR and NER saloons are also available for special occasions (eg wedding parties, conferences, etc)

Special events: Throughout the season, ring for details

Period of public operation: Daily April-31 October, Santa Specials and other Xmas services in December/January

Facilities for disabled: The NYMR welcomes disabled visitors and special attention will gladly be provided if advanced notice is given

Special notes: Operates through North York Moors National Park

Locomotives and multiple-units

Name	No	Origin	Class	Type	Built
George Stephenson	44767	LMS	5MT	4-6-0	1947
Eric Treacy	45428	LMS	5MT	4-6-0	1937
—	65894	NER	P3	0-6-0	1923
—	2238	NER	T2	0-8-0	1918
—	901	NER	T3	0-8-0	1919
Blue Peter	60532	LNER	A2	4-6-2	1948
—	62005	LNER	K1	2-6-0	1949
—	69023	LNER	J72	0-6-0T	1951
—	3814	GWR	2884	2-8-0	1940
—	6619	GWR	5600	0-6-2T	1928
—	30841	SR	S15	4-6-0	1936
Repton	30926	SR	V	4-4-0	1934
Hartland	34101	SR	WC	4-6-2	1950
—	75029*	BR	4MT	4-6-0	1951
—	80135	BR	4MT	2-6-4T	1956
Dame Vera Lynn	3672	MoS	WD	2-10-0	1943
—	90775	MoS	WD	2-10-0	1943
—	2253	USATC	S160	2-8-0	1943
—	D2207	BR	04	0-6-0DM	1953
—	08556	BR	08	0-6-0DE	1959
—	08850	BR	08	0-6-0DE	1961
Helen Turner	D5032	BR	24	Bo-Bo	1959
—	D5061	BR	24	Bo-Bo	1960
The Diana	D7541	BR	25	Bo-Bo	1965
The Sybilla	D7628	BR	25	Bo-Bo	1965
Lion	50027	BR	50	Co-Co	1961
Alycidon†	D9009	BR	55	Co-Co	1961

†not on site
*on site undergoing overhaul

Industrial locomotives

Name	No	Builder	Type	Built
—	29	Kitson (4263)	0-6-2T	1904
—	5	R/Stephenson (3377)	0-6-2T	1909
Antwerp	—	Hunslet (3180)	0-6-0ST	1944
Neil D. Barker	12139	E/Electric (1553)	0-6-0DE	1948
—	16	Drewry	0-4-0DM	1941
—	2	R/Hornsby (421419)	4wDM	1958
—	3*	R/Hornsby (441419)	4wDM	1960
—	1	Vanguard (129V)	0-4-0DM	1963
—	2	Vanguard (131V)	0-4-0DM	1963

*On loan to Middleton Railway

Stock

39 x BR Mk 1, 4 x Pullman, 2 x BR XP64, 3 x GUV, 1 x Camping Coach 1 x SR Bulleid, 10 x brake vans, 4 x diesel cranes, 2 x 45-ton steam cranes, over 70 wagons.

Owners

90775 and 30841 the Essex Locomotive Society
62005, 2238, 65894, 69023 the North Eastern Locomotive Preservation Group
60532 on loan to the North Eastern Locomotive Preservation Group
901 on loan from the National Railway Museum
Antwerp the National Mining Museum
D9009 the Deltic Preservation Society

England

Steam Centre — Northampton & Lamport Railway — Northants

Member: HRA

Headquarters: Pitsford & Brampton Station, Pitsford Road, Chapel Brampton, Northampton NN6 8BA

Location: About 5 miles north of Northampton, Pitsford Road off A5199 (formerly A50) or A508

General Manager: Mr R. Faulkner

Operating company: Northampton Steam Railway Ltd

Operating society: Northampton & Lamport Railway Preservation Society

Telephone: (01604) 820327 (mainly Sundays, recorded announcements other times)

Access by public transport: None

On site facilities: NLR souvenir shop, buffet coach, toilets

Length of line: Three-quarters of a mile at present. Work on extension under-way

Public opening: Every Sunday and Bank Holiday (except Good Friday) from 4 March to 1 January 2001, plus some Saturdays during special events

Special events: New Volunteer's Day — 16 April; Easter Egg Specials — 22-24 April; Themed Weekend — 29/30 April/1 May; Day Out with Thomas — 13/14 May; Bank Holiday Steam Up — 27-29 May; Diesels Galore — 10/11 June; Teddy Bears' Holiday — 26-28 August; Day Out with Thomas — 23/24 September; Santa Specials — weekends from 2 December including Christmas Eve; Mince Pie Specials 30/31 December, 1 January 2001

Membership details: Mr I. Rivett, Pitsford & Brampton Station, Pitsford Road, Chapel Brampton, Northampton NN6 8BA

Membership journal: *Premier Line* — 4 times a year

Locomotives and multiple-units

Name	No	Origin	Class	Type	Built
—	3862	GWR	2884	2-8-0	1942
Castell Dinas Bran	25035	BR	25	Bo-Bo	1963
—	D7629	BR	25	Bo-Bo	1965
—	26010	BR	26	Bo-Bo	1959
—	27056	BR	27	Bo-Bo	1962
The Royal Artilleryman	45118	BR	45	1Co-Co1	1962
—	PMW651	BR	97	0-6-0DM	1953
—	51367	BR	117	DMBS	1959
—	51402	BR	117	DMS	1959
—	55001	BR	122	DMBS	1958
—	55003	BR	122	DMBS	1958

Industrial locomotives

Name	No	Builder	Type	Built
Colwyn	45	Kitson (5470)	0-6-0ST	1933
Westminster	1378	Peckett 1378)	0-4-0ST	1914
—	2104	Peckett (2104)	0-4-0ST	1948
Vanguard	5374	Chrzanow (5374)	0-6-0T	1959
—	17646	Chrzanow (5387)	0-6-0T	1959
Bunty	146C	Fowler (4210018)/ rebuilt T/Hill	0-4-0DM	1950 1964
—	1	R/Hornsby (275886)	4wDM	1949
Sir Gyles Isham	764	R/Hornsby (319286)	0-4-0DM	1953

Stock

Coaches: 1 BR Mk 1 FK; 2 BR Mk 1 TSO; Mk 1 BSO; 1 BR Mk 1 BSK; 1 BR Mk 1 SK; 1 BR Mk 1 CK; 1 BR Mk 1 RBR; 1 Mk 2 BSO (trolley buffet); 1 Mk 2 SO; 1 BR Mk 1 NAV; 2 BR NJV; 2 SR PMV; 1 GWR full brake; 1 LMS CCT

Wagons: A number of various wagon types

Owners

Colwyn the Colwyn Preservation Society
17646 the Northampton Locomotive Co
51402 & 51367 the Northampton & Lamport Railway DMU Group

Location: Hunsbury Hill Industrial Museum, Hunsbury Hill Country Park, Hunsbury Hill Road, Camp Hill, Northampton
OS reference: SP 735584
Operating organisation: Northamptonshire Ironstone Railway Trust Ltd
Telephone: (01604) 702031
Contact: C. Osborn, 11 Hillside way, Weston Favell, Northampton NN3 3AW. (Tel: (01604) 405970
Access by public transport: Northampton Transport bus routes, 24, 25 to Camp Hill from Greyfriars bus station
On site facilities: Light refreshments, shop, toilets. Children's play areas and picnic areas
Length of line: 2.25 miles with yard, engine shed and workshops, 2 stations and level crossing
Public opening: Museum and shed/yard for viewing most weekdays and weekends. Train service from Easter Sunday to end of September on Sundays and Bank Holiday Mondays plus December for Santa Specials. Parties can be catered for on weekdays by appointment
Times of opening: 10.00 to 16.00 for viewing, with train service from 13.00 to 17.00 on Sundays and Bank Holidays
Facilities for the disabled: Passenger coach can accommodate wheelchairs

Multiple-unit

Name	No	Origin	Class	Type	Built
—	13004	SR	4DD	DMBS	1949

Industrial locomotives

Name	No	Builder	Type	Built
Yvonne	—	Cockerill (2945)	0-4-0 Tram	1920
Vigilant†	—	Hunslet (287)	0-4-0ST	1882
Belvedere◊	—	Sentinel (9365)	0-4-0TG	1946
Musketeer◊	—	Sentinel (9369)	0-4-0TG	1946
Hylton	—	Planet (3967)	0-4-0DH	1961
—	—	Fowler (422001)	0-4-0DH	1965
Lois	—	Fowler (422033)	0-4-0DH	1965
Muffin	46	R/Hornsby (242868)	4wDM	1946
—	16	Hunslet (2087)	0-4-0DM	1940
AMOCO	56	R/Hornsby	0-4-0DM	1956
Shire Lodge	53	R/Hornsby	0-4-0DM	1954
Sir Alfred	53	R/Hornsby (319214)	0-6-0DM	1953
—	5	R/Hornsby (338489)	0-4-0DM	1956
—*	87	Peckett (1871)	0-6-0ST	1934
Northampton†	1	Bagnall (2565)	0-4-0ST	1934
Cherwell**	—	Bagnall (2654)	0-6-0ST	1942
—	—	Grafton	Steam crane	1934

* meter gauge on loan to Irchester Country Park
◊ static display
† being rebuilt
**3ft gauge

Owners
13004 the Bulleid Double Decker Society

Special notes: Museum to the Ironstone Industry of Northamptonshire, the museum houses photographs, documents and other items connected with the ironstone industry. The railway is laid on the old trackbed of the quarry system and partly on a new formation with remains of the quarry face and cuttings available for exploration
Membership details: Mr R. Coleman, c/o above address

Member: HRA
Location: On the A60 just south of Ruddington, 3 miles south of Nottingham city centre, off A52, 7 miles north of Loughborough. Signposted
Operating society/organisation: Great Central (Nottingham) Ltd, Nottingham Heritage Centre, Mere Way, Ruddington, Nottingham NG11 6NX

Locomotives and multiple-units

Name	No	Origin	Class	Type	Built
—	37075	BR	37	Co-Co	1962
—	D4115	BR	08	0-6-0DE	1962
—	13180	BR	08	0-6-0DE	1955
—	D9520	BR	14	0-6-0DH	1964
—	52060	BR	108	DMSL	1959
—	53645	BR	108	DMBS	1958
—	53926	BR	108	DMBS	1959
—	68088	LNER	Y7	0-4-0T	1927
—	45379	LMS	5MT	4-6-0	1937

England

Telephone: (0115) 940 5905
Fax: (0115) 940 5905
Access by public transport: Buses from city centre and Broad Marsh (tel: [0115] 924 0000), via Nottingham Midland station
On site facilities: Car park, shop and café, picnic area and country park walks. 700m long passenger-carrying miniature railway. Extensive bus museum
Facilities for disabled: Accessible
Public opening: Steam Shuttle service Sundays & Bank Holidays Easter-mid October. 10.45-17.30
Special events: Not advised, please contact for details
Membership details: Great Central Northern Development

Industrial locomotives

Name	No	Builder	Type	Built
—	54	H/Clarke (1682)	0-6-0ST	1937
—	1684	Hunslet (1684)	0-4-0T	1931
Powergen No 2	—	RSH (7818)	0-4-0ST	1954
—	56	RSH (7667)	0-6-0ST	1950
—	63	RSH (7761)	0-6-0ST	1954
Staythorpe	D2959	R/Hornsby	0-4-0DE	—

Rolling stock: 1 BR Mk 1 FO, 1 BR Mk 2 BSO, 1 BR Mk 2 BFK, 1 BR (ex-WR) cinema coach, GCR coach (body) CBL No 1663 (oldest surviving GCR coach, built 1903), Barnum coach, suburban coach, 1 LNER 45-ton steam breakdown crane, 1 SR GUV, various goods wagons

Owners
37075 the Class 37 Locomotive Association

Association, c/o above address
Society journal: Quarterly

Timetable Service — Paignton & Dartmouth Steam Railway — Devon

The line from Paignton is the holiday line with steam trains running for seven miles in Great Western tradition along the spectacular Torbay coast to Churston and through the wooded slopes bordering the Dart estuary to Kingswear. The scenery is superb, with seascapes right across Lyme Bay to Portland Bill on clear days. Approaching Kingswear is the beautiful River Dart, with its fascinating craft, and on the far side, the 'olde worlde' town of Dartmouth and Britannia Royal Naval College, Butterwalk, Bayard's Cove and Dartmouth Castle
Director & General Manager: J. B. S. Cogar
Headquarters: Paignton Queen's Park Station, Paignton, Devon
Telephone: Paignton (01803) 555872
Main station: Paignton Queen's Park
Other public stations: Goodrington, Churston, Kingswear (for Dartmouth)
OS reference: SX 889606
Car parks: Paignton municipal car park, Goodrington, Dartmouth (ferry to Kingswear)
Access by public transport: Adjacent to both Paignton main line station and Devon General bus station

Locomotives and multiple-units

Name	No	Origin	Class	Type	Built
Warrior	4555	GWR	4500	2-6-2T	1924
Trojan	4588	GWR	4575	2-6-2T	1927
Goliath	5239	GWR	5205	2-8-0T	1924
—	6435	GWR	6400	0-6-0PT	1937
Lydham Manor	7827	GWR	7800	4-6-0	1951
Ardent	D2192	BR	03	0-6-0DM	1962
Volunteer	D3014	BR	08	0-6-0DE	1954
Mercury	D7535	BR	25	Bo-Bo	1965
Superb	50002	BR	50	Co-Co	1967
—	59003*	BR	116	TS	1957
—	59004*	BR	116	TS	1957
—	59488*	P/Steel	117	TCL	1959
—	59494*	P/Steel	117	TCL	1959
—	59503*	P/Steel	117	TCL	1959
—	59507*	P/Steel	117	TCL	1959
—	59513*	P/Steel	117	TCL	1959
—	59517*	P/Steel	117	TCL	1959

*converted to locomotive-hauled vehicles
Stock
15 ex-BR Mk 1 coaches; 1 Pullman observation coach; 2 auto-coaches; 1 ex-GWR coach

Owners
50002 the Devon Diesel Society (on hire to main line company)

Refreshment facilities: Paignton and Kingswear
Depot: Churston
Length of line: 7 miles
Passenger trains: Paignton-Kingswear, views of Torbay and Dart estuary, 495yd tunnel
Period of public operation: Easter to October
Facilities for disabled: Limited

Special events: Santa Specials — please see timetable and press for details. Combined river excursions available
Membership details: Devon Diesel Society (Andy Matthews)
Membership journal: Devon Diesel Society

England

Peak Rail plc

Member: HRA
Location: *Registered Office:* Matlock Station, Matlock, Derbyshire DE4 3NA
OS reference: Matlock SK 060738
Operating society/organisation: Peak Rail plc, Matlock Station, Matlock, Derbyshire DE4 3NA.
Telephone: (01629) 580381
Car parks: Matlock station, DFS Furniture Store at Darley Dale, Rowsley South station
Length of line: 4 miles — Matlock Riverside-Rowsley South
On site facilities: Shop at Matlock. Shops and buffets at Darley Dale and Rowsley South
Public opening: Not finalised, but will be every Sunday. Saturdays probably April-October. Midweek during summer. Timetable varies
Facilities for disabled: Darley Dale and Rowsley. Matlock Riverside unsuitable for disabled passengers
Period of public operation: Not advised; see timetable supplement
Special events: Not advised, please contact for details

Locomotives and multiple-units

Name	No	Origin	Class	Type	Built
—	48624	LMS	8F	2-8-0	1943
—	03158	BR	03	0-6-0DM	1960
Penyghent	D8	BR	44	1Co-Co1	1959
—	51566	BR	108	DMSL	1959
—	51567	BR	108	DMSL	1959
—	51933	BR	108	DMBS	1960
—	53627	BR	108	DMBS	1958
—	53933	BR	108	DMBS	1959
—	54484	BR	108	DTC	1960
—	54504	BR	108	DTC	1960
—	59387	BR	108	TS	1958
—	977806	BR	108	DMBS	1958

Industrial locomotives

Name	No	Builder	Type	Built
Vulcan	—	V/Foundry (3272)	0-4-0ST	1918
The Duke	2746	Bagnall (2746)	0-6-0ST	1944
Warrington*	150	RSH (7136)	0-6-0ST	1944

*at Darley Dale

Rolling Stock — coaches: 2 BR Mk 1 RMB; 1 BR Mk 1 SLF, 3 BR Mk 1 TSO, 2 BR Mk 1 SO, 1 BR Mk 1 BSOT, 3 BR Mk 1 SK, 1 BR Mk 1 BSK, 2 BR Mk 1 BG, 1 BR Mk 1 GUV, 1 BR Mk 2 SO, 1 BR Mk 2 BSO, 1 BR Mk 2 BFK, 1 LMS TK, 2 LMS BCK, 1BTK

Rolling stock — wagons: 1 MR brake van, 2 LMS brake vans, 1 LMS Shark brake van, 1 BR brake van, 1 Mess & Tool van, 1 Smith & Rodley 15-ton diesel crane, 1 Sturgeon rail wagon, 1 Lowmac wagon, 2 Dogfish ballast hoppers, 1 mineral hopper wagon, 2 LMS 16ton fish vans, 1 SR PMV, 3 BR 12-ton box van, 1 12-ton van, 1 Shell tank wagon, 2 Esso tank wagons, 3 LNER wagons, 2 LMS wagons, 1 21-ton mineral wagon, 2 ex-LMS match wagons, 1 Plasser & Theurer tamper, 1 Plasser & Theurer track slewer, 1 ex-LMR drain train water bowser, 2 Austrian ferry wagons

Owners
03158 the Amber Valley Locomotive Group
D8 the North Notts Loco Group
Vulcan the Vulcan Loco Trust

Plym Valley Railway

Member: AIRPS
A scheme dedicated to the restoration of services over the former GWR Marsh Mills-Plym Bridge line, a distance of 1.5 miles
Location: 5 miles from centre of Plymouth, Devon, north of A38. From Marsh Mills roundabout, take B3416 to Plympton, follow signs
OS reference: SX 517564

Operating society/organisation: Plym Valley Railway Co Ltd, Marsh Mills Station, Coypool Road, Marsh Mills, Plymouth, Devon PL7 4NL
Access by public transport: Buses from Plymouth, Nos 20, 20A, 21, 22A, 51 stop close to site
On site facilities: Shop and refreshments at Marsh Mills, Coypool (Sundays only)

Public opening: Sundays from 10.00, and other selected days
Length of line: Half-mile, plus sidings
Special events: Please see press for details
Special notes: Visitors are advised that, at the moment, the railway and two locomotives are still under restoration. 3 working locomotives and DMU. Steam and diesel

demonstration trains on some Sundays (tel: Alan Smith [01503] 250539)

Membership details: Pat Elbrolo, 75 Rigdale Close, Eggbuckland, Plymouth, Devon PL6 5PR

Membership journal: *Plym Valley News* — 3/year

Marketing name: The Woodland Line

Locomotives and multiple-units

Name	No	Origin	Class	Type	Built
—	75079	BR	4MT	4-6-0	1956
—	13002	BR	08	0-6-0DE	1953
—	37207	BR	37	Co-Co	1963
—	51365	BR	117	MBS	1960
—	51407	BR	117	DMS	1960

Industrial locomotives

Name	No	Builder	Type	Built
—	3	H/Leslie (3597)	0-4-0ST	1926
—	—	T/Hill (125V)	4wDH	1963
—	—	Hibberd (3281)	4wDM	1948

Rolling stock: Self-propelled Smith & Rodley diesel crane of 1956

The Railway Age, Crewe

Steam Centre — Cheshire

Location: Crewe Heritage Centre, Vernon Way, Crewe

OS reference: SJ 709552

Operating society/organisation: Crewe Heritage Trust Ltd

Telephone: (01270) 212130

Car park: On site, town centre, Forge Street, Oak Street,

Access by public transport: Main line Crewe

Refreshment facilities: Brief Encounter buffet or adjacent Safeway superstore

On site facilities: Gift shop, picnic area, children's corner, weekend train rides, standard gauge and miniature railway, exhibition hall, main line viewing area, 3 working signalboxes with 'hands-on' visitor operation

Public opening: Daily 10.00-16.00 (last admission 15.00). Family tickets available. Please contact for details of events

Facilities for disabled: Toilets

Membership details: Heritage Centre Supporters' Association, c/o above address

Notes: Steam locomotives passed for use over main line tracks are stabled between duties from time to time

Locomotives and multiple-units

Name	No	Origin	Class	Type	Built
Cornwall	3020	LNWR	—	2-2-2	1888
—	5224	GWR	4200	2-8-0T	1924
Thornbury Castle	7027	GWR	'Castle'	4-6-0	1949
Britannia	70000	BR	7MT	4-6-2	1951
—	03073	BR	03	0-6-0DM	1959
—	D8233	BR	15	Bo-Bo	1959
—	D6508	BR	33	Bo-Bo	1960
Sea King	33002	BR	33	Bo-Bo	1960
—	33023	BR	33	Bo-Bo	1961
—	33029	BR	33	Bo-Bo	1961
—	33053	BR	33	Bo-Bo	1961
—	33057	BR	33	Bo-Bo	1961
—	33108	BR	33	Bo-Bo	1960
—	D120*	BR	45	1Co-Co1	1961
Ixion	D172*	BR	46	1Co-Co1	1962
—	D1842	BR	47	Co-Co	1965
Thunderer	50008	BR	50	Co-Co	1968
—	18000	BR	—	A1A-A1A	1949
—	55032	P/Steel	121	DMBS	1960

*on site occasionally, but usually kept at private locations

Industrial locomotives

Name	No	Builder	Type	Built
Robert	—	H/Clarke (1752)	0-6-0T	1943

Rolling stock
APT vehicle Nos 48103, 48106, 48404, 48602, 48603, 48606, 49002; 1 BR Mk 1 BSK; 2 BR brake vans and other vehicles on site for repairs from time to time

Owners
Cornwall — the National Railway Museum

Ravenglass & Eskdale Railway

Cumbria

Member: HRA

Originally built to serve iron ore mines in Eskdale, this delightful line makes an ideal 'tourist' line running as it does through wooded valleys and along rugged hillsides

General Manager: Steve Wood

Headquarters: Ravenglass & Eskdale Railway, Ravenglass, Cumbria CA18 1SW

Telephone: (01229) 717171

Fax: (01229) 717011

E-mail: rer@netcomuk.co.uk

Main station: Ravenglass

Other public stations: Muncaster Mill, Irton Road, The Green, Beckfoot, Eskdale (Dalegarth)

OS reference: SD 086964

Car parks: All stations

Access by public transport: Main line services to Ravenglass; bus service from Whitehaven

Refreshment facilities: Ravenglass, Dalegarth. Bar meals at 'Ratty Arms'

Picnic areas: At both termini

Souvenir shops: Ravenglass, Dalegarth

Museum: Ravenglass

Length of line: 7 miles, 15in gauge

Passenger trains: Steam or diesel-hauled narrow gauge trains Ravenglass-Dalegarth

Locomotives

Name	No	Builder	Type	Built
River Irt	—	Heywood	0-8-2	1894
River Esk	—	Davey Paxman (21104)	2-8-2	1923
River Mite	—	Clarkson (4669)	2-8-2	1966
Northern Rock	—	R&ER	2-6-2	1976
Bonnie Dundee	—	K/Stuart (720)*	0-4-2	1901
Shelagh of Eskdale	—	R&ER/Severn-Lamb	4-6-4D	1969
				rebuilt 1998
Quarryman	—	Muir-Hill (2)	0-4-0P/Paraffin	1928
Perkins	—	Muir Hill (NG39A)	0-4-4DM	1929
Silver Jubilee	—	R&ER	DMU	1977
Lady Wakefield	—	R&ER	B-B	1980
Synolda	—	Bassett-Lowke	4-4-2	1912
—	—	Greenbat (2782)	0-4-0BE	1957
Cyril	—	Lister	0-4-0DM	1987

*rebuilt to 15in gauge 1981

Period of public operation: Daily late March-late October. Limited winter service November-March

Family ticket: All day travel at reduced price

Facilities for disabled: Special coaches for wheelchair passengers. Advance notice preferred. Wheelchair access to toilets and museum at Ravenglass; toilets, shop and café at Eskdale (Dalegarth)

Special notes: At Ravenglass the R&ER has two camping coaches and the company also operates the 'Ratty Arms' public house formed by conversion of the former BR station buildings. During the high summer, mid-July through August, five steam locomotives are normally in use Monday-Thursday.

Muncaster watermill is also worth a visit

Membership details: Mr N. Dickinson, 3 Clifton Terrace, Ravenglass, Cumbria CA18 1SE

Membership journal: *The R&ER Magazine* — quarterly

Marketing names: 'Ratty' or 'T laal Ratty'

Romney, Hythe & Dymchurch Railway

Kent

Member: HRA

This line was built in 1926/7 as a one-third size miniature main line, and is by far the longest and most fully-equipped 15in gauge railway in the world. It carries not only daytrippers and holidaymakers but also children to and from the local school at New Romney.

Headquarters: Romney, Hythe & Dymchurch Railway, New Romney Station, Kent TN28 8PL

Telephone: (01797) 362353/363256

Fax: (01797) 363591

Internet addresses: *web site:* http:\\www.rhdr.demon.co.uk

e-mail: rhdr@dels.demon.co.uk

Locomotives

Name	No	Builder	Type	Built
Green Goddess	1	Davey Paxman	4-6-2	1925
Northern Chief	2	Davey Paxman	4-6-2	1925
Southern Maid	3	Davey Paxman	4-6-2	1926
The Bug	4	Krauss (8378)	0-4-0TT	1926
Hercules	5	Davey Paxman	4-8-2	1926
Samson	6	Davey Paxman	4-8-2	1926
Typhoon	7	Davey Paxman	4-6-2	1926
Hurricane	8	Davey Paxman	4-6-2	1926
Winston Churchill	9	YEC (2294)	4-6-2	1931
Doctor Syn	10	YEC (2295)	4-6-2	1931
Black Prince	11	Krupp (1664)	4-6-2	1937
John Southland	12	TMA Birmingham	Bo-Bo	1983
—	14	TMA Birmingham	Bo-Bo	1989
—	PW1	M/Rail (7059)	4wDM	1938
—	PW2	RH&DR	4wPM	1965
Redgauntlet	PW3	Jacot/RH&DR	4wPM	1963

OS reference: TR 074249
Main station: New Romney
Other public stations: Hythe Dymchurch, Jefferstone Lane, Romney Sands, Dungeness
Car parks: Hythe, Dymchurch, New Romney, Dungeness
Access by public transport: Folkestone Central station (Connex SouthCentral) and then bus to Hythe (4 miles) or Rye station (Connex SouthCentral) and then bus to New Romney (8 miles)
Refreshment facilities: Cafeterias at New Romney and Dungeness, picnic area at New Romney. Also an observation coach on certain trains
Souvenir shops: Hythe and New Romney (plus Dymchurch and Dungeness in main season)
Toy and Model Museum: New Romney, with displays of old, and not so old, toys; plus two large operating model railways
Depot: New Romney
Length of line: 13.5 miles, 15in

Stock
42 saloon bogie coaches; 12 open bogie coaches; 3 semi-open coaches; 5 luggage/brake saloons; 1 Parlour car; 1 mess coach; 40 assorted wagons

gauge
Passenger trains: Train frequency depends on the time of year: maximum frequency is 45 minutes
Period of public operation: Trains run daily from Good Friday until last Sunday in September. Also run at weekends in March and October. Out of season the school train departs New Romney at 15.00 with limited public accommodation (Monday-Friday, term times only)
Special events: Steam & Diesel Gala — 14 May; Friends of Thomas Day — 9 July, 2/3 September. Santa Specials in December (pre-booking essential)
Special notes: Senior citizen concession Fridays, Saturdays, Sundays (return journey for single fare). Family tickets available from New Romney station only. The

'Romney Toy and Model Museum' at New Romney. Special trains can be run at most times by prior arrangement. Parties can be catered for at New Romney and Dungeness cafés
Facilities for disabled: Ramps and level crossings at all stations for easy access. Special wheelchair coach available on any train by prior arrangement. Stair lift between café and 'Toy & Model Museum'. Disabled toilets at Hythe, Dymchurch and New Romney
Membership details: RH&DR Association, 26 Norman Close, Battle, East Sussex TN33 0BD
Membership journal: *The Marshlander* — quarterly

Rother Valley Railway

Diesel Centre | East Sussex

Member: HRA
The original section of what was to become known as the Kent & East Sussex Railway was thought to be lost to preservation for ever following decisions of Transport Minister, Barbara Castle, in the late 1960s. However, more enlightened attitudes in recent years mean that work is now in hand, slowly, to reconnect Robertsbridge to Bodiam and thus the missing link of the K&ESR
Location/headquarters:
Robertsbridge Station, Robertsbridge, East Sussex
Operating society/organisation:
Rother Valley Railway (East Sussex) Ltd, 4 Coronation Cottages, Church Lane, Robertsbridge, East Sussex TN32 5PE
OS reference: TQ 734235
Access by public transport:
Connex South Eastern trains on Charing Cross and Tunbridge Wells to Hastings service call at Robertsbridge station. Arriva bus service 4 and 5 on Maidstone-Hasting service call at High Street,

Locomotive

Name	Unit No	Origin	Class	Type	Built
—	D2051	BR	03	0-60-DM	1957

Industrial locomotives

Name	No	Builder	Type	Built
Telemon	1	Vulcan/Drewry	0-4-0DM	1955

Rolling stock
Ex-GER Pullman coach Cambria, ex-SR Maunsell open 3rd, ex-SECR brake 3rd birdcage, ex-SR corridor Comp (converted to General Manager's saloon), ex-BR Mk 1 2nd open, ex-SR GBL, 4 parcels vans, 5 box wagons, 2 open wagons, 1 flat wagon, 1 hopper wagon, 2 tank wagons and 2 lowmacs
NB: Most rolling stock will be leaving the site

Owners
Most rolling stock — The Tenterden Rolling Stock Group

Robertsbridge
Car park: Robertsbridge station and Station Road, Robertsbridge
On site facilities: Former VSOE lounge housing small museum/exhibition and souvenir shop/tearoom, rolling stock under restoration, picnic area. Please note that there are no toilet facilities on site at present — the nearest public conveniences are at Station Road

car park (approx 300yd).
Facilities for disabled: Limited
Length of line: Standard gauge — c400yd at present. When restored, length to Bodiam will be 3 miles, with end-on connection to K&ESR.
Public opening: Every Sunday and Bank Holiday Monday (except Christmas and Boxing Day). 10.30-17.00 (dusk if earlier)
Special events: Annual model

railway exhibition. Monthly boot fairs
Membership secretary: Peter Coombs, 375 New Hythe Lane, Larkfield, Aylesford, Kent ME20 6RY. (Tel: 01622 717491)
Society journal: *The Phoenix* — quarterly

Steam Centre — Ruislip Lido Railway — London

Member: HRA
The 12in gauge line is operated by enthusiast volunteers as an attraction within Ruislip Lido, a country park which is maintained by the London Borough of Hillingdon
Location: Ruislip Lido, Reservoir Road, Ruislip, Middlesex
Operating society/organisation: Ruislip Lido Railway Society Ltd, Membership Secretary, Mrs S. E. Simmons, 9 Wiltshire Lane, Eastcote, Pinner, Middx HA5 2LH
Telephone: (020) 8866 9654
Car park: Available at Lido
Access by public transport: Ruislip Underground station (Metropolitan and Piccadilly lines) then by bus H13 or 331 nearby (Daily). Lido is off the A4180 road
Refreshment facilities: New family pub/restaurant (Brewers Fayre) on site. Picnic areas also available
Length of line: 1.5-mile single

Locomotives

Name	No	Builder	Type	Built
Robert	3	Severn-Lamb	B-2 DH	1973
Lady of the Lakes	5	Ravenglass & Eskdale Railway	B-B DM	1985
Mad Bess	6	RLRS	2-4-0ST+T	1998
Graham Alexander	7	Severn-Lamb	B-B DM	1990

Locomotive notes: All locomotives are available for service. Limited steam-hauled service

Stock
6 open coaches; 9 closed coaches; miscellaneous service stock

journey, 3 miles return including new extension now open which terminates beside main entrance to car park
Public opening: The line is open weekends throughout the year; Tuesdays, Wednesdays and Thursdays in May, June and September. Every day in July and August, also daily during most Hillingdon school holidays.

24-hour recorded train information service (01895) 622595
Journey time: Single 20min, return 40min
Facilities for disabled: Wheelchair passengers can travel on all trains
Membership details: c/o above address
Membership journal: *Woody Bay News* — 3 issues per year

Steam Centre — Rutland Railway Museum — Rutland

Member: HRA
This museum is dedicated to portraying the railway in industry, particularly iron ore mining, and has a wide range of industrial locomotives and rolling stock. Indeed, its collection of quarry freight rolling stock is probably the most comprehensive in the country and regular demonstrations are a feature of the 'steam days'.
Location: Cottesmore Iron Ore Mines Siding, Ashwell Road, Cottesmore, Nr Oakham, Rutland — museum situated midway between villages of Cottesmore and Ashwell, approximately 4 miles

Locomotives and multiple-units

Name	No	Origin	Class	Type	Built
NCB No 7	(D9518)	BR	14	0-6-0DH	1964
—	D9555	BR	14	0-6-0DH	1965
—	54274	BR	108	DTC	1959

Industrial locomotives

Name	No	Builder	Type	Built
Firefly	—	Barclay (776)	0-4-0ST	1896
Uppingham	—	Peckett (1257)	0-4-0ST	1912
BSC No 2	—	Barclay (1931)	0-4-0ST	1927
Dora	—	Avonside (1973)	0-4-0ST	1927
Elizabeth	—	Peckett (1759)	0-4-0ST	1928
Singapore	—	H/Leslie (3865)	0-4-0ST	1936
Drake	—	Barclay (2086)	0-4-0ST	1940
Sir Thomas Royden	—	Barclay (2088)	0-4-0ST	1940
Carlton No 3	—	Barclay (352)	0-4-0DM	1941
Salmon	8410/39	Barclay (2139)	0-6-0ST	1942

north of Oakham (locally signposted)
OS reference: SK 886137
Operating society/organisation: Rutland Railway Museum, Cottesmore Iron Ore Mines Siding, Ashwell Road, Cottesmore, Nr Oakham, Rutland LE15 7BX
Telephone: Oakham (01572) 813203
Car park: Free car park on site
Access by public transport: Nearest main line station, Oakham. Blands bus service, Leicester-Oakham-Cottesmore. Bartons buses, Nottingham-Melton Mowbray-Oakham-Ashwell, Corby/Peterborough-Oakham-Ashwell (services 117 and 125).
On site facilities: Free train rides, demonstration freight trains, refreshments, toilets, museum, shop, picnic sites, demonstration line with lineside walk and viewing areas, static displays of over 30 steam and diesel locomotives; over 50 wagons, vans and coaches (believed to be the largest collection of preserved quarry freight stock in the UK)
Length of line: Three-quarter-mile
Passenger trains: Regular shuttle service operates on open days (approximately every 15min)
Public opening: Open weekends or by arrangement, some weekdays (please telephone prior to visit). Open 11.00-17.00. (Leaflets available, SAE please)
Special events: Please contact for details
Facilities for disabled: Site relatively flat. Members willing to assist.
Special notes: The open air museum houses an extensive collection of industrial locomotives and rolling stock typifying past activity in local ironstone quarries, nationwide mines and factories. A

Name	No	Builder	Type	Built
—	1	Barclay (415)	0-4-0DH	1957
—	20-90-01	Barclay (499)	0-4-0DH	1965
—	8	Bagnall (3209)/ RSH (8364)	0-4-0DH	1962
Coal Products No 6	—	Hunslet (2868) (Rebuilt Hunslet 3883 1963)	0-6-0ST	1943
—	8	Peckett (2110)	0-4-0ST	1950
—	3	N/British (27656)	0-4-0DH	1957
—	—	R/Hornsby (305302)	4wDM	1951
—	—	R/Hornsby (306092)	4wDM	1950
—	—	R/Hornsby (347747)	0-6-0DM	1957
—	20-90-02	R/Hornsby (504565)	0-4-0DH	1965
Hays	—	R/Hornsby (544997)	0-4-0DE	1969
Phoenix	—	Hibberd (3887)	4wDM	1958
Janus	No 28	YEC (2791)	0-6-0DE	1962
—	1382	YEC (2872)	0-6-0DE	1962
—	65	Hunslet (3889)	0-6-0ST	1964
Betty	8411/04	R/Royce (10201)	0-4-0DH	1965
—	D21	R/Royce (10270)	0-6-0DH	1967
—	BSC 1	E/Electric (D1049)	0-6-0DH	1965
—	—	E/Electric (D1231)	0-6-0DH	1967
—	No 1	Hunslet (6688)	0-4-0DH	1968
—	CEGB 24	T/Hill (188c) (Rebuild of Sentinel 9597/1955)	4wDH	1967
—	24	Hunslet (2411)	0-6-0ST	1941
—	7	Sentinel (9376)	4wVBT	1947
—	21	H/Clarke (D707)	0-6-0DM	1950
—	10	T/Hill (234v)	4wDH	1971
—	ROF No 1	T/Hill (132c) (Rebuild of Fowler 22982/1942)	0-4-0DH	1963
—	4	Fowler (4240012)	0-6-0DH	1961
—	—	Fowler (4240015)	0-6-0DH	1962

Locomotive notes: In service *Dora, Singapore,* 7, D9555, 1832, *Betty,* 1, 20-90-01, 8 (Bagnal 3209), No 1 (HE6688), 21, *Phoenix,* CEGB No 24, RoF No1, No 1 and BSC 1. *Janus* currently off-site under repair

Stock
2 coaches; 4 brake vans; 14 covered goods vans; 57 wagons (includes rakes of wagons as used in local ironstone and industrial railways); 2 rail cranes

demonstration line approximately three-quarters of a mile long has been relaid on the former MR Cottesmore mineral branch (originally built to tap local ironstone quarries), on which restored locomotives and stock are run. Among the latter is the body of the only surviving Wisbech & Upwell Tramway coach and the last diesel locomotive built for BR service at Swindon Works
Membership details: Membership Secretary, c/o above address

Museum	Science Museum	London

Built on land acquired with the profits from the Great Exhibition of 1851, the Science Museum was one of the first to include industrial archaeology. The Land Transport Gallery remained closed for the whole of 1999. Railway exhibits,

Locomotive

Name	No	Origin	Class	Type	Built
Columbine	—	Grand Junction Railway	—	2-2-2	1845
Puffing Billy	—	Wylam Colliery	—	0-4-0	1813

Locomotive note: Restored to static display condition

England

including Stephenson's *Rocket*, will form part of a comprehensive new gallery due to open sometime in 2000. *Puffing Billy* remains on display in the interim; *Rocket* forms part of a temporary exhibition at the National Railway Museum, York
Location: South Kensington
OS reference: TQ 268793
Operating society/organisation: Science Museum, Exhibition Road, South Kensington, London SW7

Telephone: (020) 7938 8000
Access by public transport: South Kensington Underground station
Catering facilities: Cafe on ground floor, tea, coffee, sandwiches, etc. Picnic area in basement
On site facilities: Bookshop, toilets on most floors
Public opening: Daily 10.00-18.00. Closed 24-26 December
Special events: All organised by the National Railway Museum,

York, which is part of the Science Museum. Telephone (01904) 621261 for details
Facilities for disabled: Toilets on most floors, ramp and lifts to all floors. Parties should contact before arrival if extra assistance is required
Special notes: Static exhibits only in Land Transport Gallery

---

Timetable Service	Seaton & District Electric Tramway	Devon

Member: HRA

Devon's unique narrow gauge electric tramway, operating on the trackbed of the former Seaton branch line between Seaton, Colyford and Colyton. Panoramic views of the beautiful Axe Valley and estuary. An unforgettable experience for the family
Location: Harbour Road Car Park, Seaton; Swan Hill Road, Colyford; Station Road, Kingsdon, Colyton
OS reference: SY 252904
Operating society/organisation: Seaton Tramway Co, Harbour Road, Seaton, Devon EX12 2NQ
Telephone: Seaton (01297) 20375. 24hr talking timetable on (01297) 24703
Fax: Seaton (01297) 625626
Access by public transport: Local bus services from Axminster railway station (South West

Locomotives

Name	No	Builder	Type	Built
Claude	—	R/Hornsby (435398)	4wDM	1959

Trains), Sidmouth and Lyme Regis serve Seaton, Colyford and Colyton. Bus enquiries (01392) 382800
On site facilities: Gift shops, tea rooms, children's playground, picnic area
Length of line: 3 miles, 2ft 9in gauge
Period of public operation: Daily 8 April-29 October; Weekends 4 November-23 December; Santa Specials in December; private hire available all year round
Special events: 5th Annual Bus & Vintage Vehicle Rally — 11 June; 30th Anniversary Fortnight — 27 May-11 June

Times: Trams every 20 minutes, 09.40-17.20
Fares: Single, return and rover tickets available. Discounts for local residents, families and parties of 20 or more. Prices on application
Facilities for disabled: Tramcar No 17 carries up to 12 wheelchairs (by prior arrangement). Disabled toilets at Seaton and Colyton
Special notes: Tram driving lessons are offered every Friday and Saturday during the season, please contact for details. Services operated by open-top double-deck bogie cars with enclosed single-deck saloon cars during inclement weather

---

Timetable Service	Severn Valley Railway	Worcestershire

Member: HRA, TT

The railway hosts more main line engines than any other preserved line in the country, enjoying the back-up of a large volunteer and professional workforce and extensive engineering workshops and equipment. Railway travel like it used to be
General Manager: Alun Rees
Headquarters: Severn Valley Railway Co Ltd, Railway Station, Bewdley, Worcs DY12 1BG
Telephone: Bewdley (01299)

Locomotives and multiple-units

Name	No	Origin	Class	Type	Built
The Great Marquess	61994	LNER	K4	2-6-0	1938
Union of South Africa	60009	LNER	A4	4-6-2	1937
Gordon	AD600	LMR	WD	2-10-0	1943
—	43106	LMS	4MT	2-6-0	1951
—	46443	LMS	2MT	2-6-0	1950
—	46521	LMS	2MT	2-6-0	1953
RAF Biggin Hill	45110	LMS	5MT	4-6-0	1935
—	47383	LMS	3F	0-6-0T	1926
—	48773	LMS	8F	2-8-0	1940
—	2968	LMS	5P4F	2-6-0	1933
—	813	GWR	—	0-6-0ST	1901

403816; 24hr timetable — 0800
600900
Main stations: Bridgnorth,
Bewdley, Kidderminster Town
Other public stations: Arley,
Highley, Hampton Loade,
Northwood Halt, Country Park Halt
OS reference: Bridgnorth SO
715926, Bewdley SO 793753
Car parks: At all main stations
Access by public transport:
Midland Red bus service 192 to
Kidderminster and Bewdley and
125 & 297 to Bridgnorth. Rail
service to Kidderminster (main
line) with immediate connections to
SVR station. Through tickets
available from all manned main
line stations
Refreshment facilities: At most
stations, but not on all operating
days and on most trains. Fully
licensed bars at Bridgnorth and
Kidderminster Town
Souvenir shops: Bridgnorth,
Kidderminster Town
Depots: Bridgnorth (locomotives),
Bewdley and Kidderminster (stock)
Model railways: At Bewdley,
Kidderminster and Hampton Loade
Length of line: 16.5 miles
Passenger trains: Steam-hauled
trains running frequently from
Kidderminster Town to Bewdley
and Bridgnorth. Diesel-hauled
service on limited occasions as
advertised
Period of public operation:
Weekends year round, Santa Steam
Specials in late November and
December. Daily service 13 May to
24 September and all Bank
Holidays and school holidays.
Open for limited viewing at other
times
Special events: Day Out with
Thomas — 13/14, 20/21 May;
Heavy Horse Weekend — 10/11
June; 1940s Weekend — 1/2 July;
Day Out with Thomas — 2/3, 9/10
September; Autumn Steam Gala —
22-24 September; Diesel Gala —
2/30 September, 1 October; Classic
Vehicle Day — 8 October; Santa
Steam Specials — 2/3, 9/10, 16/17,
23/24 December. As 2000 sees the
30th Anniversary of public opening
there will be various special events
throughout the year
Facilities for disabled: Facilities
available, special vehicle available
to carry wheelchairs by prior
arrangement. Disabled people's

Name	No	Origin	Class	Type	Built
—	2857	GWR	2800	2-8-0	1918
—	5164	GWR	5101	2-6-2T	1930
—	4150	GWR	5101	2-6-2T	1947
—	5764	GWR	5700	0-6-0PT	1929
—	7714	GWR	5700	0-6-0PT	1930
—	4566	GWR	4500	2-6-2T	1924
Bradley Manor	7802	GWR	'Manor'	4-6-0	1939
Erlestoke Manor	7812	GWR	'Manor'	4-6-0	1939
Hinton Manor	7819	GWR	'Manor'	4-6-0	1939
Hagley Hall*	4930	GWR	'Hall'	4-6-0	1929
—	1501	GWR	1500	0-6-0PT	1949
—	7325	GWR	4300	2-6-0	1932
—	75069	BR	4MT	4-6-0	1955
—	80079	BR	4MT	2-6-4T	1954
Greyhound	D821	BR	42	B-B	1960
Western Ranger	D1013	BR	52	C-C	1962
Western Courier	D1062	BR	52	C-C	1963
—	D3022	BR	08	0-6-0DE	1952
—	D3586	BR	08	0-6-0DE	1953
—	12099	LMS	11	0-6-0DE	1952
—	D7029	BR	35	Bo-Bo	1962
—	D7633	BR	25	Bo-Bo	1965
—	D5410	BR	27	Bo-Bo	1962
Hood	50031	BR	50	Co-Co	1968
Ark Royal	50035	BR	50	Co-Co	1968
Exeter	D444	BR	50	Co-Co	1968
—	51935	BR	108	DMBS	1960
—	51941	BR	108	DMBS	1960
—	52064	BR	108	DMC	1960
—	56208	BR	108	DTCL	1958
—	59250	BR	108	TBS	1958

*on display at the McArthurGlen complex, Swindon

Industrial locomotives

Name	No	Builder	Type	Built
Warwickshire	—	M/Wardle (2047)	0-6-0ST	1926
The Lady Armaghdale	—	Hunslet (686)	0-6-0T	1898
—	—	Ruston (319290)	0-4-0DM	1953
Alan	—	R/Hornsby (414304)	0-4-0DM	1957
William	—	R/Hornsby (408297)	0-4-0DM	1957

Stock
27 ex-GWR coaches; 13 ex-LMS coaches; 24 ex-BR Mk 1 coaches; 8 ex-
LNER coaches; Numerous examples of ex-GWR, LMS and other freight
vehicles and two 30-ton steam cranes

Owners
813 the GWR 813 Fund
1501 the 15xx Fund
2857 the 2857 Fund
2968 the Stanier Mogul Fund
61994 the family of the late Earl of Lindsay
4150 the 4150 Locomotive Fund
4566 the 4566 Fund
5164 the 51xx Fund
5764, 7714 the Pannier Tank Fund
46521, 60009 and D1013 are private
7325 the Great Western (SVR) Association
7802 and 7812 the Erlestoke Manor Fund
7819 the Hinton Manor Fund
43106 the Ivatt 4 Fund
46443 the SVR 46443 Fund

England

toilets at Kidderminster and Bridgnorth

Special notes: A number of special enthusiasts' weekends and special events are held when extra trains are operated. In addition, supplementary trains with diesel haulage are run as advertised. 'Severn Valley Limited' and 'Severn Valley Venturer' Restaurant Car service operates on Sundays and as required on other occasions. Advanced booking required. Charter trains with or without dining facilities can be arranged

Membership details: Mrs Kate Kirk, c/o above address

47383 the Manchester Rail Travel Society
48773 the Stanier 8F Locomotive Society
50031, 50035 and D444 the 50 Fund
75069 the 75069 Fund
80079 the Passenger Tank Fund
AD600 the Royal Corps of Transport Museum Trustees
D821 and D7029 the Diesel Traction Group
D1062 the Western Locomotive Association
D3022 the Class 08 Society
D5410 Sandwell Metropolitan Council
D7633 the SVR/PW Fund
4930 and 45110 the SVR(H) plc

Membership journal: *Severn Valley Railway News* — quarterly
Share details: Mr Alun Rees, c/o above address

Steam Centre

Sittingbourne & Kemsley Light Railway

Kent

Member: HRA, TT

The Sittingbourne & Kemsley Light Railway is part of the 2ft 6in gauge railway built to convey paper and other materials between mills at Sittingbourne and Kemsley and the Dock at Ridham on the banks of the Swale. The first section of the line opened in 1906 and two of the engines then in use remain on the line today.

The railway is now leased from U.K. Paper Group and is operated as a tourist attraction. Passenger trains are normally steam-hauled and are formed of a varied selection of open and covered coaches. For the first half mile of the journey the train twists and turns through Milton Regis on a concrete viaduct which was one of the first reinforced concrete structures to be built

Headquarters: Sittingbourne & Kemsley Light Railway Ltd, PO Box 300, Sittingbourne, Kent ME10 2DZ

Telephone: Sittingbourne (01795) 424899 (talking timetable). Other enquiries: (01227) 369606 or (01622) 755313

Main station: Sittingbourne
Car park: Sittingbourne
Party bookings and enquiries: Sittingbourne & Kemsley Light Railway Ltd, PO Box 300, Sittingbourne, Kent ME10 2DZ. Tel: (01227) 369606 or (01622)

Locomotives

Name	No	Builder	Type	Built
Alpha	—	Bagnall (2472)	0-6-2T	1932
Triumph	—	Bagnall (2511)	0-6-2T	1934
Superb	—	Bagnall (2624)	0-6-2T	1940
Unique	—	Bagnall (2216)	2-4-0F	1924
Premier	—	K/Stuart (886)	0-4-2ST	1905
Leader	—	K/Stuart (926)	0-4-2ST	1905
Melior	—	K/Stuart (4219)	0-4-2ST	1924
Edward Lloyd	—	R/Hornsby (435403)	4wDM	1961
Victor	—	Hunslet (4182)	4wDM	1953

Industrial standard gauge locomotives

Name	No	Builder	Type	Built
—	4	H/Leslie (3718)	0-4-0ST	1928
Bear	—	Peckett (614)	0-4-0ST	1896
—	1	Barclay (1876)	0-4-0F	1925

Locomotive notes: In service: *Superb, Melior, Triumph*. Under repair: *Leader, Premier*. On static display: *Alpha, Unique* and standard gauge exhibits

Stock
10 bogie coaches (4 ex-Chattenden & Upnor Railway); 2 open coaches; various wagons

755313
Access by public transport: Sittingbourne main line station, A2 and M2 roads
OS reference: Sittingbourne TQ 905643, Kemsley Down TQ 920662
Refreshment facilities: Kemsley Down
Souvenir shop: Kemsley Down
Depot: Kemsley Down (access by rail only)
Length of line: 2 miles, 2ft 6in gauge
Passenger trains: Ex-industrial line Sittingbourne-Kemsley Down
Journey time: 15min each way
Period of public operation: Every Sunday 2 April to 8 October. Saturday, Sunday and Monday of Bank Holiday weekends. Wednesdays and Saturdays during

May half term and school summer holidays
Special events: Easter Events & Fun — 22-25 April; Postman Pat Day — 28 May; Fedecrail Day 11 June; Friends of Thomas the Tank Engine — 1/2 July; Steam & Beer, The Family Beer Festival — 8/9 July; Music & Steam — evenings in September (Folk, Jazz, Rock Pop Concerts, phone for details); Autumn Beer Festivals — 10, 17 September; Gala Weekend, including overnight train — 12/13 August; Santa Specials —weekends in December (phone for details)
Special notes: There is no public access to Kemsley Down other than by the railway on operating dates. When the line is closed all stock is stored in security compounds, on the mill premises. Family ticket available, special rates for parties and senior citizens. Picnic area at Kemsley Down
Membership details: David Bootle, S&KLR, PO Box 300, Sittingbourne, Kent ME10 2DZ.
Marketing name: Sittingbourne Steam Railway

Museum — Snibston Discovery Park — Leicestershire

Members: TT
Location: Snibston Discovery Park, Ashby Road, Coalville, Leicestershire LE67 3LN
Telephone: (01530) 510851
Fax: (01530) 813301
Operating group: Leicestershire County Council Museums, Arts & Records Service
Museum contact: Mr A. Coulls, Snibston Discovery Park, Ashby Road, Coalville, Leicestershire LE67 3LN
Public opening: Daily 10.00-18.00 (during British Summer Time); 10.00-16.00 at other times. Closed Christmas Day & Boxing Day
Car & coach parking: On site, free
Access by public transport: Arriva Fox from Loughborough and Nottingham (route 99); from Leicester (route 117); from Ashby de la Zouch (route 118), Mon-Sat; route 217/8 Sun & Bank Holiday Mondays. Further information, tel: (01533) 511411.
Stevensons Bus Services from Hinckley (route 179); limited service from Tamworth via Ashby (route 97). Connections at Ashby with Burton upon Trent. Further information, tel: (01283) 44662
On site facilities: Shop, toilets, car park, café. Conference facilities, tourist information centre (Tel: [01530] 813608). Family tickets, picnic areas, science play area, Sheepy Magna wheelwrights workshop. Special event days, nature reserve, golf driving range, colliery building tours
Railways on site: Approx 300yd of standard gauge track, with operation of demonstration trains on certain days — telephone for details. Track to be extended when possible. No public riding on line.
Narrow gauge railway about 350yd in length. Colliery man-riding underground train to operate in future, subject to availability of equipment

Industrial Locomotives (standard gauge)

Name	No	Builder	Type	Built
Mars II†	—	RSH (7493)	0-4-0ST	1948
—	2	Barclay (1815)	0-4-0F	1924
—*	—	Brush (314)	0-4-0ST	1906
Cadley Hill No 1	—	Hunslet (3851)	0-6-0ST	1962
—†	16	Hunslet (6289)	0-6-0DM	1966
—	—	R/Hornsby (393304)	4wDM	1955

Industrial Locomotives (2ft 6in gauge)

Name	No	Builder	Type	Built
—	—	E/Electric (2416)	4wBE	1957
—	—	H/Clarke (DM1812)	0-6-0DM	1960
—	—	Hunslet (7385)	4wDMF	1976
—	63/000/449	Hunslet (8973)	4wDH	1979

†locomotives are stored, but may be brought out for display on special events
*originally Powlesland & Mason No 6 taken over by GWR in 1924 and numbered 921
Brush (314) is now on display, *Cadley Hill* has returned to the colliery system
Plus 2ft 6in gauge English Electric battery-operated electric man-riding locomotives — ex-NCB

Museum — Somerset & Dorset Railway Trust — Somerset

Member: HRA
Situated at Washford on the West Somerset Railway, the Trust Museum houses Somerset & Dorset memorabilia and artefacts to stir memories of cross-country travel in the era of steam. The sidings and restoration shed give the visitor a chance to see locomotives, wagons and carriages in close up
Headquarters: Washford Station, Minehead Road, Washford,

Somerset TA21 0PP
Telephone: (01984) 640869
(opening hours); (01278) 683574
(otherwise)
Car park: Small car park by main
road
Access by public transport: West
Somerset Railway trains on
operating days, March to end
October. Nearest main line station:
Taunton. Southern National
Omnibus Co service 28 (Taunton-
Minehead) passes the station
On site facilities: Souvenir counter
at the station. No refreshments on
station but adjacent inn offers food
and children are welcome
Public opening: 10.30-16.30 on
WSR operating days. Other times
by arrangement, tel: (01278)

Locomotive

Name	No	Origin	Class	Type	Built
—*	53808	S&DJR	7F	2-8-0	1925

*undergoing heavy overhaul at Minehead

Industrial locomotives

Name	No	Builder	Type	Built
Isabel*	—	H/Leslie (3437)	0-6-0ST	1919
Kilmersdon	—	Peckett (1788)	0-4-0ST	1929

*undergoing restoration at Washford

Stock

3 Somerset & Dorset 6-wheeled coaches undergoing restoration. Large
wagon collection. Display of narrow gauge equipment from Sedgemoor
peat railways

683574
Membership details: S&DJR
Trust, 21 Greenhaven, Yateley,
Hampshire GU46 6NA

Membership journal: *Pines
Express* (4 issues/year, plus
newsletter)

Timetable Service	South Devon Railway - 'The Primrose Line'	Devon

Member: HRA, TT

A typical West Country branch line
meandering up the Dart Valley to
Buckfastleigh which is home to the
railway's workshops, a butterfly
and otter farm and several other
attractions. After many years of
isolation the line is now accessible
from Totnes (BR) via a new
footbridge (4min walk)
General Manager: R. Elliott
Headquarters: South Devon
Railway, Buckfastleigh Station,
Buckfastleigh, Devon TQ11 0D2
Telephone: Buckfastleigh (01364)
642338
Internet addresses: e-mail:
southdevonrailway.org
web site:
www.southdevonrailway.org
Main station: Buckfastleigh
Other public stations: Staverton,
Totnes (Littlehempston)
OS reference:
Buckfastleigh SX 747663,
Staverton SX 785638
Car park: Buckfastleigh (free),
Staverton (free). Totnes — use BR
pay & display or council car parks
Access by public transport: Bus,
X38/9 Exeter-Plymouth; 188
Newton Abbot-Buckfastleigh; X80
Plymouth-Torquay. Main line trains
to Totnes
Refreshment facilities:
Buckfastleigh

Locomotives and multiple-units

Name	No	Origin	Class	Type	Built
—	0298	LSWR	0298	2-4-0WT	1874
—	1420	GWR	1400	0-4-2T	1933
—	1369	GWR	1366	0-6-0PT	1934
—	3205	GWR	2251	0-6-0	1946
—	3803	GWR	2884	2-8-0	1939
Dumbleton Hall	4920	GWR	'Hall'	4-6-0	1929
—	5526	GWR	4500	2-6-2T	1929
—	5786	GWR	5700	0-6-0PT	1930
—	D3666	BR	09	0-6-0DE	1959
—	D8110	BR	20	Bo-Bo	1962
—	20118	BR	20	Bo-Bo	1962
—	D7612	BR	25	Bo-Bo	1966
—	51592	BR	127	DMBS	1959
—	51604	BR	127	DMBS	1959
—	59659	BR	115	TS	1960
—	59719	BR	115	TCL	1960
—	59740	BR	115	TS	1960

Broad gauge — 7ft 0.25in

Name	No	Origin	Class	Type	Built
Tiny†	—	SDR	—	0-4-0VBT	1868

Industrial locomotives

Name	No	Builder	Type	Built
Ashley	1	Peckett (2031)	0-4-0ST	1942
Lady Angela	1690	Peckett (1690)	0-4-0ST	1926
—	1738	Peckett (1690)	0-4-0ST	1937
Sapper	WD132	Hunslet (3163)	0-6-0ST	1943
Glendower	—	Hunslet (3810)	0-6-0ST	1954
Carnarvon	47	Kitson (5474)	0-6-0ST	1935
—	—	Fowler (421014)	0-4-0DM	1958
Errol Lonsdale	68011	Hunslet (3796)	0-6-0ST	1953
Meteor	31	RSH (7609)	0-6-0T	1950

Stock

13 ex-BR Mk 1 coaches; 7 ex-GWR coaches; 3 ex-GWR auto trailers;
25 wagons

Souvenir shop: On the train
Museum: Buckfastleigh
Depot: Buckfastleigh
Length of line: 7 miles
Passenger trains: Buckfastleigh-Totnes (Littlehempston) alongside the River Dart
Period of public operation: Telephone above for details
Facilities for disabled: Good
Membership details: South Devon Railway Association, c/o above address
Membership journal: *Bulliver* — quarterly
Marketing name: The Primrose Line

Owners
0298 on loan from the National Railway Museum
Tiny, 7ft 0.25in gauge, part of the National Collection
3803 the South Devon Railway Trust
Glendower is privately owned
Errol Lonsdale the South Devon Railway Trust
1420 the South Devon Railway Association
5526 the 5526 Ltd
D8110 the Class 20 Group
20118 the South Devon Diesel Traction Group
5786 the Worcester Locomotive Society
Sapper & 4920 the South Devon Railway Trust
1369 the South Devon Railway Association

Timetable Service	South Tynedale Railway	Cumbria

Member: HRA, TT
A narrow gauge line passing through the attractive scenery of the South Tyne valley, in the North Pennine area of outstanding natural beauty
Location: Approximately 0.75-mile north of Alston town centre, on A686 Hexham road
OS reference: NY 717467
Operating society: South Tynedale Railway Preservation Society, The Railway Station, Alston, Cumbria CA9 3JB
Telephone: Alston (01434) 382828 (timetable information); (01434) 381696 (other enquiries)
Car park: Alston station
Access by public transport: Wright Bros buses, Haltwhistle-Alston and Newcastle-Alston-Keswick. Also summer buses from Durham and Stanhope. Bus links from Langwathby in connection with Settle-Carlisle line trains on certain dates (Details of all buses: [01228] 606000.)
On site facilities: Book and souvenir shop, tourist information centre, picnic area, toilets (including disabled persons), parking, lineside footpath
Catering facilities: Most trains serve coffee, tea, soft drinks and snacks at Kirkhaugh from a converted brake van on the train. (Tearoom at Alston is not operated by Society). Confectionery, ice cream and soft drinks on sale in the railway shop at Alston
Length of line: 2.25 miles, 2ft

Locomotives

Name	No	Builder	Type	Built
Phoenix	1	Hibberd (2325)	4wDM	1941
Sao Domingos	3	O/K (11784)	0-6-0WT	1928
Naworth	4	H/Clarke (DM819)	0-6-0DM	1952
Thomas Edmondson	6	Henschel (16047)	0-4-0T	1918
—	9	Hunslet (4109)	0-4-0DM	1952
Naklo	10	Chrzanow (3459)	0-6-0WTT	1957
Cumbria	11	Hunslet (6646)	0-4-0DM	1967
Chaka's Kraal No 6	12	Hunslet (2075)	0-4-2T	1940
—	13	Hunslet (5222)	0-4-0T	1958
Helen Kathryn	14	Henschel (28035)	0-4-0T	1948
—	—	Hunslet (4110)	0-4-0DM	1952
—	—	H/Clarke (DM1167)	0-6-0DM	1960
—	15	H/Clarke (DM1366)	0-6-0DM	1965
—	—	EE/Baguley (2519/3500)	4wBE	1958
—	—	Hunslet (1859)	0-4-2ST	1937
Permanent Way	DB965062			
Trolley	Wickham		4WDM	?

Owners
1, 6, 9, 10 & 1859 the South Tynedale Railway Preservation Society
4, 11, 4110, DM1107, 2519/3500) & DB965082 the Durham Narrow Gauge Group
12 the North Gloucestershire Narrow Gauge Co
13 the Ayle Colliery Co
3, 14 & 15 privately owned

Stock
6 bogie coaches; 2 brake vans; 1 bogie open wagon; 3 4-wheel open wagons; 1 4-wheel box van; 4 4-wheel flat wagons; 1 4-wheel fuel tank wagon; 2 bogie well wagons, 4 4-wheel skip wagons; 6 bogie flat wagons; 6 bogie hopper wagons; 1 4-wheel hopper wagon; 1 4-wheel weedkiller wagon; 1 bogie compressor wagon

gauge
Public opening: Weekends and Bank Holidays — 15 April-24 September; daily — Easter week, Spring Bank Holiday week and 24

July to 3 September; Tuesdays, Wednesdays and Thursdays 4 June-20 July and 24-26 October
  Steam haulage scheduled at weekends from Spring Bank

England

Holiday until September, also Easter and May Day Weekends, daily 24 July to 5 September, and most special event days
Special events: Easter Bunny Day — 24 April; Teddy Bears' Picnic — 17/18 June; Gala Weekend — 2/3 September; Santa Specials — 3, 9/10, 16/17 December; . Friends of Thomas the Tank Engine — 29/30 April, 1 May, 21/22 October (subject to confirmation)
Special notes: The line has been constructed on the trackbed of the former BR Haltwhistle-Alston branch. the .75-mile extension of The line from Kirkhaugh is now open, with a further 2.25 miles, in progress towards Slaggyford.
Membership details: Membership Secretary, c/o above address
Membership journal: *Tynedalesman* — quarterly
Marketing name: England's Highest Narrow Gauge Railway

Museum — South Yorkshire Railway — South Yorkshire

Member: HRA
Location: Barrow Road Railway Sidings, Barrow Road, Meadowhall, Wincobank, Sheffield S9 1HN
OS Reference: SK 391914
General Manager: John Wade
Operating society: South Yorkshire Railway
Telephone: Mr A. L. Dyson, Rotherham (01709) 368040
Car park: Car parking facilities available; more facilities being developed nearby
Access by public transport: From Sheffield: By bus, No 93 Firth Park, alight at the top of Barrow Road, and follow the signposts. From Rotherham, Doncaster and Sheffield No X77 bus alighting on Barrow Road.
By rail: Meadowhall, 100yd
By Supertram: From city centre to Meadowhall Interchange
On site facilities: Small shop
Length of line: 3.5 miles in total, although only three-quarters of a mile is currently occupied
Period of public operation: Not operating a service as yet
Journey time: See above
Membership Secretary: G. Barnes
Membership details: c/o above address
Membership journal: *41Z* — quarterly

Locomotives and multiple-unit

Name	No	Origin	Class	Type	Built
—	D2953	BR	01	0-4-0DM	1956
Peter	02003	BR	02	0-4-0DH	1960
—	D2854	BR	02	0-4-0DH	1960
—	D2866	BR	02	0-4-0DH	1961
—	D2867	BR	02	0-4-0DH	1961
—	D2868	BR	02	0-4-0DH	1961
—	03018	BR	03	0-6-0DM	1958
—	03020	BR	03	0-6-0DM	1958
—	03037	BR	03	0-6-0DM	1959
—	03099	BR	03	0-6-0DM	1960
—	D2118	BR	03	0-6-0DM	1959
—	D2134	BR	03	0-6-0DM	1960
—	D2139	BR	03	0-6-0DM	1960
—	03180	BR	03	0-6-0DM	1962
—	03197	BR	03	0-6-0DM	1961
—	D2199	BR	03	0-6-0DM	1961
—	D2229	BR	04	0-6-0DM	1955
Bluebell	D2246	BR	04	0-6-0DM	1956
Alfie	D2272	BR	04	0-6-0DM	1960
—	D2284	BR	04	0-6-0DM	1960
—	D2302	BR	04	0-6-0DM	1960
—	D2310	BR	04	0-6-0DM	1960
Judith	D2324	BR	04	0-6-0DM	1961
Dorothy	D2337	BR	04	0-6-0DM	1961
—	D2587	BR	05	0-6-0DM	1959
—	06003	BR	06	0-4-0DM	1958
—	07012	BR	07	0-6-0DE	1962
—	D3000	BR	08	0-6-0DE	1952
Gwyneth	D3019	BR	08	0-6-0DE	1953
—	D3023	BR	08	0-6-0DE	1953
—	08133	BR	08	0-6-0DE	1955
—	08216	BR	08	0-6-0DE	1956
—	08390	BR	08	0-6-0DE	1958
—	08507	BR	08	0-6-0DE	1960
—	08707	BR	08	0-6-0DE	1960
—	D3476	BR	10	0-6-0DE	1957
Christine	D4092	BR	10	0-6-0DE	1962
—	12074	BR	11	0-6-0DE	1950
—	12083	BR	11	0-6-0DE	1950
—	12098	BR	11	0-6-0DE	1952
—	D9500	BR	14	0-6-0DM	1964
—	D9502	BR	14	0-6-0DM	1964
—	26038	BR	26	Bo-Bo	1959
Earl Mountbatten of Burma	33203	BR	33	Bo-Bo	1962

Name	No	Origin	Class	Type	Built
—	53556	BR	104	DMCL	1958

Industrial locomotives

Name	No	Builder	Type	Built
WD75133	2	Hunslet (3183)	0-6-0ST	1944
—	7	H/Clarke (1689)	0-4-0ST	1937
Cathyrn	—	H/Clarke (1884)	0-4-0ST	1955
George	—	Sentinel (9596)	4wVBT	1955
Ken	67	Sentinel (10180)	0-6-0DH	1964
Bigga	—	Fowler (4200019)	0-4-0DH	1947
Rotherham	2	YEC (2480)	0-4-0DE	1950
—	—	Hibbard (3817)	0-4-0DM	1956
—	44	Hunslet (6684)	0-6-0DH	1968
—	47	T/Hill (249V)	0-6-0DH	1974
—	8	T/Hill (288V)	0-6-0DH	1980
—	—	Barclay (335)	0-4-0DM	1939
Speedy	—	Barclay (361)	0-4-0DM	1942
Hotwheels	—	Barclay (422)	0-6-0DM	1958
Toffo	2	R/Hornsby (432479)	4wDM	1959
—	20	YEC (2688)	0-4-0DE	1959

Rolling stock

2 diesel-electric cranes; 4 BR Mk 1 coaches; 6 BR Mk 1 General Utility Vehicles; 1 BR Mk 1 bogie van; 2 Covered Carriage Trucks; 2 LNER brake vans; Several other wagons

Timetable Service — Spa Valley Railway — Kent

Member: HRA

The shed at Tunbridge Wells West is an original LBSCR design dating from 1891 and consists of four roads which house various items of rolling stock and motive power

Location: Tunbridge Wells West station

Operating society/organisation: Spa Valley Railway, Tunbridge Wells West Station, Nevill Terrace, Tunbridge Wells, Kent TN4 8HL

Telephone: (01892) 537715

Internet address: Web site: www.spavalleyrailway.co.uk

Access by public transport: Buses to Tunbridge Wells, direct services from London and Hastings. All services stop at Sainsbury's, 15min walk away

Refreshment facilities: Buffet car at Tunbridge Wells West

Souvenir shop: Tunbridge Wells West (within engine shed)

Museum: Tunbridge Wells West (within engine shed)

Length of line: 3 miles Tunbridge Wells-Groombridge

Passenger trains: Weekends from March and Tuesdays, Wednesdays and Thursdays in July and August

Special events: Please contact for details

Locomotives and multiple-units

Name	No	Origin	Class	Type	Built
—	15224	BR	12	0-6-0DE	1949
—	51669	BR	115	DMBS	1960
—	51849	BR	115	DMBS	1960

Industrial locomotives

Name	No	Builder	Type	Built
Scottie	1	R/Hornsby (412427)	4wDM	1957
North Downs	3	RSH (7846)	0-6-0T	1955
Princess Margaret	6	Barclay (376)	0-4-0DM	1947
Lady Ingrid	3	Barclay (2315)	0-4-0ST	1951
Telemon	9	Drewry/Vulcan (D295)	0-4-0DM	1955
Topham	10	Bagnall (2193)	0-6-0ST	1922
Fonmon	—	Peckett (1936)	0-6-0ST	1924
Paxman	11	Sentinel (10007)	0-4-0DE	1959
Spartan	—	Chrzanow (3135)	0-6-0T	1954
Hotspur	—	Chrzanow	0-6-0T	1950s

Stock

5 BR Mk 1 coaches; 1 BR Mk 2 coaches; 2 ex-London Transport T stock coaches; Various freight wagons

Membership details: c/oTunbridge Wells West Station

Visitors in action during an early season gala on the West Somerset Railway. BR Standard No 76079 (East Lancs) and Ivatt-designed 2-6-2T No 41312 (Mid-Hants) are seen at Castle Hill on 19 March 1999.
Alan P. Barnes

Jonathan, **a Hunslet-built 0-4-0ST, at the head of a train on the West Lancashire Railway.** *John Simm*

England

Museum — Steam: Museum of the Great Western Railway — Wiltshire

Member: HRA

Replacing the old Great Western Railway Museum which closed after 37 years in 1999, this new museum will tell the story of the people and machines that made Swindon famous. Situated on the old Swindon Railway Works site, the museum is housed in a 72,000sq ft Victorian machine shop. As well as locomotives, carriages and wagons the story will be told through reconstructions of workshops, videos and interactive exhibits. The museum will open at the end of May 2000

Keeper: T. Bryan AMA

Location: Kemble Drive, Swindon, Wiltshire SN2

OS reference: tba

Operating society/organisation: Swindon Borough Council

Telephone: Swindon (01793) 466646. (For enquiries before opening 01793 466555)

Locomotives

Name	No	Origin	Class	Type	Built
—	2516	GWR	2301	0-6-0	1897
—	4248	GWR	4200	2-8-0T	1916
Caerphilly Castle	4073	GWR	'Castle'	4-6-0	1923
King George V	6000	GWR	'King'	4-6-0	1927
—	9400	GWR	9400	0-6-0PT	1947
North Star*	—	GWR	—	2-2-2	1837
—	4	GWR	Diesel railcar	Bo-Bo	1934

*broad gauge (7ft 0.25in) replica

Owners

All locomotives are part of the National Railway Museum Collection

Car park: Shared with the Great Western Designer Outlet Village complex

Access by public transport: Swindon main line station 1-mile (20 minutes walk)

On site facilities: Café, shop

Facilities for disabled: Fully accessible

Period of Public opening: Following opening in late May 2000 — Monday to Sunday 10.00-18.00, (except Thursdays 10.00-20.00). Closed Christmas Day, Boxing Day, New Year's Day

Membership details: The Friends of Swindon Railway Museum, c/o Steam

Membership journal: North Star — quarterly

Steam Centre — Stephenson Railway Museum & North Tyneside Railway — Northumberland

Member: HRA

A display in buildings which began life as the Tyne & Wear Metro Test Centre now features locomotives and exhibitions which illustrate railway development from waggonways to the present day

Location: Middle Engine Lane, West Chirton

OS reference: NZ 396576

Operating society/organisation: Tyne & Wear Museums operates the Stephenson Railway Museum, and the North Tyneside Steam Railway Association operates the North Tyneside Railway for North Tyneside Council, address c/o Stephenson Railway Museum, Middle Engine Lane, West Chirton, North Shields NE29 8DX

Car park: On site

Length of line: North Tyneside

Locomotive and multiple-unit

Name	No	Origin	Class	Type	Built
—	03078	BR	03	0-6-0DM	1959
—	3267	NER	—	DMLV	1904

Industrial locomotives

Name	No	Builder	Type	Built
Billy	—	Killingworth or RS & Co (1)	0-4-0	c1826
—	A No 5	Kitson (2509)	0-6-0PT	1883
Ashington No 5	5	Peckett (1970)	0-6-0ST	1939
MEA No 1	1	RSH (7683)	0-6-0T	1951
—	E4	Siemens-Schuckert (457)	Bo-BoWE	1909
Thomas Burt MP 1837-1902	401	Bagnall (2994)	0-6-0ST	1950
—	10	Consett Iron Co	0-6-0DM	1958

Stock

1 LNER Gresley BFK; 3 BR Mk 1 non-gangwayed coaches, 2 BR Mk 2 coaches, 1 LNER Gresley BGP

Owners

NER van National Railway Museum

Railway, 3 miles, Stephenson Railway Museum to California Siding (for Royal Quays)
Access by public transport: Tyne & Wear Metro to Percy Main when North Tyneside Railway is in operation
Public opening: Weekends and Bank Holidays only — Easter to September. Write or phone (0191) 200 7145 for details, including early/late season variations and special events
Special notes: Stephenson Railway Museum and North Tyneside Railway share facilities in buildings. North Tyneside Steam Railway Association operates and maintains exhibits from the Museum Collection
Facilities for disabled: Access for wheelchairs to Museum building at Middle Engine Lane. Access to stations; also wheelchair ramp onto train

---

Swanage Railway — 'The Purbeck Line'

Timetable Service — Dorset

Member: HRA
Overlooked by the historic ruins of Corfe Castle, this railway is slowly extending towards Wareham and a connection to the Railtrack network
Location: Swanage station
Operations Manager: Paul McDonald
Passenger Services Manager: David Green
Operating society/organisation: Swanage Railway Co Ltd, Station House, Swanage, Dorset BH19 1HB
Telephone: Swanage (01929) 425800. Talking Timetable — (01929) 425800
Fax: (01929) 426680
Main station: Swanage
Other public stations: Herston Halt, Harman's Cross, Corfe Castle and Norden
OS reference: SZ 026789
Car park: Norden park & ride signposted off A351 Wareham-Swanage road on the approach to Corfe Castle. Limited parking available at Swanage station
Access by public transport: Regular bus services operated by Wilts & Dorset from Bournemouth, Poole and Wareham to Swanage and Norden park & ride
On site facilities: Souvenir shop at Swanage. Buffet car on most trains. Picnic areas at Swanage, Harman's Cross and Norden. Exhibition and cinema coach at Corfe. 5in gauge railway at Swanage on some weekends. Travel Agency at Swanage station
Length of line: 6 miles, Swanage-Herston Halt-Harman's Cross-Corfe Castle-Norden
Public opening: Swanage station open every day except Christmas Day. Trains operate weekends all year round. Daily from 1 April until

Locomotives and multiple-units

Name	No	Origin	Class	Type	Built
—	6695	GWR	5600	0-6-2T	1928
—	30053	LSWR	M7	0-4-4T	1905
Harry A. Frith	E828	SR	S15	4-6-0	1923
Eddystone	34028	SR	WC	4-6-2	1946
257 Squadron	34072	SR	BB	4-6-2	1948
Port Line	35027†	SR	MN	4-6-2	1948
—	80078	BR	4MT	2-6-4T	1954
—	80104	BR	4MT	2-6-4T	1955
—	1708	MR	1F	0-6-0T	1880
—	30075	JZ	USA	0-6-0T	1950s
—	D3591	BR	08	0-6-0DE	1958
—	D9521	BR	14	0-6-0DH	1964
Stan Symes	D6515	BR	33	Bo-Bo	1960
—	52048	BR	108	DMCL	1960
—	51919	BR	108	DMBS	1956

†expected to arrive spring 2000

Industrial locomotives

Name	No	Builder	Type	Built
Cunarder	47160	Hunslet (1690)	0-6-0T	1931
May	2	Fowler (4210132)	0-4-0DM	1957
Beryl	—	Planet (2054)	4wPM	1937
Progress	—	Peckett (1611)	0-4-0ST	1923
—	2150	Peckett (2150)	0-6-0T	1954
Rosedale	110070		0-4-0DE	—

Locomotive notes: 30053, 80078 and 80104 will be away periodically on short-term loan. *Cunarder* is on loan to the Lavender Line

Stock
3 ex-LSWR coach bodies; 4 ex-SR vans; 9 ex-SR coaches; 18 ex-BR Mk 1 coaches; 15 various types of wagons; 1 ex-BR Mk 3 Sleeping coach; 1 ex-SR 15-ton diesel-electric crane; 1 ex-London Transport Plasser & Theurer ballast tamper; 1 ex-BR Corridor 2nd converted to disabled persons' coach. Brake vans from SR, LMS, LSWR, GWR

Owners
6695 the Great Western Railway Preservation Group
Cunarder the 1708 Locomotive Preservation Trust Ltd
1708 the 1708 Locomotive Preservation Trust Ltd
34028, 34072, 35027, 80078 and 80104 the Southern Locomotives Ltd
30053 the Drummond Locomotive Society
30075 the Project 62 Group
E828 the Eastleigh Preservation Society
D6515 the 71A Locomotive Group

31 October. Also 26 December 2000 to 2 January 2001
Special events: Hot Cross Bun Specials — 21 April; Easter Egg Specials — 23/24 April; 8th Annual Classic Vehicle Weekend (Harman's Cross) — 8/9 July; 8th Annual Exemption Dog Show — 16 July; Grand Steam Gala &

Vintage Transport Weekend — 9/10 September; Diesel Day — 28 November; Santa Specials — 25/26 November, 2/3, 9/10, 16/17, then daily until 24 December
Facilities for disabled: Access to shop and toilets; disabled facilities on most trains
Membership details: Sue Payne,

c/o Southern Steam Trust at above address
Membership journal: *Swanage Railway News* — quarterly
Marketing name: The Purbeck Line

Steam Centre | Swindon & Cricklade Railway | Wiltshire

Member: HRA, TT
This is the only preserved section of the former Midland & South Western Junction Railway, the society having had to re-lay track and associated works. The line has been extended to a new station at Hayes Knoll, and serves the engine shed complex
Location: Tadpole Lane, Blunsdon (approximately midway between Blunsdon St Andrew and Purton)
Chairman: J. Larkin
Operating society/organisation: Swindon & Cricklade Railway, Blunsdon Station, Blunsdon, Swindon, Wiltshire SN2 4DZ
Telephone: Swindon (01793) 771615 (weekends only)
Internet address: *Web site:* http://members.aol.com/blunsdon/homepage/.htm
Station: Blunsdon
OS reference: SU 110897
Length of line: 1-mile
Car park: Tadpole Lane, Blunsdon
Refreshment facilities: Blunsdon station amenities building. Buffet car at Hayes Knoll on open days. Picnic area
Toilet: Blunsdon station amenities building
Souvenir shop: Blunsdon station amenities building. Various sales stands on Open Days around station area. Museum in converted coach
Depot: Blunsdon
Public opening: Saturdays and Sundays throughout the year.
Passenger trains: Trains run between 11.00 and 16.00 on the dates shown below, except for Halloween which is an evening event (please phone to confirm actual times)

Locomotives and multiple-units

Name	No	Origin	Class	Type	Built
Foremarke Hall	7903	GWR	'Hall'	4-6-0	1949
—*	5637	GWR	56xx	0-6-2T	1924
—	3845	GWR	2884	2-8-0	1942
—	D2022	BR	03	0-6-0DM	1960
—	D2152	BR	03	0-6-0DM	1960
—	13261	BR	08	0-6-0DE	1956
—	51386	P/Sreel	117	MBS	1959
—	51434	Met/Cam	101	MBS	1958
—	51503	Met/Cam	101	DMC	1959
—	52005	BR	107	DMBS	1960
—	52025	BR	107	DMBS	1960
—	59117	Met/Cam	101	TC	1958

*on loan to East Somerset Railway

Industrial locomotives

Name	No	Builder	Type	Built
Swordfish	—	Barclay (2138)	0-6-0ST	1941
Richard Trevithick	—	Barclay (2354)	0-4-0ST	1955
Woodbine	—	Fowler (21442)	0-4-0DM	1936
—	—	Fowler (4210137)	0-4-0DM	1958
—	23	Fowler (4220031)	0-4-0DH	1964
—	—	H/Clarke (1857)	0-6-0T	1952
Slough Estates No 5	—	H/Clarke (3138)	0-6-0ST	1915
Merlin/Myrddin	1371	Peckett (1967)	0-4-0ST	1939

Stock
6 BR Mk 1 coaches; 2 GWR coaches; selection of goods rolling stock; Wickham railcar

Owners
7903 the Foremarke Hall Locomotive Group
5637 the 5637 Locomotive Group
Slough Estates the Slough & Windsor Railway Society

Special events: Easter Bunny — 23/24 April; Day Out with Thomas — 20/21 May; Teddy Bears' Special — 18 June; Fire Engine Weekend — 23/24 September; Halloween Party Night — 31 October (Tuesday); Santa Specials — 9/10, 16/17, 23 December

Facilities for disabled: Access to shop and refreshments
Membership details: Membership Secretary c/o above address
Membership journal: S&CR Newsletter — quarterly
Marketing name: Tiddlydyke

England

Tanfield Railway

Member: HRA

The oldest railway in the world, featuring 1725 route, 1725 Causey embankment, 1727 Causey arch, 1766 Gibraltar bridge and 1854 Marley Hill engine shed. Also collection of local engines, Victorian carriages and vintage workshop

Location: Off the A6076 Sunniside to Stanley road

OS reference: NZ 207573

Operating society/organisation: The Tanfield Railway, Marley Hill Engine Shed, Sunniside, Gateshead NE16 5ET

Telephone: (0191) 388 7545

Main stations: Andrews House, Sunniside, Causey, East Tanfield

Car park: Marley Hill, Causey picnic area, East Tanfield

Access by public transport: X30 (weekdays) stops outside main entrance; 705, 706, 770 Sundays to Sunniside only, near to Sunniside station

Catering facilities: Light refreshments available on operating days

On site facilities: Shop and toilets

Length of line: 3 miles

Public opening: Trains run every Sunday and Bank Holiday Monday from January to November. Also Wednesdays and Thursdays from 26 July-31 August. Santa trains in December before Christmas. Marley Hill engine shed open daily for viewing

Special events: Tanfield Railway 275th Anniversary Month (special events on each operating day — 2-31 August; Santa Steamings — 2/3, 9/10, 16/17, 23/24 December; Mince Pie Specials — 26/27 December

Family tickets: Available

Facilities for disabled: Access to East Tanfield and Andrews House stations and Marley Hill engine shed. Toilets at Causey car park and Andrews House station

Membership details: Miss E. Martin, 33 Stocksfield Avenue, Fenham, Newcastle upon Tyne NE5 2DX

Membership journal: *Tanfield Railway News* — 4 times/year

Locomotives

Name	No	Origin	Class	Type	Built
—	M2*	TGR	M	4-6-2	1951

*3ft 6in gauge, Tasmanian Government Railways (RSH 7630)

Industrial locomotives

Name	No	Builder	Type	Built
—	9	AEG (1565)	4w-4wE	1913
Gamma	—	Bagnall (2779)	0-6-0ST	1945
Horden	—	Barclay (1015)	0-6-0ST	1904
—	6	Barclay (1193)	0-4-2ST	1910
—	17	Barclay (1338)	0-6-0T	1913
—	32	Barclay (1659)	0-4-0ST	1920
—	3	E. Borrows (37)	0-4-0WT	1898
—	6	Fowler (4240010)	0-6-0DH	1960
Enterprise	—	R&W Hawthorn (2009)	0-4-0ST	1884
Cyclops	112	H/Leslie (2711)	0-4-0ST	1907
—	2	H/Leslie (2859)	0-4-0ST	1911
Stagshaw	—	H/Leslie (3513)	0-6-0ST	1923
—	3	H/Leslie (3575)	0-6-0ST	1923
—	13	H/Leslie (3732)	0-4-0ST	1928
—	3	H/Leslie (3746)	0-6-0F	1929
Irwell	—	H/Clarke (1672)	0-4-0ST	1937
—	38	H/Clarke (1823)	0-6-0T	1949
—	501	Hunslet (6612)	0-6-0DH	1965
—	4	Sentinel (9559)	0-4-0T	1953
Twizell†	3	Stephenson (2730)	0-6-0T	1891
—	L2	R/Hornsby (312989)	0-4-0DE	1952
—	35	R/Hornsby (418600)	0-4-0DE	1958
—	158	RSH (6980)	0-4-0DM	1940
Hendon	—	RSH (7007)	0-4-0CT	1940
—	62	RSH (7035)	0-6-0ST	1940
—	3	RSH (7078)	4w-4wE	1940
—	49	RSH (7098)	0-6-0ST	1943
Progress	—	RSH (7298)	0-6-0ST	1946
Cochrane	—	RSH (7409)	0-4-0ST	1948
—	44	RSH (7760)	0-6-0ST	1953
—	38	RSH (7763)	0-6-0ST	1954
—	21	RSH (7796)	0-4-0ST	1954
—	47	RSH (7800)	0-6-0ST	1954
—	1	RSH (7901)	0-4-0DM	1958
—	16	RSH (7944)	0-6-0ST	1957
FGF	—	Barclay (D592)	0-4-0DH	1969
—	2	A/Whitworth (D22)	0-4-0DE	1933
Escucha	11	B/Hawthorn (748)	0-4-0ST	1883
—	—	Clayton (133141)	4wBE	1984
—	—	Hunslet(7332	4wDM	1973
—	—	L/Blackstone (53162)	4wDM	1962
—	—	L/Blackstone (54781)	4wDM	1962
—	—	R/Harnsby (323587)	4wDM	1952
—	—	R/Hornsby (244487)	4wDM	1946
—	25	RSH (8201)	4wBE	1960
—	—	W/Rogers	4wBE	—

†on loan from Beamish
2ft gauge

99

Special notes: Families can alight at Causey station for 2 miles of walks through the picturesque Causey Woods; picnic facilities and toilet available in car park

Stock
19 4-wheel carriages; 3 6-wheel carriages; 1 6-wheel van; 14 hopper wagons; 9 contractors' bogies; 3 brake vans; 3 steam cranes; 8 covered wagons; 4 open wagons; 4 black wagons; 3 flat wagons

| Steam Centre | # Telford Horsehay Steam Trust | Shropshire |

Member: HRA

The railway is now extended northwards to Lawley Common, and southwards to 'Cheshire Cheese Field'. Excavation of Lawley Common cutting was begun by the Army before re-assignment, but will recommence soon

Location: Horsehay, Telford, Shropshire

OS reference: SJ 675073

Operating society/organisation: Telford Horsehay Steam Trust, The Old Loco Shed, Horsehay, Telford, Shropshire TF4 2LT

Web site: http://www.thad.demon.co.uk.tsr

On site facilities: Model railway, tearoom, picnic area, children's play equipment, narrow gauge steam tramway, miniature railway (separate charge); ticket gives unlimited travel (except miniature railway)

Public opening: Easter until last Sunday in September including Bank Holidays 11.00-16.00 (-17.00 on Bank Holiday weekends). Last Sundays in month usually steam-hauled, but steam tram every Sunday

Locomotives and diesel multiple-units

Name	No	Origin	Class	Type	Built
—	5619	GWR	5600	0-6-2T	1925
—	53531	BRCW	104	DMC	1957
—	53479	BRCW	104	DMBS	1957

Industrial locomotives

Name	No	Builder	Type	Built
—	MP1	Barclay (1944)	0-4-0F	1944
—	MP1	Bagnall (2461)	0-4-0ST	19--
Tom	27414	N/British (27414)	0-4-0DH	1954
Ironbridge No 3	—	Peckett (1990)	0-4-0ST	1940
—	9535	Sentinel (9535)	4wVBT	1952
—	D2959	R/Hornsby (382824)	4wDM	1955
—	—	R/Hornsby	0-4-0DH	1968
—	—	R/Hornsby	0-4-0DE	1959
—	—	R/Hornsby	0-4-0DE	1969
Thomas	—*	Kierstead	4wVBT	1979
—	—	Sentinel	0-4-0DH	1968
—	—	Sentinel	0-4-0DH	1969

*2ft gauge

Stock
1 ex-BR Mk 1 coach; 1 ex-GWR auto-trailer; 1 ex-GWR Toad brake van; 1 ex-GWR 3-ton hand crane; 1 Wickham trolley; various wagons

| Museum | # Vintage Carriages Trust Museum | West Yorkshire |

Member: HRA, TT, AIM, ABTEM

A fascinating collection of elderly railway carriages and small locomotives, interestingly presented. Sit in a fully restored, prize winning 1876-built Manchester, Sheffield & Lincolnshire Railway carriage or relive the dark days of wartime travel in one of the three Metropolitan Railway carriages. Listen to the 'Travellers' Tales' and view the collection of railway posters and other items. Video presentation. The carriages and locomotives have appeared in over 30 cinema and television productions including *The Unknown Soldier*, *The Woman in White*, *The Secret Agent*, *The Railway Children* and *Fairy Tale — A True Story*.

Location: Vintage Carriages Trust Museum, Ingrow Station Yard, Halifax Road, Keighley, West Yorkshire BD22 8NJ. On the A629 road

Operations Manager: Michael Cope, Hon Secretary, VCT

Operating society/organisation: Vintage Carriages Trust (a Registered Charity No 510776)

Telephone: Keighley (01535) 680425 during opening hours, or (01535) 646472 when closed

Fax: (01535) 646472

Internet address: website:

http://www.neotek.demon.co.uk/vct/
The website includes a database on over 3,100 preserved carriages

Car park: Yes. Also coach parking at Ingrow station

Access by public transport: Northern Spirit through trains from Carlisle, Settle, Morecambe, Lancaster to Keighley (one mile). Fast and frequent Metro Train services from Bradford Forster Square, Leeds, Shipley, and Skipton to Keighley. Then either KWVR train to Ingrow West (adjacent) or buses 500, 502, 663, 664, 665, 696, 697 from Keighley bus station. Calderline bus 500 (limited winter service) from Hebden Bridge. Calderline bus 502 from Huddersfield and Halifax. Keighley & District buses 663, 664, 665 (Sunday only) from Bradford, via Bingley, Saltaire and Keighley rail and bus stations. Keighley & District buses 696 and 697 from Bradford via Thornton and Denholme. Numerous buses from Keighley bus station. Tel: (0113) 245 7676 for bus and Metro Train information

On site facilities: Transport relics shop specialising in out of print magazines, lamps and hardware. Soft drinks, ice cream and chocolate available. Toilets with full disabled access. A determined effort has been made to provide a museum which will interest the casual visitor who is not knowledgeable about railways

Public opening: Daily 11.30-17.00 (or dusk if earlier), openings outside these times can be arranged for groups

Facilities for disabled: The museum building is level with easy access for wheelchair users. A

Stock

Railway	BR or previous owner Number	Date type	built	Seats	Weight	Length
MS&LR	176	4-wheel 1st/2nd/3rd/ luggage	1876	34	12T	28ft 0in
ECJS	143	6-wheel 3rd brake	1888	40	14T	34ft 11in
MR	358	6-wheel 1st/3rd/ luggage	1886	32	15T	34ft 0in
Met	427	BS	1910	84	30T	54ft 0in
Met	465	S	1919	108	30T	54ft 0in
Met	509	F	1923	84	30T	54ft 0in
SR (SECR)	S3554S	BSK	1924	42	33T	65ft 3in
BR (SR)	S1469S	TSO	1951	64	32T	67ft 1in
GN	2856	Non vestibule composite, lav brake	1898	34	?	45ft 0in

(also two oil tank wagons: MR, c1890, and Esso, 1939)

Industrial locomotives

Name	No	Builder	Type	Built
Bellerophon	—	Haydock Foundry (C)	0-6-0WT	1874
Sir Berkeley	—	M/Wardle (1210)	0-6-0ST	1891
Lord Mayor	—	H/Clarke (402)	0-4-0ST	1893

stairlift has been provided to allow wheelchair users to view carriage interiors, and enter guards' brake areas, though naturally wheelchairs are too wide to enter individual passenger compartments. Toilets with full access for wheelchair users. Braille leaflet, guidebook and audio tape for loan during visit. Special facilities for visitors with hearing difficulties. Wheelchair available for loan.

Winner of the 1998 Adapt Museum Award for best practice in access for disabled and older people. Runners up for the 1998 Yorkshire Electricity/Yorkshire &

Humberside Museums Council Access Awards. Highly commended in the 1999 White Rose Tourist For All Awards

Special notes: Visitors are welcome to either browse in the shop or visit the museum. *Bellerophon* and *Sir Berkeley* are both operational and may be visiting a number of other railways during the year. Please telephone for details

Membership details: Membership Secretary, c/o above address

Marketing names: Vintage Carriages Trust or VCT

Wells & Walsingham Light Railway

Timetable Service

Norfolk

Member: HRA, TT

One man's railway, the life and love of retired naval commander, Roy Francis, this delightful line which is totally uncommercialised runs along the old Wells branch to Walsingham where the old station has been transformed into a Russian Orthodox Church by the addition of an onion-shaped dome

to its roof. A must if you find yourself nearby

Location: On A149, Stiffkey Road, Wells next the Sea, Norfolk

General Manager: Lt-Cdr R. W. Francis

Operating organisation: Wells & Walsingham Light Railway, Wells next the Sea, Norfolk NR23 1RB

Car park: Yes

Access by public transport: Eastern Counties buses

On site facilities: Souvenir shop, toilets and tea shop

Length of line: 4 miles, 10.25in gauge

Public opening: Daily from Good Friday to the end of October

Special notes: Journey may be commenced at either end. Believed to be the world's longest 10.25in gauge line. Built on the old Wells & Fakenham Railway trackbed. Old Swainsthorpe signalbox on site at Wells. Motive power is provided by a Garratt locomotive.

Life passes in the form of a gilt edged enamel medallion now available, please enquire for details **Membership details:** Membership Secretary, Wells & Walsingham Light Railway Support Group, c/o

above address
Membership journal: Newsletter — quarterly

Steam Centre | West Lancashire Light Railway | Lancashire

Location: Alty's Brickworks. Station Road, Hesketh Bank, Nr Preston, Lancashire PR4 6SP
OS reference: SD 448229
Operating society/organisation: The West Lancashire Light Railway Association, Secretary, 8 Croft Avenue, Orrell, Wigan, Lancs WN5 5TW
Telephone: (01772) 815881 Railway (24hr) or (01645) 622654 Secretary (evenings)
Internet address: *Web site:* http://www.djr12ecg.demon.co.uk/wllr/wllr. html
Car parks: On site
Access by public transport: Main line rail to Preston or Southport. Bus route 100 and 102, between Preston and Southport
On site facilities: Gift shop, light refreshments, picnic tables, 2ft gauge line
Public opening: Easter weekend (not Saturday); May Day Bank Holiday Sunday and Monday; Spring Bank Holiday. Every Sunday 2 April to last Sunday in October. Opening times 12.30-17.30
Special events: Friendly Engines Day — 2 April; Teddy Bear's Picnic — 14 May; Father's Day— 18 June; Family Fun Day — 2 July; Annual Gala Day — 13 August, Industrial Day — 1 October; Santa Specials — 16/17, 23 December

Industrial locomotives

Name	No	Builder	Type	Built
Clwyd	1	R/Hornsby (264251)	4wDM	1951
Tawd	2	R/Hornsby (222074)	4wDM	1943
Irish Mail	3	Hunslet (823)	0-4-0ST	1903
Bradfield	4	Hibberd (1777)	4wPM	1931
—	5	R/Hornsby (200478)	4wDM	1940
—	7	M/Rail (8992)	4wDM	1946
Pathfinder	8	H/Hunslet (4480)	4wDM	1953
Joffre	9	K/Stuart (2405)	0-6-0T	1915
—	10	Hibberd (2555)	4wDM	1946
—	16	R/Hornsby (202036)	4wDM	1941
—	19	Lister (10805)	4wPM	1939
—	20	Baguley (3002)	4wPM	1937
—	21	H/Hunslet (1963)	4wDM	1939
—	25	R/Hornsby (297054)	4wDM	1950
—	26	M/Rail (11223)	4wDM	1963
Mill Reef	27	M/Rail (7371)	4wDM	1939
—	30	M/Rail (11258)	4wDM	1964
Montalban	34	O&K (6641)	0-4-0WT	1913
Utrillas	35	O&K (2378)	0-4-0WT	1907
—	36	R/Hornsby (339105)	4wDM	1953
Jonathan	37	Hunslet (678)	0-4-0ST	1898
—	38	Hudswell (D750)	0-4-0DM	1949
—	39	Hibberd (3916)	4wDM	1959
—	40	R/Hornsby (381705)	4wDM	1959
—	41	Lister (29890)	4wPM	1946
—	42	Hunslet (8917)	4wDM	1980
—	43	Greenbat (1840)	4wBE	1942
Welsh Pony	44	Wingrove (640)	4wWE	1926
—	45	Chrzanow (3506)	0-6-0T+WT	1957
Stanhope	46	K/Stuart (2395)	0-4-2ST	1917

Stock
Toastrack coach built 1986 by WLLR
Semi-open coach built 1993 by WLLR
Brake van built 1987 by WLLR
Large collection of goods rolling stock

Timetable Service | West Somerset Railway | Somerset

Member: HRA, TT
Running for 20 miles, this is Britain's longest preserved railway and evokes all the atmosphere of a country railway from a more

Locomotives and multiple-units

Name	No	Origin	Class	Type	Built
—	53808*	S&DJR	7F	2-8-0	1925
—	3850	GWR	2884	2-8-0	1942
—	4160	GWR	5101	2-6-2T	1948

England

leisured age. The line is host to several societies and groups, and several stations have their own museum, such as the Somerset & Dorset Trust at Washford. There are some idyllic country stations in the Quantock Hills, and Dunster station serves as the model for Hornby Dublo's branch line station

Managing Director: Mark L. Smith

Headquarters: West Somerset Railway, The Railway Station, Minehead, Somerset

Telephone: Minehead (01643) 704996. Talking timetable: (01643) 707650

Internet address: Website: www.west-somerset-railway.co.uk E-mail: info@west-somerset-railway.co.uk

Main station: Minehead

Other public stations: Dunster, Blue Anchor, Washford, Watchet, Williton, Doniford Beach Halt, Stogumber, Crowcombe, Bishops Lydeard

OS reference: Minehead SS 975463, Williton ST 085416, Bishops Lydeard ST 164290

Car parks: Minehead, Williton, Bishops Lydeard. Some parking at all stations except Doniford Beach

Access by public transport: Nearest main line station, Taunton. Southern National Omnibus Co (01823) 272033

Refreshment facilities: Minehead, Bishops Lydeard (limited opening). Wine and Dine trains, contact (01984) 623873. Buffet car on most steam trains

Souvenir shops: Minehead, Bishops Lydeard

Museum: Somerset & Dorset Railway Museum Trust, Washford (open WSR operating days March-end October). GWR Museum at Blue Anchor (open Sundays & Bank Holidays WSR operating season)

Depots: Bishops Lydeard, Williton, Washford, Minehead

Length of line: 20 miles

Passenger trains: Steam and diesel trains to Bishops Lydeard

Period of public operation: 23-26, 30 March; daily April (EXCEPT 3, 7, 10, 14, 17); daily May (EXCEPT 5, 12, 15, 19, 22); daily June to 24 September; 26-28, 30 September; daily October (EXCEPT 2, 6, 9, 13, 16, 27, 30); 2/3, 9/10, 16/17, 22-24, 27-31 December; 1 January 2001

Name	No	Origin	Class	Type	Built
—	4561	GWR	4500	2-6-2T	1924
—	5193	GWR	5101	2-6-2T	1934
—	5542†	GWR	4575	2-6-2T	1928
—	6412	GWR	6400	0-6-0PT	1934
Dinmore Manor	7820	GWR	'Manor'	4-6-0	1950
Odney Manor	7828	GWR	'Manor'	4-6-0	1950
Braunton	34046	SR	WC	4-6-2	1946
Sir Keith Park	34053	SR	BB	4-6-2	1947
—	D2119	BR	03	0-6-0DM	1959
—	D2133	BR	03	0-6-0DM	1959
—	D2271	BR	04	0-6-0DM	1952
—	D3462	BR	08	0-6-0DE	1957
—	D9526	BR	14	0-6-0DH	1964
—	D9551	BR	14	0-6-0DH	1965
—	33048	BR	33	Bo-Bo	1961
—	D7017	BR	35	B-B	1962
—	D7018	BR	35	B-B	1964
—	D7523	BR	25	Bo-Bo	1963
Defiance	50149	BR	50	Co-Co	1967
Western Campaigner	D1010	BR	52	C-C	1962
—	50413	P/Royal	103	DMBS	1957
—	51663	BR	115	DMBS	1960
—	51852	BR	115	DMBS	1960
—	51887	BR	115	DMBS	1960
—	56097	M/Cam	101	DTC	1957
—	56169	P/Royal	103	DTCL	1957
—	59678	BR	115	TC	1960

†undergoing restoration at Bridgnorth, Severn Valley Railway
*undergoing restoration at Minehead

Industrial locomotives

Name	No	Builder	Type	Built
Isabel	—	H/Leslie (3437)	0-6-0ST	1919
Kilmersdon	—	Peckett (1788)	0-4-0ST	1929
—	24	Ruston (210479)	4wDM	1941
—	—	Ruston (183062)	4wDM	1937
—	57	Sentinel (10214)	0-6-0DM	1964
—	501	Brush/Bagnall (3066)	0-4-0DE	1954
—	512	Brush/Bagnall (3102)	0-4-0DE	1954

Stock
22 ex-BR Mk 1 coaches; 1 ex-BR Mk 2 coach; 2 ex-BR Restaurant cars; 1 ex-BR Sleeping Car; 3 ex-S&DJR 6-wheel coaches, 7 ex-GWR camping coaches; 1 ex-GWR Sleeping Coach; 1 ex-GWR 5-ton hand crane; more than 40 freight vehicles

Owners
53808, *Isabel, Kilmersdon* the Somerset & Dorset Museum Trust
D1010, D7017, D7018 & D9526 the Diesel and Electric Preservation Group
D2119, D3462 and D752 Dr John F. Kennedy
5542 the 5542 Fund
3850 and 7820 the Dinmore Manor Locomotive Ltd
4160 the 4160 Ltd
D2271 & D9551 the WSR plc

Special events: Steam Gala Weekend — 24-26 March; Teddy Bears' Picnic — 3/4 June; Bishop Lydeard 21st Anniversary Party — 10/11 June; Days Out with Thomas — 1/2 July; Vintage Rally at Bishops Lydeard — 5/6 August; Autumn Steam Weekend — 8-10 September; 60s Weekend — 23/24 September; Santa Specials — 2/3, 9/10, 16/17, 22-24 December

Facilities for disabled: Parking space level with entrance. No steps to shop or booking office, level access to toilets (disabled toilets at Bishops Lydeard and Minehead stations). Special saloon accommodates 14 wheelchairs and has disabled toilet. Advanced booking essential. Catering facilities can be reached without difficulties. Groups can be catered for.

Membership details: West Somerset Railway Association, The Railway Station, Bishops Lydeard, Taunton TA4 3BX

Membership journal: *WSR Journal* — quarterly

Museum	**Winchcombe Railway Museum**	Glos

One mile from Winchcombe station on the Gloucestershire Warwickshire railway, the diverse collection includes signalling equipment, lineside fixtures, horse-drawn road vehicles, tickets, lamps, etc. Indoor and outdoor displays set in half an acre of traditional Victorian Cotswold garden. Visitors are encouraged to touch and operate exhibits

Location: 23 Gloucester Street, Winchcombe, Gloucestershire
OS reference: SP 023283
Operating society/organisation: Winchcombe Railway Museum Association, 23 Gloucester Street, Winchcombe, Gloucestershire
Telephone: Winchcombe (01242) 620641
Car Park: On street at entrance
Access by public transport: Bus service from Cheltenham operated by Castleways Ltd

On site facilities: Relic, refreshments and souvenir shop
Public opening: Not advised, please contact for details
Facilities for disabled: Access to all parts except toilets
Special notes: Many visitor-operated exhibits, picnic area, pet animals

Scotland

Steam Centre	**Alford Valley Railway**	Aberdeenshire

The Alford Valley Railway operates from the restored station yard which once marked the terminus of the branch line linking the villages of upper Donside with Kintore Junction, thence to Aberdeen

Location: On A944, 25 miles west of Aberdeen, adjacent to Grampian Transport Museum
Headquarters: Alford Valley Railway Co Ltd, Alford Station, Alford, Aberdeenshire
Main station: Alford
Car park: On site
Length of line: 3km, 2ft gauge

Industrial locomotives

Name	No	Builder	Type	Built
Saccharine	—	Fowler (13355)	0-4-2T	1914
Hamewith	—	Lister (3198	4wDM	c1930
—	—	M/Rail (9215)	4wDM	1946
—	—	M/Rail (9381)	4wDM	1948
—	—	M/Rail (22129)	4wDM	1962
—	—	M/Rail (2221)	4wDM	1964
Aberdeen Corporation Gas Works	3*	A/Barclay (1889)	0-4-0ST	1926

*standard gauge

Rolling stock
Two 24-seat coaches, 50-seat coach, 24-seat ex-Aberdeen tramcar; various wagons

Museum: Grampian Transport Museum adjacent
Depot: Alford station
Period of public operation: Railway operates: April, May September — weekends only (13.00-17.00); June, July and August — daily 13.00-17.00. Trains depart at 30min intervals.

Seasonal tickets available. Alford Heritage Centre is open daily (10.00-17.00)
Special notes: Steam-operated on first Sunday of each month from April to September. Special bookings available, tel: (01975) 562811
Special events: Santa Specials;

please contact for details
Membership details: Membership Secretary, AVR Association, Creagmwor, Main Street, Alford, Aberdeenshire AB33 8AD

Almond Valley Heritage Trust

Museum   **West Lothian**

Member: HRA
Part of a wide ranging heritage centre containing a museum of Scotland's shale oil industry with award-winning children's exhibits, working watermill, farmsteading with traditional livestock. indoor play areas, countryside walks and farmhouse kitchen tearoom.
Operating society/organisation: Almond Valley Heritage Centre, Millfield, Livingston Village, West Lothian EH54 7AR.
OS reference: NT 034667
Telephone: (01506) 414957
Fax: (01506) 497771
Internet address: e-mail: almondheritage@cableinet.co.uk
Access by public transport: Main line trains to Livingston North (1-mile), or SMT D27 bus from Edinburgh
On site facilities: Children's exhibits, indoor play areas, tearoom

Industrial locomotives

Name	No	Builder	Type	Built
05/576	—	Barclay (557)	4wDH	1970
Oil Company No 2	—	Baldwin (20587)	4wDE	1902
—	20	Brook Victor (612)	4wBE	1972
—	38	Brook Victor (698)	4wBE	1972
—	42	Brook Victor (700)	4wBE	1972
—	—	Brook Victor (1143)	4wBE	1972
3585	13	Greenwood (1698)	4wDE	1940
ND3059	Yard No B10	Hunslet (2270)	0-4-0DM	1940
—	7330	Hunslet (7330)	4wDM	1973
—	—	Simplex (40SPF522)	4wDM	1981

Note
Barclay 557 and Hunslet 2270 operate passenger services

Public opening: Daily (except 25/26 December, 1/2 January) 10.00-17.00.
Trains operate weekends from March-September, daily July and August and certain public holidays

Length of line: 500m 2ft 6in gauge line from Livingston Mill to Almondhauge stations, with plans to extend
Facilities for disabled: Full disabled access

Bo'ness & Kinneil Railway

Timetable Service   **West Lothian**

Member: HRA, TT, Registered Museum
Historic railway buildings, including the station and train shed, have been relocated from sites all over Scotland. In a purpose-built exhibition hall, the Scottish Railway Exhibition tells the story of the development of the railways in Scotland, and their impact on the people. The rich geology of the area, with its 300-million-year old fossils, is explained during a

Locomotives

Name	No	Origin	Class	Type	Built
Sovereign	44871	LMS	5MT	4-6-0	1945
—	419	CR	439	0-4-4T	1908
Morayshire	246	LNER	D49	4-4-0	1928
Glen Douglas	256	NBR	D34	4-4-0	1913
—	42	NBR	Y9	0-4-0ST	1887
Maude	673	NBR	J36	0-6-0	1891
—	80105	BR	4MT	2-6-4T	1955
—	08443 (D3558)	BR	08	0-6-0DE	1958
—	14901 (D9524)	BR	14	0-6-0DH	1964
—	D8020	BR	20	Bo-Bo	1959
—	25235 (D7585)	BR	25	Bo-Bo	1965

conducted tour of the caverns of the former Birkhill Fireclay Mine

Operating society/location: Scottish Railway Preservation Society, Bo'ness Station, Union Street, Bo'ness, West Lothian, EH51 9AQ

Access by public transport: Nearest ScotRail station — Linlithgow. Bus services from Linlithgow, Falkirk, Stirling, Edinburgh and Glasgow

OS reference: NT 003817

Telephone: Bo'ness (01506) 822298

Main station: Bo'ness

Other station: Birkhill

Car parks: At Bo'ness and Birkhill (free)

Refreshment facilities: Extensive (unlicensed) buffet at Bo'ness. Picnic tables at both stations

Souvenir shop: Bo'ness

Depot: Bo'ness

Length of line: 3.5 miles

Period of public operation: Weekends April-October, daily (except Mondays) 1 July-27 August

Special events: Easter Egg Specials — 21-24 April; Day Out with Thomas — 20-22 May, 12/13 August; Vintage Vehicle Rally — 18 June; Diesel Gala Weekend — 2/3 September; Santa Specials — weekends 2-24 December. Black Bun Specials — 30/31 December

Facilities for disabled: Disabled access to platform and a specially adapted carriage for wheelchair users. Toilets at Bo'ness station

Special notes: The S&T Department were winners of the 1998 Westinghouse Signalling Award in the Ian Allan Railway Heritage Awards. Achieved full museum registration in 1999

Name	No	Origin	Class	Type	Built
—	26004 (D5303)	BR	26	B0-Bo	1958
—	26024 (D5323)	BR	26	Bo-Bo	1959
—	27001 (D5347)	BR	27	Bo-Bo	1961
—	D5351	BR	27	Bo-Bo	1961
—	47643	BR	47	Co-Co	1968
Rodney	50021	BR	50	Co-Co	1968

Industrial locomotives

Name	No	Builder	Type	Built
Clydesmill	3	Barclay (1937)	0-4-0ST	1928
—	3	Barclay (2046)	0-4-0ST	1937
—	24	Barclay (2335)	0-6-0T	1953
Texaco	—†	Fowler (4210140)	0-4-0DM	1958
(Lord King)	—	H/Leslie (3640)	0-4-0ST	1926
—	19	Hunslet (3818)	0-6-0ST	1954
DS3	—	R/Hornsby (275883)	4wDM	1949
DS4	P6687	R/Hornsby (312984)	0-4-0DE	1951
(Ranald)	—	Sentinel (9627)	4wVBT	1957
—	970214	Wickham (6050)	2w-2PMR	c1951
—	—	Matisa (48626)	—	—
—	5	Hunslet (3837)	0-6-0ST	1955
—	(7)	Bagnall (2777)	0-6-0ST	1945
Borrowstounness	—*	Barclay (840)	0-4-0T	1899
—	—*	M/Rail (110U082)	4wDH	1970
—	—	Wickham (10482)	2w-2PMR	1970
—	(17)	Hunslet (2880)	0-6-0ST	1943
—	970213	Wickham (6049)	2w-2PMR	c1951
—	17†	Barclay (2296)	0-4-0ST	1952
Lady Victoria	3	Barclay (1458)	0-6-0ST	1916
The Wemyss Coal Co Ltd	20	Barclay (2068)	0-6-0T	1939
—	(6)	Barclay (2127)	0-4-0CT	1942
No 1	—	Barclay (343)	0-6-0DM	1941
City of Aberdeen	—	B/Hawthorn (912)	0-4-0ST	1887
F82 (Fairfield)	—	E/Electric (1131) (244)	4wBE	1940
Kelton Fell	13	Neilson (2203)	0-4-0ST	1876
Lord Roberts	1	N/Reid (5710)	0-6-0T	1902
(Tiger)	—	N/British (27415)	0-4-0DH	1954
Kilbagie	DS2	R/Hornsby (262998)	4wDM	1949
—	—	R/Hornsby (321733)	4wDM	1952
DS6	(1)	R/Hornsby (421439)	0-4-0DE	1958
St Mirren	(3)	R/Hornsby (423658)	0-4-0DE	1958
—	D88/003	R/Hornsby (506500)	4wDM	1965
(Denis)	—	Sentinel (9631)	4wVBT	1958
—	—	Arrols (Glasgow)	2w-2DM	c1966

*3ft 0in gauge
†at present off-site at Lathalmond Bus Museum

Stock
A large selection of coaching stock, many built by Scottish pre-Grouping companies, ex-BR Class 126 DMU, and an appropriate collection of early freight vehicles

Owners
80105 and (Denis) owned by Scottish Locomotive Owners Group
246 and 24 owned by Royal Museum of Scotland
256 the Glasgow Museum of Transport
44871 the Sovereign Preservation Group
27001 the Class 27 Preservation Group
26004 and 26024 the 6LDA Group

Caledonian Railway (Brechin)

Member: HRA

This Scottish country steam railway is a classic branch line starting at the Strathmore line junction station of Bridge of Dun. Last stomping ground of the Gresley 'A4' Pacific locomotives and climbs up some steep gradients through some scenic farmland with assorted wildlife. The summit is reached at the Edzell & Forfar junction just short of Brechin station, itself one of the most impressive of Britain's preserved railways.

The National Trust for Scotland property House of Dun, built by William Adam in 1730 is approximately 1-mile from Bridge of Dun station, which is also close to the Montrose Basin, a tidal wildlife centre. Brechin itself has many attractions including the cathedral and round tower and the new Pictavia centre

The railway is run entirely by volunteer members of the Brechin Railway Preservation Society which celebrates its 21st anniversary this year.

Headquarters: Caledonian Railway (Brechin) Ltd, The Station, 2 Park Road, Brechin, Angus DD9 7AF

Telephone: (01334) 655965 after 4.30pm Mon-Fri or (01674) 810318

Talking timetable: (01356) 622992

Information enquiries: Mrs Ena Wilkie, 248 High Street, Laurencekirk, Kincardineshire AB30 1BP. Tel: (01356) 622992

Main stations: Brechin and Bridge of Dun

OS reference: NO 603603

Car parks: Brechin, Bridge of Dun

Access by car: Via A90 Dundee/Aberdeen to Brechin bypass. Brown tourist signs to stations. Free parking

Access by public transport: By ScotRail, GNER and Virgin services to Montrose (5 miles). By bus from Montrose, Strathtay Scottish — Dundee (01382) 228054/227201

Refreshment facilities: Light refreshments at Brechin on operating days

Locomotives and multiple-units

Name	No	Origin	Class	Type	Built
Brechin City	D3059	BR	08	0-6-0DE	1954
—	25083	BR	25	Bo-Bo	1963
—	D5314	BR	26	Bo-Bo	1959
—	26035	BR	26	Bo-Bo	1959
—	27024	BR	27	Bo-Bo	1962
Mrs Slocombe	51993	BR	107	DMBS	1960
Mr Humphries	52012	BR	107	DMCL	1960

Industrial locomotives

Name	No	Builder	Type	Built
Patricia	68189	Peckett (1376)	0-4-0ST	1915
—	1	Barclay (1863)	0-4-0ST	1926
Menelaus	—	Peckett (1883)	0-6-0ST	1935
Dewar Highlander	—	R/Hornsby (458957)	4wDM	1961

Service stock
1 ex-BR Mk 2A BFK, 2 ex-BR Mk 2 TSO, 1 ex-BR Mk 1 SO, 1 ex-BR Mk 1 BFK, 2 ex-BR Mk 1 TSO

Stock under restoration
1 ex-BR Mk 1 BSO, stored — 2 ex-BR Mk 1 TSO, 1 ex-BR Mk 1 RK

Engineer's stock
1 ex-BR diesel-electric crane, 2 Dogfish, 1 Mermaid, 4 warflats, 3 rectanks, 1 Ferry van, 2 Lowmacs, 2 minfit, 1 21-ton minfit, 2 LNER vans, 2 LMS vans, 2 demountable tank wagons, 1 ex-BR bolster

Dapartmental stock
1 LMS GUV, 1 CR origin electrification coach, 1 ex-BR BCK, various vans

Locomotives expected in service during 2000
13059, D5314, 27024, 26035, No 1, DMU and *Dewar Highlander*

Locomotives under restoration
Menelaus, 25083 (to re-enter service in 2000)

Owners
No 1 and *Menelaus* the Angus Railway Steam Engineers
68189 private
D5314 the Class Twenty Six Preservation Group
13059, 26035 and 27024 the Caledonian Diesel Group
51993 and 52012 the DMU Group

Picnic area: Bridge of Dun
Souvenir shop: Brechin
Museum: Brechin
Length of line: 4 miles 22 chains
Depot: Brechin
Passenger trains: Industrial steam and heritage diesel-hauled trains between Brechin and Bridge of Dun
Period of public operation: SAE to above address. Generally Sundays from end of May until beginning of September

Special events: Easter Sunday Specials — Easter Sunday, Father's Day, Teddy Bears' Picnic, December Santa Specials. Please call for special event details, approx one a month
Facilities for disabled: Ramp access to both stations. Vehicular access to Brechin platforms by prior arrangement. Wheelchair ramp on most trains
Family tickets: Available
Disclaimer: The Caledonian

Railway (Brechin) Ltd reserves the right to amend, cancel or add to these events. And whilst every effort will be made to maintain the above services, the company does not guarantee that trains will depart or arrive at the time stated and reserves the right to suspend or alter any train without notice and will not accept any liability for loss, inconvenience or delay thereby caused

Membership details: Murray Duncan, 2 Binghill Crescent, Milltimber, Aberdeen AB13 0HP. Tel: (01224) 861963
Membership journal: Quarterly
Marketing name: The Friendly Line

Glasgow Museum of Transport

Museum   Glasgow

Glasgow's magnificent railway collection represents one of the best efforts by a municipal authority to preserve a representative collection of items appropriate to the 'locomotive builders of the Empire'. In 1989 the collection opened to view once again in its new setting at the former Kelvin Hall

Access by public transport: Strathclyde PTE Underground. Kelvinhall: Strathclyde Buses 6, 6A, 8, 8A, 9, 9A, 16, 42, 42A, 44A, 57, 57A, 62, 62A, 62B, 64; Kelvin Scottish Buses 5, 5A; Clydeside Scottish Buses 17

Operating society/organisation: Glasgow City Council, Dept of Cultural & Leisure Services
Location: Museum of Transport, Kelvin Hall, 1 Bunhouse Road, Glasgow G3 8DP
Telephone: (0141) 287 2623 or (0141) 287 2721
Fax: (0141) 287 2692

Locomotives

Name	No	Origin	Class	Type	Built
—	123	CR	123	4-2-2	1886
—	9	G&SWR	5	0-6-0T	1917
—	103	HR	—	4-6-0	1894
Gordon Highlander	49	GNSR	F	4-4-0	1920

Industrial locomotives

Name	No	Builder	Type	Built
—	1	Barclay (1571)	0-6-0F	1917
—	—	Chaplin (2368)	0-4-0TG	1888
—	—	BEV (583)	B	1927

Stock
Glasgow District Subway car 39T; Glasgow Corporation Underground cars 1 and 4; LMS King George VI's saloon 498 of 1941

Car park: Opposite Museum entrance
On site facilities: Toilets, cafeteria, shop and public telephone, cloaking facility
Public opening: Monday-Thursday 10.00-17.00; Friday and Sunday 11.00-17.00. Closed 1/2 January and 25/26 December only. Please check before travelling
Facilities for disabled: Both single-sex and uni-sex disabled facilities now available. A passenger lift to allow disabled access at the front entrance is now in operation

Leadhills & Wanlockhead Railway

Steam Centre   Lanarkshire

Member: HRA
Situated in the Lowther Hills between Abington and Sanquhar, the society was formed in 1983 to construct and operate a 2ft gauge tourist railway between the villages of Leadhills and Wanlockhead. The track now extends to the old county boundary between Lanarkshire and Dumfriesshire. The highest adhesion worked railway in Great Britain at 1,498ft above sea level. Signalbox under construction, with a variety of pre-Grouping signalling & telegraph equipment (eg North

British Railway lever frame and Caledonian Railway lattice post signal.

Operating society/organisation: Leadhills & Wanlockhead Railway c/o Douglas Boyd, The Saltings, Battlehill, Annan DG12 6SN

Main station: Leadhills

Access by public transport: ScotRail trains stop at Sanquhar on Nith Valley Line (approx 10 miles) every 1hr 30min-2 hours. Bus service (Western Scottish Stagecoach) to Leadhills (please check for times). Nearest motorway — M74 — J14 from south/J15 from north. From A76 take B797 to Leadhills

Length of line: 1-mile

Journey time: Approx 40min

On site facilities: Shop, ticket office, small museum and picnic tables. Extensive country walks.

Industrial locomotives

Name	No	Builder	Type	Built
—	—	O&K	0-4-0T	1913
The Gulliver	1	Fowler (18892)	4wDM	1931
Elvan	2	M/Rail (9792)	4wDM	1955
Luce	4	R/Hornsby (7002/0467/2)	4wDM	1966
Little Clyde	5	R/Hornsby (7002/0467/6)	4wDM	1966
Clyde	6	Hunslet (6347)	4wDH	1975
Nith	7	H/Clarke (DM1002)	0-4-0DMF	1956

Rolling stock

2 air-braked passenger coaches and guard's van built at Leadhills. 1 air-braked coach chassis built by Talyllyn Railway, with the L&WR completing the bodywork, assorted permanent way wagons

Also on 'Southern Uplands Way'. Scottish Lead Mining Museum at Wanlockhead (1-mile)

Period of public operation: Easter weekend; weekends May-October. Saturdays 12.00-17.00, Sundays 11.00-17.00. Schools and private charters by prior arrangement

Special events: Steam Fair weekend (usually late July/early August)

Membership details: c/o above address

Society journal: Quarterly

Timetable Service	**Mull Rail**	Isle of Mull

Member: HRA, TT

Commercial Manager: Graham E. Ellis

Operations Manager: D. Moseley

Operating society/organisation: Mull & West Highland (NG) Railway Co Ltd, Old Pier Station, Craignure, Isle of Mull PA65 6AY

Telephone: (01680) 812494

Fax: (01680) 300595

OS reference: NM 725369

Car park: At Craignure, free

Access by public transport: Caledonian MacBrayne ferry from Oban (40min sail)

On site facilities: Gift shop, car park (free)

Family ticket: Available (2 adults & 2 children under 14)

Length of line: 1.25 miles/10.25in gauge

Public opening: Easter week, to mid-October

Facilities for disabled: No steps on railway, two compartments for wheelchairs

Membership details: Friends of Mull Rail, David Crombie, 1 Mulberry Drive, Dunfermline, Fife KY11 5BZ. Tel: (01383) 728652

Locomotives

Name	No	Builder	Type	Built
Lady of the Isles	—	Marsh	2-6-4T	1981
Waverley	—	Curwen	4-4-2	1948
—	—	Alcock	4w-4PM	1973
Glen Auldyn	—	Davies	8wDH	1986
—	—	Mouse Boiler Works, Sheffield	8wDH	2000
Victoria*	—	Vere	2-6-2T	1993

*Largest tank engine built for 10.25in gauge

Rolling stock

12 coaches (two with wheelchair accommodation); 3 bogie wagons; 1 4-wheel wagon

Owners

Waverley — The Waverley Group

Membership journal: Crankpin Journal — annual

Special notes: First island passenger railway in Scotland, runs to Torosay Castle and 12 acres of gardens, superb panoramic views of mountains and sea. Joint discounted sail/rail tickets only from Caledonian MacBrayne, Oban. Group discount available for 20+ pre-booked passengers. Special trains can be chartered within and outside timetable hours. Ride the Railway by the Mull Experience and visit Torosay and Duart Castles, Tel: (01680) 812309 for details. The Waverley Groups are willing to consider special charters for groups not exceeding 30, contact Roger Nicholas, Merlin, Craignure, Isle of Mull PA65 6AY (tel: 01680 812400)

Paddle Steamer Preservation Society

Member: HRA, TT, Heritage Afloat
Paddle steamers: *Waverley* & *Kingswear Castle*. Pleasure cruise ship: *Balmoral*
The paddle steamer *Waverley* was built for the London & North Eastern Railway in 1946, and replaced a vessel of the same name which was sunk off Dunkirk during May 1940. Sold to the PSPS — a Registered Charity — in 1974, *Waverley* sails on day trips and afternoon cruises from ports and piers in most coastal areas and river estuaries of the United Kingdom,

from Easter until October each year. Also in the 'fleet' is the traditional motor cruiser *Balmoral* and the river paddle steamer *Kingswear Castle* which sails from Chatham Historic Dockyard on the River Medway
Commercial Director: Ellie Newlands
Operations Director: Ian McMillan
Headquarters: Waverley Excursions Ltd, Waverley Terminal, Anderston Quay, Glasgow G3 8HA
On ship facilities: Self service

restaurants, bars, toilets (disabled toilets on *Waverley*)
Membership details: Paddle Steamer Preservation Society, PO Box 385, Hazlemere, High Wycombe HP11 1AE
Membership journal: *Paddlewheels* — quarterly. Details of the full programme of cruises operated by the three ships can be obtained from the National Booking Office, Waverley Excursions Ltd, Waverley Terminal, Anderston Quay, Glasgow G3 8HA.
Tel: (0141) 221 8152.

Prestongrange Industrial Heritage Museum

Location: On the B1348 between Musselburgh and Prestonpans.
OS reference: NT 734737
Operating society/organisation: East Lothian Museum Service, Library & Museum Headquarters, Dunbar Road, Haddington, East Lothian EH41 3PJ
Telephone: (0131) 653 2904 (Prestongrange Visitor Centre), (01620) 828203 (Museum Service)
Car park: On site
On site facilities: Once part of the Scottish Mining Museum, Prestongrange is being developed as a museum which tells the story of people and industries in East Lothian — local coal deposits encouraged the growth of numerous other industries such as pottery, pipe making, soap, glycerine, brewing and weaving
Visitor centre: Changing exhibitions of local industries. Displays of local art and crafts — one-off events, demonstrations, workshops. Cornish beam engine, installed 1874 to pump water from the mine. Colliery locomotives restored by Prestongrange Railway

Industrial locomotives

Name	No	Builder	Type	Built
—	6	A/Barclay (2043)	0-4-0ST	1937
—	17	A/Barclay (2219)	0-4-0ST	1946
Prestongrange	7	G/Ritchie (536)	0-4-2ST	1914
Tomatin	1	M/Rail (9925)	4wDM	1963
—	—*	Hunslet (4440)	4wDM	1952
—	32	R/Hornsby (458960)	4wDM	1962
George Edwards	33	R/Hornsby (221647)	4wDM	1943
—	—	E/Electric (D908)	4wDM	1964

*2ft gauge

Rolling stock
Steam crane, Whittaker No 30, c1890, occasionally in steam

Society are housed here
Toilets: Visitor Centre
Refreshment facilities: Available at Visitor Centre
Public opening: April to October, 11.00-16.00, last tour at 15.00
Length of line: 400m (standard gauge), extension in progress
Facilities for disabled: Access and toilet at Visitor Centre. Access to powerhouse exhibition, and footpaths along the site
Special events: Steam days are held on the first Sunday of each

month April to October and the last Sunday in October, also third Sunday of July and August. Passenger rides available. Advanced notice for larger parties
Membership details: Friends of Prestongrange. Contact Peter Gray, Museums Officer — c/o operating organisation
Contact: For Prestongrange Railway Society — Colin Boyd, 3 Stuart Wynd, Craigmount View, Edinburgh EH2 8XU

Member: HRA, TT, AIM

The Scottish Industrial Railway Centre is based on part of the former Dalmellington Iron Co railway system which was one of the best known industrial railway networks in Britain. Steam worked up until 1978 when the system closed and it is the aim of the centre to re-create part of the railway. The Ayrshire Railway Preservation Group also owns the former G&SWR station at Waterside, 2 miles from the Centre, and has access to the former NCB locomotive shed and wagon workshops at Waterside. These locations are not yet open to the general public. Working in conjunction with the Dalmellington & District Conservation Trust it is hoped to create an industrial heritage centre at Waterside based on the iron, coal and brickmaking industries. A passenger train service may operate between the two stations on certain Sundays

Location: Scottish Industrial Railway Centre, Minnivey Colliery, Dalmellington, Ayrshire

OS reference: NS 476074

Operating society/organisation: Ayrshire Railway Preservation Group

Telephone: Doon Valley Heritage Office (01292) 531144. The Secretary (01292) 313579 (evenings & weekends)

Length of line: Half mile

Access by public transport: Nearest rail station, Ayr (14 miles). Stagecoach bus service from Ayr. Tel: (01292) 263382

On site facilities: Steam-hauled brake van rides (over half-mile section). Guided tours of centre, museum of railway relics and photographs, souvenir shop, buffet, locomotive shed, narrow gauge demonstration line

Public opening: Open for static display, with limited facilities, every Saturday from the beginning

Locomotives

Name	No	Origin	Class	Type	Built
—	MP228 (12052)	BR	11	0-6-0DE	1949
—	MP229 (12093)	BR	11	0-6-0DE	1951

Industrial locomotives

Name	No	Builder	Type	Built
—	16	A/Barclay (1116)	0-4-0ST	1910
—	8	A/Barclay (1296)	0-6-0T	1912
—	19	A/Barclay (1614)	0-4-0ST	1918
—	8	A/Barclay (1952)	0-4-0F	1928
Harlaxton	—	A/Barclay (2107)	0-6-0ST	1941
—	10	A/Barclay (2244)	0-4-0ST	1947
NCB No 23	—	A/Barclay (2260)	0-4-0ST	1949
—	25	A/Barclay (2358)	0-6-0ST	1954
—	1	A/Barclay (2368)	0-4-0ST	1955
—	118	A/Barclay (366)	0-4-0DM	1940
—	7	A/Barclay (399)	0-4-0DM	1956
Lily of the Valley	—	Fowler (22888)	0-4-0DM	1943
Tees Storage	—	N/British (27644)	0-4-0DH	1959
—	—	R/Hornsby (224352)	4wDM	1943
Blinkin Bess	—	R/Hornsby (284839)	4wDM	1950
Johnnie Walker	—	R/Hornsby (417890)	4wDM	1959
—	—	R/Hornsby (421697)	0-4-0DM	1959
—	107	Hunslet (3132)	0-4-0DM	1944
—	—	Sentinel (10012)	4wDM	1959
—	—	Donnelli (163)	4wDMR	1979

3ft gauge

—	—	R/Hornsby (256273)	4wDM	1949
—	—	Hunslet (8816)	4wDH	1981

2ft 6in gauge

—	2	R/Hornsby (183749)	4wDM	1937
—	3	R/Hornsby (210959)	4wDM	1941
—	1	R/Hornsby (211681)	4wDM	1942

Note: Not all vehicles on public display

Stock

1 BR Mk 1 TSO, 1 BR Mk 1 BSK, 2 Wickham trolleys; 1 steam crane; various other items

of June to the end of September

Special events: Steam days (with at least one engine in steam) will be held on: 30 April, 28 May, 25 June, 2, 9, 16, 23, 30 July, 6, 13, 20, 27 August, 3 September. Open times 11.00-16.30

Membership details: Mr Frank Beattie, 1 McKnight Avenue, Waterside, Fenwick, Kilmarnock, Ayrshire

Special notes: For further information and details of special events, telephone the Doon Valley Heritage Office (01292) 531144 daytime, (01292) 313579 evenings and weekends, or write to Gordon Thomson, 8 Burnside Place, Troon, Ayrshire KA10 6LZ

Strathspey Railway

Member: HRA, TT

Scotland's steam railway in the Highlands connects the busy tourist resort at Aviemore to the more traditional highland village of Boat of Garten, famed as one of the few nesting places of the osprey (viewing site 3 miles from station). The bridge at Bridge of Garten has been replaced and the four miles of track between Bridge of Garten and Broomhill has been laid. A great deal of work still needs to be done but, subject to labour and finance being available, the railway would like to open to Broomhill for Easter 2001

Commercial Manager: Laurence Grant

Enquiries: Aviemore Station, Dalfaber Road, Aviemore, Inverness-shire PH22 1PY (SAE for copy of timetable brochure)

Telephone: (01479) 810725.

Main station: Aviemore. The railway occupies one platform at the main line Aviemore station

Other public station: Boat of Garten

OS reference: Aviemore NH 898131, Boat of Garten NH 943789

Car parks: Aviemore (Strathspey Railway side of station (off Dalfaber Road) for railway customers only and at Boat of Garten

Access by public transport: ScotRail services and express bus to Aviemore. Local service to Boat of Garten

Refreshment facilities: On-train buffet car or facilities on many trains. Picnic tables at Boat of Garten (for use of ticket purchasers). No refreshment facilities on DMU services

Souvenir shop: Boat of Garten and Aviemore

Museum: Small relics display at Boat of Garten. Extension progress display at Aviemore

Depot: Aviemore (not open to public) sidings at both stations are not open to the public

Length of line: 5.5 miles

Journey time: 19min, return within the hour possible on most

Locomotives and multiple-units

Name	No	Origin	Class	Type	Built
—	5025	LMS	5MT	4-6-0	1934
—	46512	LMS	2MT	2-6-0	1952
—	828	CR	812	0-6-0	1899
—	08490	BR	08	0-6-0DE	1958
—	D5302	BR	26	Bo-Bo	1958
—	26025	BR	26	Bo-Bo	1959
—	D5394	BR	27	Bo-Bo	1962
—	51990	BR	107	DMBS	1960
—	52008	BR	107	DMBS	1960
—	52030	BR	107	DMC	1960
—	54047	BR	114	DTC	1960

Industrial locomotives

Name	No	Builder	Type	Built
—	48	Hunslet (2864)	0-6-0ST	1943
Cairngorm	9	RSH (7097)	0-6-0ST	1943
—	60	Hunslet (3686)	0-6-0ST	1948
Niddrie	6	Barclay (1833)	0-6-0ST	1924
Forth*	10	Barclay (1890)	0-4-0ST	1926
Balmenach	2	Barclay (2020)	0-4-0ST	1936
	17	Barclay (2017)	0-6-0T	1935
Inveresk	14	R/Hornsby (260756)	0-4-0DM	1950
Inverdon	15	Simplex (5763)	4wDM	1957
—	16	North British (27549)	0-4-0DM	1951
Queen Anne	20	R/Hornsby (265618)	4wDM	1948

*not on site

Locomotive notes: In service 9, 828, 08490, D5302, 54047 & 52008. Under restoration 60, 46512 (possibly in traffic late 2000)

Stock

18 ex-BR coaches; 4 ex-LMS coaches; 1 Pullman coach; 3 ex-LMS sleeping cars; 1 ex-LNER sleeping car; 1 ex-HR coach; 1 ex-NBR coach; 1 ex-GNSR coach; Numerous examples of rolling stock

Owners

6, 17 and 46512 the Highland Locomotive Co Ltd
828 the Scottish Locomotive Preservation Trust Fund
D5302 and 26025 the Highland Diesel Locomotive Co Ltd

services

Passenger trains: Steam-hauled services. Boat of Garten-Aviemore. DMU on most Saturdays in March, April, May, June, September and October

Period of public operation: 22/23, 25/26, 29/30 March; 1/2, 5/6, 8/9, 12/13, 15/16, 19-27, 29/30 April; 1, 3/4, 6/7, 10/11, 13/14, 17/18, 20/21, 24/25 May; Daily 27 May-30 September; 1, 4/5, 7/8, 11/12, 15, 18/19, 21/22, 25/26, 28/29 October; 16/17, 23/24, 26, 31 December; 1/2 January 2001.

DMU service on all Saturdays from 25 March to 28 October (except 22, 29 April, 27 May, Saturdays in July and August, 2 September and 21, 28 October when a steam branch line service [1 engine and 1 or 2 carriages] will operate)

Special events: Day Out with Thomas — 29/30 April, 1 May, 2/3 September; Enthusiasts' Day — 27/28 May (27th mainly diesel, 28th mainly steam).

Facilities for disabled: Access possible at Boat of Garten and

Aviemore. Please contact in advance for directions and if a party involved

Special notes: First and third class travel available on most trains. Family fares available for third class travel. Special rates/arrangements for parties. Luncheon on the train — Wednesdays in July and August. Bicycles carried free — groups must give prior notice (bicycles must not be ridden on platforms or pedestrian pathways)

Membership details: Strathspey Railway Association at above address
Membership journal: *Strathspey Express* — quarterly

Museum — Summerlee Heritage Park — Lanarkshire

Social and industrial history museum, interprets the communities in the west of Scotland in the 19th and 20th centuries. Working machinery in reconstructed workshops; miners' rows, reconstructed coal mine, art gallery, working tramway
Manager: Jim McCann
Operating society/organisation: Summerlee Heritage Park, Heritage Way, Coatbridge, ML5 1QD (operated by North Lanarkshire Council)
Telephone: (01236) 431261
Fax: (01236) 440429
Public opening: Daily 10.00-17.00, except 25/26 December and 1/2 January. Park closes at 16.00 between November and March
Access by public transport: STP electric service from Glasgow Queen Street Low Level to Coatbridge Sunnyside (Airdrie/Drumgelloch line). Or

Locomotives

Name	No	Origin	Class	Type	Built
Springbok	4112	SAR	GMAM	4-8-2+2-8-4	1956

(3ft 6in gauge/built by North British Loco Co)

Industrial locomotives

Name	No	Builder	Type	Built
—	—	Barclay (472)	0-4-0DH	1966
—	—	H/Clarke (895)	0-6-0T	1909
—	—	G/Hogg	0-4-0T	1898
Robin	—	Sentinel (9628)	4wTG	1957

Stock
2 rail-mounted steam cranes

from Glasgow Central via Motherwell to Coatbridge Central. Trains also run from Cumbernauld to Coatbridge Central, but not on Sundays
Car park: Opposite site
On site facilities: Tearoom (summer only), gift shop. Working electric tramway with cars from Motherwell, Düsseldorf, Brussels and Graz; underground mine tour and miners' cottages
Special events: Organised events from April-October, details on request
Facilities for disabled: Toilets, wheelchair available

Wales

Timetable Service — Bala Lake Railway (Rheilffordd Llyn Tegid) — Gwynedd

Member: HRA, TT
This delightful narrow gauge railway follows the route of the former Bala-Dolgellau Railway, along the shore of Wales' largest natural lake. The railway's headquarters are to be found in the fine old station building at Llanuwchllyn at the south-western end of the line. Do not be deterred by the fact that the railway runs down the opposite shore of the lake to the main road — it is well worth the detour
General Manager: Roy Hardiman
Headquarters: Rheilffordd Llyn Tegid (Bala Lake Railway) Llanuwchllyn, Bala, Gwynedd LL23 7DD
Telephone: Llanuwchllyn (01678) 540666
Main station: Llanuwchllyn
Other public stations: Llangower, Bala. Request halts at Pentrepiod and Bryn Hynod
OS reference: Llanuwchllyn SH 880300, Bala SH 929350
Car parks: Llanuwchllyn, Llangower and Bala town centre
Access by public transport: Bus Gwynedd service No 94 to both Bala and Llanuwchllyn (from Wrexham or Barmouth)

Road access: Off the A494 Bala-Dolgellau road
Refreshment facilities: Llanuwchllyn. Large picnic site with toilet facilities by lake at Llangower
Souvenir shop: Llanuwchllyn
Depot: Llanuwchllyn
Length of line: 4.5 miles, 1ft 11.625in gauge
Passenger trains: Llanuwchllyn-Bala. Journey takes 25min in each direction
Period of public operation: 15 April-1 October
Facilities for disabled: Facilities available on most trains
Special notes: Small parties (10/12) may just turn up, but a day's notice required for larger groups
Family tickets: Available for all round trip journeys
Membership details: Membership Secretary, c/o Llanuwchllyn Station

Industrial locomotives

Name	No	Builder	Type	Built
Holy War	3	Hunslet (779)	0-4-0ST	1902
Maid Marian	5	Hunslet (822)	0-4-0ST	1903
Triassic	—	Peckett (1270)	0-6-0ST	1911
Meirionydd	11	Severn Lamb (7322)	Bo-Bo	1973
Chilmark	12	R/Hornsby (194771)	4wDM	1939
Bob Davies	—	YEC (L125)	4wDM	1994
Indian Runner	—	R/Hornsby (200744)	4wDM	1940
—	—	Lister (34025)	4wDM	1949
—	—	Motorail (5821)	4wDM	1934
—	—	R/Hornsby (189972)	4wDM	1938
—	—	Hibberd (FH2544)	4wDM	1941
—	—	Hunslet (1974)	4wDM	1939
Cernyw	—	R/Hornsby (200748)	4wDM	1940
Lady Madcap	—	R/Hornsby (283512)	4wDM	1949

Locomotive notes: *Holy War* and *Maid Marian* are in regular use, remainder are on static display.
Triassic is currently away on loan

Membership journal:
Llanuwchllyn Express — approx 4 times a year

Brecon Mountain Railway
Timetable Service
Merthyr Tydfil

A narrow gauge passenger-carrying railway close to Merthyr Tydfil built on part of the trackbed of the former Brecon & Merthyr Railway. Gradually being extended northward, the railway has some interesting narrow gauge steam locomotives imported from East and West Germany and South Africa.
General Manager: A. J. Hills
Headquarters: Brecon Mountain Railway, Pant Station, Dowlais, Merthyr Tydfil CF48 2UP
Telephone: Merthyr Tydfil (01685) 722988
Fax: (01685) 384854
Main station: Pant
Car park: Pant station
OS reference: SO 063120
Access by public transport: Bus to Pant Cemetery — half hour frequency from Merthyr bus station. BR rail service to Merthyr from Cardiff Central
Depot: Pant
Length of line: 3.5 miles, 1ft 11.75in gauge

Locomotives

Name	No	Builder	Type	Built
—	2	Baldwin (61269)	4-6-2	1930
Sybil	—	Hunslet (827)	0-4-0ST	1903
Graf Schwerin-Löwitz	—	Arn Jung (1261)	0-6-2WT	1908
Pendyffryn	—	de Winton	0-4-0VBT	1894
Redstone	—	Redstone	0-4-0VBT	1905
Rhydychen	—	Simplex (11177)	4wDM	1961
—	77	Hanomag (10629)	2-6-2+2-6-2	1928
—	—	Brecon MR (001)	0-6-0DH	1987

Stock
Two balcony-end 39-seat coaches; 2 balcony-end 40-seat coaches; 1 19-seat Caboose; miscellaneous rail-carrying and ballast wagons; Wickham petrol trolley

Period of public operation: Daily 1 April-29 October. EXCEPT for: 3-7, 10-14, 17-20 April; 5, 8, 12, 15, 19, 22 and 26 May; 15, 18, 22, 25 and 29 September; 2, 6, 9, 13, 16, 20, 25 and 27 October
Refreshment facilities: Cafés at Pant and Pontsticill
Special events: Santa Specials — December

Facilities for disabled: Facilities for disabled include ramps, toilets and carriage designed to carry wheelchairs
Special notes: There is no road access to Pontsticill

Museum | Corris Railway Museum | Gwynedd

Member: HRA

In the heart of Wales' 'narrow gauge country', the Corris Railway Museum, situated in the remaining buildings of Corris station, displays relics and photographs of mid-Wales' first public narrow gauge railway

Location: In Corris village off A487 trunk road. Turn opposite Braichgoch Hotel, five miles north of Machynlleth and 11 miles south of Dolgellau

OS reference: SH 755078

Operating society: The Corris Railway Society, Corris Station Yard, Gwynedd (postal address: Corris, Machynlleth, Powys SY20 9SH)

Telephone: (01654) 761303

Internet address: *E-mail:* alfo@corris.co.uk

Car park: Adjacent

Access by public transport: Central Trains services to Machynlleth. Bus Gwynedd services 2 (Aberystwyth-Dolgellau-Machynlleth), 30 (Machynlleth-Tywyn) and 34 (Machynlleth-Aberllefenni); Dyfi Valley service 530 (Tywyn-Machynlleth-Abergynolwyn)

Catering facilities: Snacks, teas and light refreshments

Locomotives

Name	No	Builder	Type	Built
Alan Meaden	5	M/rail (22258)	4wDM	1965
—	6	R/Hornsby (51849)	4wDM	1966
—	7	Winson	0-4-2ST	19—
—	8	Hunslet	4wDM	—

Locomotive notes: 5 and 6 operational on works trains. 7 under construction at Winson Engineering, based on Corris No 4 (now Talyllyn No 4) *Edward Thomas*. 8 undergoing restoration off-site

Stock

Two carriages, brake van, 17 works wagons and 5 historic wagons

Owners

8 on loan from the National Mining Museum

On site facilities: Souvenir shop, toilets and children's playground; close to Corris Craft Centre and King Arthur's Labyrinth; two miles from Centre for Alternative Technology

Length of line: Three-quarter-mile, 2ft 3in gauge track between Corris and Maespoeth has been reinstated, and, subject to legal process, passenger services will recommence during 2000. Planning permission for a further two miles of track has been granted

Public opening: Easter, May Day and Spring Bank Holidays, June-September. Half term week in October, other times by prior arrangement. Times as advertised locally. Please write for full details

Special events: Model Railway Exhibition, Machynlleth — 26-28 August

Facilities for disabled: Access to display area of Museum and shop

Internet address: http//www.apricot.co.uk/hosts/corris/corris.htm

Membership details: Membership Secretary, c/o above address

Timetable Service | Fairbourne Railway | Gwynedd

Member: Britain's Great Little Railways

Since 1986 this railway has been regauged from 15in to 12.25in and has been transformed by the introduction of new locomotives and rolling stock, a tunnel through the sand dunes, signalboxes, new workshops and a café overlooking the Mawddach estuary. Under new ownership since April 1995, there has been a big investment in the rolling stock maintenance so that all four steam locomotives are now

Locomotives

Name	No	Builder	Type	Built
Beddgelert	—	Curwen	0-6-4ST	1979
Yeo	—	Curwen	2-6-2T	1978
Sherpa	—	Milner	0-4-0STT	1978
*Russell**	—	Milner	2-6-4T	1985
Lilian Walter†	—	FLW	A1-1AD	1985
Gwril	—	FLW	4wBE	1987

FLW — Fairbourne Locomotive Works

*built as replica of Leek & Manifold *Elaine*, rebuilt to present form 1985 at FLW

†originally buit by G&S Engineering in 1961 as 15in gauge *Sylvia*. Rebuilt at Fairbourne in 1985

in service. During the main season a two-train service is in operation. A new indoor nature attraction is open at Fairbourne terminus
Headquarters: North Wales Coast Light Railway Co Ltd, Fairbourne & Barmouth Steam Railway, Beach Road, Fairbourne, Gwynedd LL38 2PZ
Telephone: (01341) 250362
Fax: (01341) 250240
Internet address: *e-mail:* enquiries@fairbourne-railway.co.uk
Main station: Gorsaf Newydd (Fairbourne)
Other public stations: Gorsafawddachaidraigodanhed-dogleddollonpenrhynareudraeth-ceredigion, Porth Penrhyn (Barmouth Ferry Station)
OS reference: SH 616128
Car parks: Gorsaf Newydd
Access by public transport: Fairbourne railway station. Bus Gwynedd service (No 28)

Stock
12.25in gauge — 18 coaches (1st, 2nd class); 15 freight

Note: The railway offers a range of driver experience courses (when no public trains are running). Please write for details

Refreshment facilities: Porth Penrhyn cafe, tea shop on platform at Gorsaf Newydd (Fairbourne)
Souvenir shop: Gorsaf Newydd (Fairbourne)
Depot: Fairbourne
Length of line: 2.5 miles, 12.25in gauge
Passenger trains: A 2.5-mile journey connecting with ferry at Porth Penrhyn to Barmouth. 20min single journey. Through tickets to Barmouth (including ferry) available
Period of public operation: Daily service 12 April to 24 September and 21-29 October. Santa Specials operate 16/17 December
Special events: Spring Steam Gala

— 29 April to 1 May; Day Out with Thomas — 31 May to 3 June and 17-20 August; Kite Festival — 17/18 June; Craft Festival — 30/31 July; Ride Lifeboat along the line at Penrhyn Point — 2 August; Summer Steam Gala — 26-28 August; Santa Specials — 11/12 December
Membership details: Fairbourne Railway Supporters' Association, contact Hon Sec at above address
Special notes: During inclement weather the service may be restricted or cancelled. Extra trains and special parties by arrangement with the manager

Timetable Service	Ffestiniog Railway	Gwynedd

Member: HRA
In many ways, evocative of the early Swiss mountain railways as it climbs high above Porthmadog with some breathtaking views, the railway still operates an interesting variety of locomotives including some unusual Victorian survivors. Passengers have replaced slate as the principal traffic over this former quarry line
General Manager: Alan Heywood
Headquarters: Ffestiniog Railway Co, Harbour Station, Porthmadog, Gwynedd, LL49 9NF
Telephone: Porthmadog (01766) 512340
Web site: http://www.festrail.co.uk
Main stations: Porthmadog Harbour, Blaenau Ffestiniog
Other public stations: Boston Lodge, Minffordd, Penrhyn, Plas Halt, Tan-y-Bwlch, Dduallt, Tanygrisiau
OS reference: SH 571384
Car parks: Porthmadog, Tan-y-Bwlch, Tanygrisiau, Blaenau Ffestiniog
Access by public transport:

Locomotives

Name	No	Builder	Type	Built
Princess	1	G/England (199/200)	0-4-0STT	1863
Prince	2	G/England	0-4-0STT	1863
Palmerston	4	G/England	0-4-0STT	1863
Welsh Pony	5	G/England (234)	0-4-0STT	1867
Earl of Merioneth	—	FR	0-4-4-0T	1979
Merddin Emrys	10	FR	0-4-4-0T	1879
David Lloyd George	12	FR	0-4-4-0T	1992
Taliesin	—	FR	0-4-4T	1999
Moelwyn	—	Baldwin (49604)	2-4-0DM	1918
Blanche	—	Hunslet (589)	2-4-0STT	1893
Linda	—	Hunslet (590)	2-4-0STT	1893
Britomart*	—	Hunslet (707)	0-4-0ST	1899
Mountaineer	—	Alco (57156)	2-6-2T	1917
Livingston Thompson†	3	FR	0-4-4-0T	1886
Harlech Castle	—	Baguley-Drewry (3767)	0-6-0-DH	1983
Ashover	—	Hibberd (3307)	4wDM	1948
Conway Castle	—	Hibberd (3831)	4wDM	1958
Moel Hebog	—	Hunslet (4113)	0-4-0DM	1955
Mary Ann	—	M/Rail (596)	4wDM	1917
Criccieth Castle	—	FR	0-6-0DH	1995
Monarch*	—	Bagnall (3024)	0-4-4-0T	1953
The Colonel	—	M/Rail (8788)	4wDM	1943
Diana	—	M/Rail (21579)	4wDM	1957
Stefcomatic	—	Matisa (48589)	2-2-0DH	1956
Vale of Ffestiniog	—	Funkey	Bo-Bo	1968

*privately owned
†on loan to National Railway Museum

Minffordd and Blaenau Ffestiniog main line stations. Porthmadog, Minffordd and Blaenau Ffestiniog served by local buses
Refreshment facilities: Licensed restaurant at Porthmadog, cafe at Tan-y-Bwlch (summer only), refreshments also on most trains
Souvenir shops: Porthmadog, Tan-y-Bwlch (summer only), Blaenau Ffestiniog
Museum: Porthmadog
Depot: Boston Lodge
Length of line: 13.5 miles, 1ft 11.5in gauge
Passenger trains: Porthmadog-

Stock
32 bogie coaches; 6 4-wheel coaches; 3 brake vans, plus numerous service vehicles

Blaenau Ffestiniog
Period of public operation: Daily late March-early November, limited winter service
Special events: A Day out with Thomas — 29 April-1 May. Santa Specials — 9/10, 16/17 December. Please phone to confirm all special event dates and for further details
Facilities for disabled: Porthmadog and Blaenau Ffestiniog

easily accessible for wheelchairs. Facilities on trains for disabled in wheelchairs by prior arrangement
Special notes: Reduced return rates available for off-peak services
Membership details: Ffestiniog Railway Society (see above address)
Membership journal: *Ffestiniog Railway Magazine* — quarterly

---

Timetable Service | **Great Orme Tramway** | **Conwy**

Member: HRA
A cable-hauled street tramway to the summit of the Great Orme is operated as two sections involving a change half-way. Opened in July 1903, it involves gradients as steep as 1 in 3.9
Location: Great Orme Tramway, Victoria Station, Church Walks, Llandudno
OS reference: SH 7781
Operating society/organisation:

Contract Services, Maesdu, Llandudno LL30 1HF
Telephone: Llandudno (01492) 574237
Car park: Approximately 100yd from Lower Terminal or adjacent to Summit Terminal
Access by public transport: Good
On site facilities: Shop
Period of public operation: April to end of October (daily) 10.00-18.00 (17.00 October). Can be

subject to change
Special notes: The only remaining cable-hauled street tramway in Britain. 1-mile long, rising to 650ft (3ft 6in gauge)
Stock: 4 tramcars each seating 48, built 1902/3
Family tickets: Available, along with joint tickets for Great Orme Mine — Bronze Age Heritage Centre

---

Timetable Service | **Gwili Railway (Rheilffordd Gwili)** | **Carmarthenshire**

Member: HRA, TT
Runs alongside the River Gwili on part of the former Carmarthen-Aberystwyth line. Attractions include a fully restored signalbox and historic station building. Extension towards Cynwyl Elfed in progress. A 7.25in gauge miniature railway operates at Llwyfan Cerrig.
Headquarters: Gwili Railway Co Ltd, Bronwydd Arms Station, Bronwydd Arms, Carmarthen, SA33 6HT
Telephone: Carmarthen (01267) 230666
OS reference: Bronwydd Arms SN 417239
Llwyfan Cerrig SN 405258
Main station: Bronwydd Arms

Locomotives

Name	No	Origin	Class	Type	Built
—†	12061	BR	11	0-6-0DE	1949
—**	D2178	BR	03	0-6-0DM	1962

Industrial locomotives

Name	No	Builder	Type	Built
—	1	H/Clarke (1885)	0-6-0ST	1955
Idris	—	R/Hornsby (207103)	4wDM	1941
Trecatty	—	R/Hornsby (421702)	0-6-0DM	1959
Olwen	—	RSH (7058)	0-4-0ST	1942
Welsh Guardsman	71516	RSH (7170)	0-6-0ST	1944
Nellie	02101	YEC(2779)	0-4-0DE	1960
Rosyth No 1•	—	A/Barclay (1385)	0-4-0ST	1914
Victory••	—	A/Barclay (2201)	0-4-0ST	1945
Sir John†	—	Avonside (1680)	0-6-0ST	1914
—†	3	H/Clarke (D1246)	0-4-0DM	1961
Gunby	—	Hunslet (2413)	0-6-0ST	1941
Swansea Vale No 1*	—	Sentinel (9622)	4wVBTG	1958
Swansea Jack*	—	R/Hornsby (393302)	4wDM	1955

Other public station: Llwyfan Cerrig (Danycoed section to be opened during 2000 season)
Car park: Bronwydd Arms (free) (not 20-23 April when park & ride from Carmarthen must be used)
Access by public transport: Carmarthen railway station, then First Cymru services Nos 441, 460, 461
Refreshment facilities: Bronwydd Arms, Llwyfan Cerrig (picnic site). Bar on train
Souvenir shop: Bronwydd Arms
Depot: Llwyfan Cerrig, stock also kept at Bronwydd Arms and Cynwyl
Length of line: 2 miles
Passenger trains: Bronwydd Arms-Llwyfan Cerrig, approximately 1¼ hour service
Period of public operation: 20-23, 29/30 April; 1, 7, 14, 21, 28-31 May; 1/2, 4, 7, 11, 14, 18, 21, 25, 28 June; 2, 5, 9, 12, 16, 19, 22-31 July; Daily — August; 3, 10, 17, 24 September; 22, 25/26 October; 9/10, 16/17, 20-24 December
Public opening: Trains leave Bronwydd Arms at 11.15, 12.30, 14.00, 15.15 and 16.30 on most operating days. A more frequent service operates in December

Name	No	Builder	Type	Built
Dylan Thomas*	—	N/British (27654)	0-4-0DH	1956
Folly	—	R/Hornsby (183062)	4wDM	1937
—	114	N/British (27878)	0-4-0DH	1962
—	21	H/Leslie (3931)	0-6-0ST	1938
Haulwen†*	—	V/Foundry (5272)	0-6-0ST	1945

Stock
8 ex-BR Mk 1 coaches; 1 ex-BR griddle car; 1 ex-BR Mk 3 sleeper; 1 ex-TVR coach (built 1891); Coles diesel rail crane; 1 Booth diesel-hydraulic crane; 2 ex-GWR Mink vans; 2 ex-GWR Fruit D; 1 ex-GWR Crocodile; 1 GWR Bloater; 2 ex-GWR Loriot D; 3 GWR Toad brake vans; 2 GWR bogie bolster wagons; 1 SECR Parcels Van; 2 SR Parcels vans; 1 SR bogie parcel van; 1 LMS 20-ton brake van; 1 LNER open wagon; 5 LNER vans; 2 Army vans; 6 BR open wagons; 2 BP tank wagons; 2 tar tankers; 3 open wagons

Owners
*The Railway Club of Wales
** Caerphilly Railway Society
†Vale of Neath Railway Society
†*National Museum of Wales Industrial & Maritime Museum in care of Caerphilly Railway Society

Facilities for disabled: access to stations and trains
Special events: Friends of Thomas the Tank Weekend — 20-23 April; Teddy Bear Specials — 11 June. Santa Specials — 9/10, 16/17, 20-24 December, details: Booking Officer, Bronwydd Arms Station, Carmarthen SA33 6HT (Tel: [01267] 230666)
Special notes: Family tickets available except for Friends of Thomas and Santa Special events. Trains may be hired for special events, tour parties, birthdays, etc

---

(Timetable Service) **Llanberis Lake Railway (Rheilffordd Llyn Padarn)** (Gwynedd)

Member: HRA
A narrow gauge passenger-carrying railway starting at the historic Dinorwic Quarry workshops (now part of the National Museum of Wales) and running along the shores of Llanberis Lake using the trackbed of the former slate railway line to Port Dinorwic. Excellent views of Snowdonia and good picnic spots along the line
General Manager:
Mr B. Yarborough
Headquarters: Llanberis Lake Railway, Gilfach Ddu, Llanberis, Gwynedd LL55 4TY
Telephone: Llanberis (01286) 870549
Internet address: *E-mail:* llr@lake-railway.freeserve.co.uk
Web site: www.lake-railway.freeserve.co.uk

Industrial locomotives

Name	No	Builder	Type	Built
Elidir	1	Hunslet (493)	0-4-0ST	1889
Thomas Bach/Wild Aster	2	Hunslet (849)	0-4-0ST	1904
Dolbadarn	3	Hunslet (1430)	0-4-0ST	1922
—	7	R/Hornsby (441427)	4wDM	1961
Twll Coed	8	R/Hornsby (268878)	4wDM	1956
—	—	R/Hornsby (425796)	4wDM	1958
Garrett	11	R/Hornsby (198286)	4wDM	1939
—	18	M/Rail (7927)	4wDM	1941
Llanelli	19	R/Hornsby (451901)	4wDM	1961
Una*	—	Hunslet (873)	0-4-0ST	1905

*Not part of the railway's motive power stock. Housed at the adjacent slate museum and can sometimes be seen working demonstration freight trains

Stock
13 bogie coaches; 20 wagons

Main station: Llanberis (Padarn station/Gilfachddu)
Other public stations: Cei Llydan
OS reference: SH 586603
Car park: Llanberis (Padarn station)
Refreshment facilities: Padarn station

Souvenir shop: Padarn station
Length of line: 2 miles, 1ft 11.5in gauge
Passenger trains: Llanberis-Penllyn-Llanberis
Journey time: 40min round trip
Period of public operation: Mondays to Thursdays in March and October. Mondays to Fridays in April. Sundays to Fridays, May through September. Saturdays July and August. Family tickets available, under 5s free
Facilities for disabled: Level approaches throughout shop, café and to train. Special toilet facilities provided. Specially adapted carriage for wheelchair users
Marketing names: Rheilffordd Llyn Padarn Cyfyngedig (Padarn Lake Railway Ltd); Llanberis Lake Railway

---

Llangollen Railway

Member: HRA, TT

The line, which is presently 7.5 miles long, is the only operational preserved standard gauge line in North Wales. Situated in the Dee Valley, it follows the course of the River Dee for much of its route, and affords good views of the dramatic Welsh countryside between Llangollen and Carrog. It is the eventual aim to reach Corwen, some 10 miles from Llangollen, where a new terminus will be built. The most recent extension to Carrog opened on 2 May 1996. The railway was the winner of the Ian Allan Independent Railway of the Year Award in 1996. There are many pleasant walks beginning and ending at the railway's stations. Picnic facilities are available at all stations and camping can be arranged at Carrog station

Location: Llangollen station, A542 from Ruthin, A539 from Ruabon, A5 from Shrewsbury/Betws-y-coed

Commercial Manager: Mr C. Keyse

Operating organisation: Llangollen Railway plc

Supporting organisation: Llangollen Railway Trust Ltd, The Station, Abbey Road, Llangollen, Denbighshire LL20 8SN (both organisations)

Telephone: Talking timetable (24hr): Llangollen (01978) 860951. Other enquiries: (01978) 860979 (office hours only). Llangollen Railway Trust Ltd (24hr answerphone) (01978) 861143

Main station: Llangollen

Other stations: Berwyn, Deeside

Locomotives and multiple-units

Name	No	Origin	Class	Type	Built
—	2859	GWR	2800	2-8-0	1918
—	4141	GWR	4101	2-6-2T	1946
—	5199	GWR	5101	2-6-2T	1934
—	5532	GWR	4575	2-6-2T	1928
—	6430	GWR	6400'	0-6-0PT	1937
—	7754	GWR	5700	0-6-0PT	1930
Foxcote Manor	7822	GWR	'Manor'	4-6-0	1950
—	7298	LMS	3F	0-6-0T	1924
Magpie	44806	LMS	5MT	4-6-0	1944
*Scots Guardsman**	46115	LMS	'Royal Scot'	4-6-0	1927
—	5197	USATC	S160	2-8-0	1942
—	80072	BR	4MT	2-6-4T	1954
—	2162	BR	03	0-6-0DM	1960
—	D3265	BR	08	0-6-0DE	1956
—	D8142	BR	20	Bo-Bo	1966
—	D7629	BR	25	Bo-Bo	1965
Chirk Castle	25313	BR	25	Bo-Bo	1966
—	46010	BR	46	1Co-Co1	1961
—	47449	BR	47	Co-Co	1962
—	50454	BRCW	104	DMBS	1957
—	50528	BRCW	104	DMC	1957
—	51618	BR	127	DMBS	1959
—	51907	BR	108	DMBS	1960
—	53447	BRCW	104	DMBS	1957
—	53454	BRCW	104	DMBS	1958
—	54456	Cravens	105	DMBS	1958
—	54490	BR	108	DTC	1960
—	50416†	Wickham	108	MBS	1958

†undergoing restoration at the Midland Railway Centre, Butterley
D7629 on loan to Northampton & Lamport Railway
*arrival from Birmingham Railway Museum still to be confirmed

Industrial locomotives

Name	No	Builder	Type	Built
Jessie	—	Hunslet (1873)	0-6-0ST	1937
*Darfield No 1**	—	Hunslet (3783)	0-6-0ST	1953
Eliseg	—	Fowler (22753)	0-4-0DM	1939
Richboro†	—	H/Clarke (1243)	0-6-0T	1917
Austin No 1	—	Kitson (5459)	0-6-0ST	1932
—	14	H/Clarke (D1012)	0-4-0DM	1956
Pilkington	1	YEC/BTH	0-4-0D	c1950

*undergoing overhaul at Bury
†on display at the Dr Who Exhibition at Lower Dee Mill, Llangollen

Halt (by request), Glyndyfrdwy, Carrog

OS reference: SJ 214422

Car park: Llangollen (Market St) and Mill St (Lower Dee Mill), also at Carrog station on B5437 off the A5 west of Llangollen

Access by public transport: Nearest station: Ruabon (approx 2hrly Central Trains service), then Bryn Melyn bus (Wrexham-Llangollen) half-hourly Monday-Saturday (at 26 and 56min past the hour at Ruabon station); or Arriva 94 Wrexham-Barmouth service (6 a day). For bus times call Wrexham Bus Enquiries: (01978) 266166

Refreshment facilities: Llangollen, Berwyn*, Glyndyfrdwy* and Carrog (*weekends only)

Souvenir shop: Llangollen

Length of line: 7.5 miles

Passenger trains: Llangollen-Carrog

Period of public operation: Most weekends throughout the year plus school holidays, including half term. Daily services 2 May-end of October

Special events: Cambrian Coast Weekend — 1/2 April, Day Out with Thomas — 29/30 July; Vintage Military Weekend — 29/30 April; Spring Steam Gala — 20/21 May; Transport Extravaganza — 16/17 September; Day Out with Thomas — 23/24, 30/31 October; Santa Specials — 2/3, 9/10, 16/17, 21-24 December;

Stock: *coaches* — 17 BR Mk 1 coaches; 5 BR Mk 1 sleepers (3 ex-'Queen of Scots'); 1 BR BG (converted to generator van); 1 BR Mk 3 sleeper; 4 GWR coaches; 1 LNER Thompson saloon coach

Stock: *wagons* — 4 wagons; 1 Bolster wagon; 1 LNWR tool van; 3 GWR brake vans; 1 GWR Mink D wagon; 1 SR 'BY' parcels van; 3 tank wagons; 1 LNER parcels van; 2 BR Fruit vans; 1 ex-LNWR brake van; 1 Matisa track tamper; 1 BR ballast wagon; 1 Coles diesel/electric 5-ton crane; 1 BR generator van; 1 LMS guard's van; 1 GWR Siphon G coach; 1 LMS box van; 1 GWR Mink A van; 1 BR Presflow bulk cement wagon; 1 BR CCT; 2 LMS Sole ballast wagons, 1 BR Shark ballast plough, 1 chemicals tanker

Stock: *maintenance* — ARD96718 45-ton Cowans breakdown crane, 1 Matisa Track Recording Machine; 1 BR Bridge/Viaduct Inspection Unit, Unimog road-rail vehicle, Permaquip Permaclipper, 1 Trackmaster Light Shunting Vehicle

Owners
2859 and 5532 the Llangollen Railway GW Locomotive Group
5199 the 5199 Project
7822 the Foxcote Manor Society
7754 and *Austin No 1* the Llangollen Railway Trust Ltd
80072 the 80072 Steam Locomotive Co Ltd
46115 the 46115 (Scots Guardsman) Steam Locomotive Trust Ltd
2162 the Wirral Borough Council

Mince Pie Specials — 26-31 December

Special notes: The 'Berwyn Belle' operates midday Sunday and Saturday evening dining train, tel: (01978) 860583 for details. Driver experience courses are offered on both diesel and steam locomotives. Party rates available for groups of more than 10

Facilities for disabled: Special passenger coach for wheelchairs. During 2000 extensive restoration

work is expected to be undertaken at Llangollen and Berwyn stations, subject to access to Lottery funds and the granting of a new lease. Access to shop at Llangollen. Toilets available at Glyndyfrdwy and Carrog stations. Advance notice required for special coach

Membership details: Mr Graham Hoyland, Llangollen Railway Trust Ltd, c/o above address

Membership journal: *Steam at Llangollen* — quarterly

Museum | Penrhyn Castle Industrial Railway Museum | Aberconwy

Member: HRA

A collection of historic industrial steam locomotives, both standard and narrow gauge, displayed in Penrhyn Castle, a well-known National Trust property in the area regularly open to visitors

Location: Llandegai, near Bangor. One mile east of Bangor on the A5

OS reference: SH 603720

Operating society/organisation: National Trust, Penrhyn Castle, Industrial Railway Museum, Llandegai, Nr Bangor LL57 4HN

Telephone: Bangor (01248) 353084

Industrial locomotives

Name	No	Builder	Type	Built
Kettering Furnaces No 3	—	B/Hawthorn (859)	0-4-0ST	1885*
Watkin	—	de Winton	0-4-0VBT	1893*
Fire Queen	—	Horlock	0-4-0	1848†
Hawarden	—	H/Clarke (526)	0-4-0ST	1899
Vesta	—	H/Clarke (1223)	0-6-0T	1916
Charles	—	Hunslet (283)	0-4-0ST	1882§
Hugh Napier	—	Hunslet (855)	0-4-0ST	1904§
—	1	Neilson (1561)	0-4-0WT	1870
Haydock	—	Stephenson (2309)	0-6-0T	1879
Acorn	—	R/Hornsby (327904)	0-4-0DM	1948

*3ft gauge
†4ft gauge
§1ft 10.75in gauge

Car park: Within castle grounds
Access by public transport: By rail: Bangor (3 miles). Bus: Crosville Cymru 5, Purple 6/7 and D&E 65/6
On site facilities: The castle is open to the public and contains a gift shop. Light refreshments are available
Public opening: Daily 22 March-4 November (except Tuesdays), 11.00-17.00 (last admission 30min

Stock
10 narrow gauge rolling stock exhibits from the Padarn/Penrhyn system. The small relics section includes a comprehensive display of railway signs and model locomotives in the upper stable block

before closing)
Facilities for disabled: Access to castle and museum
Special notes: For those interested in stately homes the castle is well worth a visit. The entrance fee

covers both the castle and the railway exhibits housed in the castle courtyard. *Acorn* can be seen operating on some occasions during opening times

---

Steam Centre	Pontypool & Blaenavon Railway	Torfaen

Member: HRA
The historic Blaenavon site, complete with its railway installations and locomotives, can easily be included in a visit to Big Pit Mining Museum
Location: Just off the B4248 between Blaenavon and Brynmawr. Signposted as you approach Blaenavon
OS reference: SO 237093
Operating society/organisation: Pontypool & Blaenavon Railway Co (1983) Ltd, Council Offices, High Street, Blaenavon NP4 9PT
Telephone/Fax: (01495) 792263
Car park: Adjacent to railway terminus
On site facilities: Light refreshments and souvenir shop
Public opening: Sundays Easter-end of September, and Bank Holiday Mondays. Plus first Saturday in May, June, July and August
Special events: Friends of Thomas the Tank Engine, Santa Special. Please contact for details
Special notes: The railway incorporates the former mineral/LNWR passenger lines running through Big Pit. Both north and southward extensions are being considered. Service currently operates between Furnace Sidings platform and Whistle Inn platform. The railway runs near to the Garn Lakes — ideal for picnics after a train ride
Membership details: c/o above address, or phone (01873) 857539

Locomotives

Name	No	Origin	Class	Type	Built
—	2874	GWR	2800	2-8-0	1918
—	3855	GWR	2884	2-8-0	1942
—	4253	GWR	4200	2-8-0T	1917
—	5668	GWR	5600	0-6-2T	1926
Bickmarsh Hall	5967	GWR	'Hall'	4-6-0	1937
—	9629	GWR	5700	0-6-0PT	1946
Renown	50029	BR	50	Co-Co	1968
Repulse	50030	BR	50	Co-Co	1968
Eagle	50043	BR	50	Co-Co	1968
—	51074	GRCW	119	DMBC	1958
—	51104	GRCW	119	DMS	1958
—	51942	BR	108	DMCL	1960
—	52044	BR	108	DMCL	1960
—	54270	BR	108	DTCL	1960
—	53632	BR	108	DMCL	1960

Industrial locomotives

Name	No	Builder	Type	Built
Nora	5	Barclay (1680)	0-4-0ST	1920
Harry	—	Barclay (1823)	0-4-0ST	1926
—	8	RSH (7139)	0-6-0ST	1944
Llanwern	104	E/Electric (D1249)	0-6-0DH	1968
—	106	E/Electric (D1226)	0-6-0DH	1971
—	1	Fowler (22497)	0-6-0DM	1938
—	—	Hunslet (5511)	0-6-0DM	1960
Ebbw Vale	170	Hunslet (7063)	0-8-0DH	1971
—	10083	R/Royce (10083)	0-4-0DH	1961

Stock
7 ex-BR Mk 1 coaches, 5 ex-GWR coaches, 2 ex-LSWR coaches, 36 other vans, china clay, coke and tank wagons

Owners
50029 and 50030 Operation Collingwood

Rheilffordd Eryri — Welsh Highland Railway (Caernarfon)

The Welsh Highland Light Railway Ltd has been incorporated to reconstruct much of the original WHR line. The new northern terminus is at Caernarfon, with re-opening to Porthmadog in stages over the next 10 years.

General Manager: Alan Heywood
Headquarters: Ffestiniog Railway Co, Harbour Station, Porthmadog LL49 9NF
Telephone: Porthmadog (01766) 512340
Main station: Caernarfon
Other public station: Dinas
OS reference: SH 481625
Car parks: Caernarfon
Access by public transport: Caernarfon is served by local buses. The station at Bangor is served by Virgin and First North Western Railways. There is a regular bus service between Bangor and Caernarfon
Depot: Dinas
Length of line: 3 miles, 1ft 11.5in gauge
Passenger trains: Caernarfon-Dinas

Locomotives

Name	No	Builder	Type	Built
—†	K1	B/Peacock (5292)	0-4-0+0-4-0	1909
—**	133	S. F. Belge	2-8-2	1953
—**	134	S. F. Belge	2-8-2	1953
—*	138	B/Peacock	2-6-2+2-6-2	1958
—*†	140	B/Peacock	2-6-2+2-6-2	1958
—*	143	B/Peacock	2-6-2+2-6-2	1958
Castell Caernarfon	—	Funkey	Bo-Bo	1968
Upnor Castle	—	Hibberd (3687)	4wDM	1954

*former South African Railways NGG16 class locomotives
**former South African Railways NG15 class locomotives
†not on site
The above locomotives may not be on site. Ffestiniog Railway Co locomotives may operate some services

Stock
6 bogie coaches. Numerous service vehicles

Future extensions: Dinas-Waunfawr (summer 2000), Waunfawr-Rhyd Ddu, Rhyd Ddu-Porthmadog
Period of public operation: Easter-end of October
Facilities for disabled, refreshments & souvenirs: Please phone for availability of space in disabled carriage. Limited snacks and souvenirs available in Caernarfon
Membership details: Welsh Highland Railway Society (see above address)
Membership journal: Snowdon Ranger — quarterly

Snowdon Mountain Railway

Member: HRA
The only public rack and pinion railway in the British Isles, opened in 1896, this bustling line climbs the slopes of Snowdon, often through the clouds, to the hotel at the top. The trip should not be missed

General Manager: A. P. Hopkins
Engineering Manager: M. Kressman
Headquarters: Snowdon Mountain Railway, Llanberis LL55 4TY
Telephone: Llanberis (01286) 870223
Fax: (01286) 872518
Internet address: web site: www.snowdonrailway.force9.co.uk

Locomotives

Name	No	Builder	Type	Built
Enid	2	SLM (924)	0-4-2T	1895
Wyddfa	3	SLM (925)	0-4-2T	1895
Snowdon	4	SLM (988)	0-4-2T	1896
Moel Siabod	5	SLM (989)	0-4-2T	1896
Padarn	6	SLM (2838)	0-4-2T	1922
Ralph*	7	SLM (2869)	0-4-2T	1923
Eryri*	8	SLM (2870)	0-4-2T	1923
Ninian	9	Hunslet (9249)	0-4-0DH	1986
Yeti	10	Hunslet (9250)	0-4-0DH	1986
Peris	11	Hunslet (9305)	0-4-0DH	1991
George	12	Hunslet (9312)	0-4-0DH	1992

All steam locomotives were built by Swiss Locomotive Works, Winterthur
All diesel locomotives were built by Hunslet Engine Co, Leeds
*currently stored out of service (boilerless)

e-mail: enquiries@snowdonrailway.force9.co.uk

Main station: Llanberis
Other public stations: Summit, also Clogwyn/Rocky Valley when Summit is inaccessible
OS reference: SH 582597
Car park: Llanberis
Access by public transport: Bangor railway station then by bus, either direct, or alternatively via Caernarfon. Snowdon Sherpa Services to/from Beddgelert and Betws-y-coed stop outside the station
Refreshment facilities: Llanberis, Summit

Stock
8 closed bogie coaches; 1 bogie works car; 1 4-wheel open wagon; a 3-car diesel-electric railcar set built 1995 by HPE Tredegar (fleet Nos 21, 22, 23 [Works Nos 1074/5/6])

Souvenir shops: Llanberis, Summit
Depot: Llanberis
Length of line: 7.5km, 800mm gauge
Passenger trains: Llanberis-Summit. Journey time approx 60min. Departures from Llanberis at 30min intervals during peak periods. Round trip approx 2hr 30min
Period of public operation: Daily 15 March-1 November

Special notes: All trains are subject to weather and traffic restrictions. Prior to mid/late May and after October upper section to Summit is normally closed and trains terminate at Clogwyn or Rocky Valley. Parties welcome by prior arrangement. Family ticket (2 adults, 2 children) available on early morning trains up to and including 10.00. Any train may be steam- or diesel-hauled

---

Museum — Swansea Maritime & Industrial Museum — Swansea

Member: HRA

This Museum houses a number of relics from Swansea's industrial and maritime past, one of which is stationed outside the Museum. The Tramshed Annexe houses a restored Swansea City double-deck tram (Brush Electrical Engineering 1923/24 model) and a replica of the early Mumbles railway carriage, in addition to the sole surviving example of the Mumbles Railway rolling stock, the front section of the tramcar, manufactured by the Brush Electrical Engineering Co in 1928.

Artefacts from the Mumbles Railway are also displayed within a graphic presentation, as are examples of Brunel's 'GWR' broad gauge rail track.
Location: On the south side of the city between the shopping centre

Industrial locomotives

Name	No	Builder	Type	Built
Sir Charles*	—	A/Barclay (1473)	0-4-0F	1919
—	—	Peckett (1426)	0-6-0ST	1916

Notes
*not on public display

and the sea in the newly created Maritime Quarter
OS reference: SS 659927
Operating society/organisation: City & County of Swansea Museum Services, Maritime & Industrial Museum, Museum Square, Maritime Quarter, Swansea SA1 1SN
Telephone: Swansea (01792) 650351
Car park: Public car parks nearby
Access by public transport: Reached on foot from shopping centre, central bus depot, or by car

On site facilities: Café in summer months, otherwise no refreshments in the Museum but several cafés close by. Museum shop selling souvenirs and produce of the Woollen Mill which operates in the Museum throughout the year. Education Service available on request to Education Officer
Public opening: 10.00-17.00 six days a week, closed Mondays and 25/26/27 December and New Year's Day. Last admission 16.45
Facilities for disabled: Available

Timetable Service — Swansea Vale Railway — Swansea

Member: HRA
Location/headquarters: Swansea Vale Railway Upper Bank, Pentrechwyth, Swansea SA1 7DB
Telephone: (01792) 653615

Marketing Manager: Mike Meyrick
Main stations: Six Pit Junction, Nant-Y-Ffin Road, Llansamlet (Swansea)
Other stations: Cwm Halt Upper

Bank Junction (awaiting restoration)
OS reference: Six Pit Junction — SN 683969, Upper Bank Junction — SN 668953
Car parks: Six Pit Junction, Upper

Bank Works

Access by public transport: To Six Pit Junction (ask for Llansamlet) — by train Llansamlet (1-mile); by bus South Wales Transport (from Quadrant Bus Stn) 30B/31/31B/32/33/34.
To Upper Bank bus 34. Bus Info (01792) 580580

Refreshment facilities: On train on operating days only (snacks & drinks)

Souvenir shop: On train on operating days only

Depot: Upper Bank

Facilities for disabled: Six Pit platform will have wheelchair ramp

Period of public operation: Open all year for viewing. April-October 11.00-17.00; October-April 11.00-16.00

Operating days: Not advised, please contact for details

Special events: Not advised; please contact for details

Membership details: G. Fuller, Swansea Vale Railway Society, 21 Elmhurst Crescent, St Thomas, Swansea SA1 8EA

Membership journal: *Vale News* — quarterly

Locomotives and multiple-units

Name	No	Origin	Class	Type	Built
—	4270	GWR	4200	2-8-0T	1919
—	51135	BR	116	DMBS	1958
—	51148	BR	116	DMS	1958
—	52061	BR	108	DMSL	1960
—	53982	BR	108	DMBS	1959
—	55026	P/Steel	121	DMBS	1960
—	59445	BR	116	TS	1959

Industrial locomotives

Name	No	Builder	Type	Built
Llantarnam Abbey	—	Barclay (2074)	0-6-0ST	1939
—	—	Hunslet (3829)	0-6-0ST	1955
—	1	Peckett (1345)	0-4-0ST	1914
—	12514	H/Clarke (D1254)	0-6-0DM	1962
—	2	N/British (27914)	0-4-0DM	1961
—	—	R/Hornsby (312433)	4wDM	1951

Owners
51135, 51148 and 59445 the Llanelli & District Railway Society
Llantarnam Abbey the Llantarnam Abbey Locomotive Association

Stock: *coaches* — 1 BR suburban SO; 1 BR Mk 2 BSK
Stock: *wagons* — 1 GWR brake van, 1 BR brake van, 3 4-wheel tar tanks (ex-NCB), 3 LMS 12-ton mineral wagons, 1 BR 'Gane A' bogie bolster, 1 GWR 'Mink' 10-ton van, 3 GWR 10-ton vans, 1 10-ton open, 2 GWR 'tunney' wagons, 1 LNER low-fit, GWR Pooley van, BR 13-ton single bolster wagon

Stock: *cranes* — Smith & Rodley 4-wheel steam crane, Cowans & Sheldon LMS rail-mounted hand crane, Jones 72-ton rail-mounted diesel crane

---

Timetable Service — Talyllyn Railway — Gwynedd

Member: HRA, TT

The very first railway in the country to be rescued and operated by enthusiasts, the line climbs from Tywyn through the wooded Welsh hills past Dolgoch Falls to Nant Gwernol. The trains are hauled by a variety of veteran tank engines, all immaculately maintained by the railway's own workshops at Tywyn Pendre

Managing Director: David Mitchell

Traffic manager: David Leech

Headquarters: Talyllyn Railway Co, Wharf Station, Tywyn, Gwynedd LL36 9EY

Telephone: Tywyn (01654) 710472

Fax: (01654) 711755

Internet address: *Web site:* www.talyllyn.co.uk

Locomotives

Name	No	Builder	Type	Built
Talyllyn	1	F/Jennings (42)	0-4-2ST	1865
Dolgoch	2	F/Jennings (63)	0-4-0WT	1866
Sir Haydn	3	Hughes (323)	0-4-2ST	1878
Edward Thomas	4	K/Stuart (4047)	0-4-2ST	1921
Midlander	5	R/Hornsby (200792)	4wDM	1940
Douglas	6	Barclay (1431)	0-4-0WT	1918
*Tom Rolt**	7	Barclay (2263)	0-4-2T	1949
Merseysider	8	R/Hornsby (476108)	4wDH	1964
Alf	9	Hunslet (4136)	0-4-0DM	1950
Bryn Eglwys	10	Simplex (101T023)	0-4-0DM	c1985

Locomotive notes: In service — Nos 1, 2, 3, 4, 6 and 7
*virtually a new locomotive rebuilt from the original at Pendre Works

Stock
13 4-wheel coaches/vans; 10 bogie coaches; 45 wagons

Main station: Tywyn Wharf
Other public stations: Tywyn
Pendre, Rhydyronnen, Brynglas,
Dolgoch Falls, Abergynolwyn,
Nant Gwernol
OS reference: SH 586005 (Tywyn
Wharf)
Car parks: Tywyn Wharf,
Dolgoch, Abergynolwyn
Access by public transport:
Tywyn BR station. Bus Gwynedd
services to Tywyn
Refreshment facilities: Tywyn
Wharf, Abergynolwyn hot and cold
snacks available. Picnic areas at
Dolgoch Falls and Abergynolwyn.
Picnic site at Dolgoch Falls
Souvenir shops: Tywyn Wharf,
Abergynolwyn
Museum: Tywyn Wharf
Depot: Tywyn Pendre
Length of line: 7.25 miles, 2ft 3in
gauge
Passenger trains: Tywyn-Nant
Gwernol
Period of public operation:
Sundays 20 February-19 March.
Daily 26 March to 28 October,
26 December-2 January 2001
Journey times: Tywyn-Nant

Narrow Gauge Museum, Tywyn

Name	No	Builder	Type	Built
Dot	—	B/Peacock (2817)	0-4-0ST	1887
Rough Pup	—	Hunslet (541)	0-4-0ST	1891
—	2	K/Stuart (721)	0-4-0WT	1902
Jubilee 1897	—	M/Wardle (1382)	0-4-0ST	1897
George Henry	—	de Winton	0-4-0T	1877
—	13	Spence	0-4-0T	1895
Nutty*	—	Sentinel (7701)	0-4-0VB	1929

*not currently on site

Stock
Various wagons and miscellaneous equipment

Gwernol — single 55min, return
2hr 15min
Special events: Not advised; please
contact for details
Family tickets: Available
Facilities for disabled: No
problem for casual visitors,
advance notice preferred for
groups. Access to shop and
cafeteria possible at Tywyn and
Abergynolwyn. Disabled toilet
facilities at Tywyn and
Abergynolwyn. Access possible to
lower floor of museum. Limited
capacity for wheelchairs on trains.

New vehicle for wheelchairs now
in operation
Special notes: Parties and private
charter trains by arrangement.
Children under 5 years of age free.
Narrow gauge 'Wanderer' four-
and eight-day tickets accepted
Membership details: Mr A.
Johnston, 9 Reynolds Way,
Croydon, Surrey CR0 5JW
Membership journal: *Talyllyn
News* — quarterly
Marketing names: One of the
Great Little Trains. The first
preserved railway in the world

Timetable Service	**Teifi Valley Railway**	Ceredigion

Member: HRA
Operating society/organisation:
Teifi Valley Railway, Henllan
Station, Nr Newcastle Emlyn
SA44 5TD
Manager: Tony Ridgewell
Telephone: (01559) 371077
Main station: Henllan
Other public stations: Forest Halt,
Pontprenshitw, Llandyfriog
Car park: Henllan (on B4334)
OS reference: SN 358407
Access by public transport: BR
station — Carmarthen (14 miles).
Bus service 461 to Henllan or 460
Refreshments: Henllan
Souvenirs: Henllan
On site facilities: Children's play
areas, woodland water fall, nature
trails, crazy golf and crazy quoits,
GWR library, picnic area, plus
quarter-mile 7.25in gauge miniature
railway. Display of standard gauge
freight wagons

Industrial locomotives

Name	No	Builder	Type	Built
Alan George	—	Hunslet (606)	0-4-0ST	1894
Sgt Murphy	—	K/Stuart (3117)	0-6-2T	1918
Sholto	—	Hunslet (2433)	4wDM	1941
Simon	—	M/Rail (7126)	4wDM	1936
Sammy	—	M/Rail (605)	4wDM	1959

Depot: Henllan, engine shed open
to public
Facilities for disabled: All
facilities including portable steps
and wide door for wheelchairs in
two coaches
Period of public operation: Good
Friday to end of October
Special events: Halloween, Santa
Specials
Membership details: Teifi Valley
Railway Society, c/o Henllan
station
Membership journal: *Right Away*
— quarterly

Steam Centre — Vale of Glamorgan Railway — Vale of Glamorgan

Member: HRA
Steam hauled rides over 800yd of track. This will increase to 1.5 miles when the extension to Barry (No 1 Dock) opens in the early summer of 2000
Location: Barry Island Station, Barry Island, South Wales
Operating society: Vale of Glamorgan Railway Co
Car park: Large public car park near site
Access by public transport: Frequent train services from Cardiff to Barry Island for cross platform interchange (Cardiff Railway Co)
On site facilities: Museum, shop, light refreshments
Public opening: Open for viewing every Saturday thoughout the year. Services operate: Saturdays — Easter to end of October. Sundays — June, July and August and Bank Holiday Mondays.
Special events: Santa Specials — weekends in December until Christmas. See local press for details of other events or please telephone (01446) 748816
Length of line: 800yd (1.5 miles from early summer)
Further information: The Chairman, Vale of Glamorgan Railway Co, Barry Island Station,

Locomotives and multiple-unit

Name	No	Origin	Class	Type	Built
—	2861	GWR	2800	2-8-0	1918
—	4115	GWR	4101	2-6-2T	1936
—	5227	GWR	5205	2-8-0T	1924
—	5538	GWR	4575	2-6-2T	1928
—	5539	GWR	4575	2-6-2T	1928
—	6686	GWR	5600	0-6-2T	1928
Willington Hall	7927	BR	'Hall'	4-6-0	1950
—	44901	LMS	5MT	4-6-0	1945
—	48518	LMS	8F	2-8-0	1944
—	80150	BR	4MT	2-6-4T	1956
—	92245	BR	9F	2-10-0	1958
—	54279	BR	108	DTC	1959

Locomotive notes: In store, not on public view, except 5538 on site

Industrial locomotives

Name	No	Builder	Type	Built
Sir Gomer	—	Peckett (1859)	0-6-0ST	1932
Pamela	—	Hunslet (3840)	0-6-0ST	1956
—	7705	RSH (7705)	0-4-0ST	1952
—	52/001	Barclay (1966)	0-4-0F	1929
—	107	North British (27932)	0-6-0DM	1959
Bill Caddick	—	H/Clarke (1168)	0-6-0DM	1959
—	—	Unilok (2183)		1964

Stock
BR Mk 1 coaches, TVR coach No 153, operational steam crane, various freight vehicles

South Wales CF36 5TH
Membership details: Membership Secretary c/o above address

Timetable Service — Vale of Rheidol Railway — Ceredigion

Member: HRA
This narrow gauge railway offers a 23-mile round trip from Aberystwyth to Devil's Bridge providing spectacular views which cannot be enjoyed by road. At Devil's Bridge there are walks to the Mynach Falls and Devil's Punch Bowl. Many artists have been inspired by the magnificence of Devil's Bridge and the Rheidol Valley
General Manager: N. Thompson
Headquarters: Vale of Rheidol Railway, The Locomotive Shed,

Park Avenue, Aberystwyth
SY23 1PG
Telephone: (01970) 625819
Fax: (01970) 623769
Main station: Aberystwyth
(adjacent to main line station)
Other public stations: Devil's
Bridge, Rhiwfron, Rheidol Falls,
Aberffrwd, Nantyronen, Capel
Bangor, Glanrafon, Llanbadarn
OS reference: SN 587812
Car parks: Aberystwyth, Devil's
Bridge
Access by public transport:
Aberystwyth BR station and bus
services to Aberystwyth
Refreshment facilities:
Aberystwyth (not railway owned),
Devil's Bridge (not railway
operated)

Locomotives

Name	No	Origin	Ex-BR Class	Type	Built
Owain Glyndwr	7	GWR	98	2-6-2T	1923
Llywelyn	8	GWR	98	2-6-2T	1923
Prince of Wales	9	GWR	98	2-6-2T	1924
—	10	Brecon MR (002)	98/1	0-6-0DH	1987

Stock

16 bogie coaches; 1 4-wheel guard's van; 11 wagons for maintenance use; 1 inspection trolley

Souvenir shop: Aberystwyth
Depot: Aberystwyth (not open to the public)
Length of line: 11.75 miles, 1ft 11.75in gauge
Journey time: Single 1hr, return 3hr
Passenger trains: Aberystwyth-

Devil's Bridge
Period of public operation: Daily 21 April-28 October, with some exceptions in May, September and October

---

Steam Centre	# Welsh Highland Railway	Gwynedd

Member: HRA
The Welsh Highland Railway Ltd operates services at the south-western end of the old Welsh Highland line and has its base in the bustling holiday town of Porthmadog. The company is developing an exciting project to enhance visitor facilities at the Gelert's Farm site. The WHR is very much a family orientated attraction and adults have the opportunity to purchase a footplate pass
Location: Tremadog Road, Porthmadog, adjacent to Cambrian line station
OS reference: SH 571393
General Manager: Ray Ollier
Operating society/organisation:
Welsh Highland Light Railway Ltd, Gelert's Farm Works, Madoc Street West, Porthmadog, LL49 9DY
Telephone: Porthmadog (01766) 513402
Internet address:
http:/www.roke.co.uk/WHR/WHR. html
Car park: Tremadog Road (free)
Catering facilities: 'Russells' supplying a range of

Locomotives

Name	No	Builder	Type	Built
Moel Tryfan	—	Bagnall (3023)	0-4-2T	1953
Gelert	—	Bagnall (3050)	0-4-2T	1953
Russell	—	Hunslet (901)	2-6-2T	1906
Pedemoura	—	O&K (10808)	0-6-0WT	1924
Karen	—	Peckett (2024)	0-4-2T	1942
Glaslyn	1	R/Hornsby (297030)	4wDM	1952
Kinnerley	2	R/Hornsby (354068)	4wDM	1953
Cnicht	36	M/Rail (8703)	4wDM	1941
Katherine	9	M/Rail (605363)	4wDM	1968
—	4	M/Rail (605333)	4wDM	1963
—	5	Hunslet (6285)	4wDM	1968
—	3	R/Hornsby (370555)	4wDM	1953
Jonathon	6	M/Rail (11102)	4wDM	1959
—	7	Hunslet (7535)	4wDM	1977
—	10	R/Hornsby (481552)	4wDM	1962
—	11	Hunslet (3510)	4wDM	1947
Sezela No 4	—	Avonside (1738)	0-4-0T	1915
Beddgelert*	NG120	S. F. Belge	2-8-2	1950
Edward Saunders	—	Bagnall (2287)	4-4-0T	1926
Snowdonia/Eryri†	—	Buch (23389)	0-6-0DM	1977
—†	—	Buch (2405)	0-6-0DH	1980
—	—	Barclay (554)	4wDH	1970
—	—	Barclay (555)	4wDH	1970
—	—	M/Rail (22237)	4wDM	1965

*ex-South African Railways Class NG15
†ex-Polish State Railways class LYD2

Locomotive notes: 2000 steam service will be worked by WHR veteran *Russell*, assisted by *Gelert* and possible guest locomotives

adult/children's meals and light refreshments
Access by public transport: Central Trains to Porthmadog station. Bus Gwynedd services 1 and 3 to Porthmadog
On site facilities: Souvenir and railway book/video shop, disabled toilet facilities, information boards and extended shed tours. Footplate courses available
Length of line: To Pen-y-Mount, Tremadog. Three-quarter mile, 1ft 11.5in gauge
Passenger trains: Porthmadog-Pen-y-Mount. Return journey

Stock
Passengers will have the opportunity to travel in the historic 'Gladstone' coach, other replica Welsh Highland coaches in the course of construction

approx 40min incorporating works tours. Steam-hauled Bank Holidays, every weekend and daily from early July to end of August (all other trains are diesel-hauled
Family tickets: Available, 2 adults + 2 children
Period of public operation: Easter, then May-October
Special events: Not advised; please contact for details

Facilities for disabled: Toilets. Disabled passengers can be accommodated without prior notice
Membership details: Membership Secretaries, R. & P. Hughes, Cil-y-nant, Gladestry, Kington, Herefordshire HR5 3NR. Instant membership available at the shop
Membership journal: *The Journal* — quarterly

Welshpool & Llanfair Light Railway

Timetable Service — Mid Wales

Member: HRA
There is a decidedly foreign atmosphere to the trains over this line. The steam locomotive collection embraces examples from three continents, and the coaches are turn-of-the-century balcony saloons from Austria or 1960s bogies from Africa. The line follows a steeply graded route (maximum 1 in 24) through very attractive rolling countryside, and is rather a gem in an area too often missed by the traveller heading for further shores
General Manager: Terry Turner
Headquarters: Welshpool & Llanfair Light Railway Preservation Co Ltd, The Station, Llanfair Caereinion SY21 0SF
Telephone: Llanfair Caereinion (01938) 810441
Fax: (01938) 810861
Main station: Welshpool (Raven Square)
Other public stations: Castle Caereinion, Sylfaen, Llanfair Caereinion
OS reference: SJ 107069
Car parks: Llanfair Caereinion, Welshpool (both free)
Access by public transport: Main line station at Welshpool, one mile from Raven Square. Arriva buses from Shrewsbury, Oswestry and Newtown to Welshpool

Locomotives

Name	No	Builder	Type	Built
The Earl	1	B/Peacock (3496)	0-6-0T	1902
The Countess	2	B/Peacock (3497)	0-6-0T	1902
Chattenden	7	Drewry (2263)	0-6-0DM	1949
Dougal	8	Barclay (2207)	0-4-0T	1946
Sir Drefaldwyn	10	S. F. Belge(2855)	0-8-0T	1944
Ferret	11	Hunslet (2251)	0-4-0DM	1940
Joan	12	K/Stuart (4404)	0-6-2T	1927
SLR 85	14	Hunslet (3815)	2-6-2T	1954
Orion	15	Tubize (2369)	2-6-2T	1948
Scooby	16	Hunslet (2400)	0-4-0DM	1941

Locomotive notes: Locomotives expected in service 2000 — *The Earl. Orion, SLR* No 85. The remainder can be seen at Llanfair station, No 12 is displayed with access to the footplate

Stock
1 Wickham trolley; 6 W&LLR wagons; 8 ex-Admiralty wagons; 2 ex-Bowater wagons; 5 ex-Zillertalbahn coaches; 4 ex-Sierra Leone coaches, 2 Hungarian Railway State Coaches

Refreshment facilities: Light refreshments at Llanfair Caereinion. Picnic areas at Welshpool and Llanfair
Souvenir shops: Welshpool, Llanfair Caereinion
Depot: Llanfair Caereinion
Length of line: 8 miles, 2ft 6in gauge
Passenger trains: Welshpool-Llanfair Caereinion
Period of public operation: Easter

to October. Daily in school holidays
Special events: Santa trains on three weekends before Christmas; Friends of Thomas the Tank Engine — 1/2 July; Narrow Gauge Steam Gala — 2/3 September
Facilities for disabled: Specially adapted coaches for wheelchairs now available. Easy access to shops. Disabled toilet facility at Welshpool

128

Membership details: David Barker, 458 Oxford Road, Gomersal, Cleckheaton, West Yorks BD19 4LB
Membership journal: *The Journal* — quarterly
Marketing name: Llanfair Railway
Special notes: New buildings at Raven Square largely a reconstruction of the 1863 station from Eardisley in Herefordshire. Restored station at Llanfair. Access to No 12 at Llanfair, steps up to footplate. Children can see how an engine works. Open balcony coaches — travel right next to the engine at the front of the train. Or see the line rolling away behind the back end!

No 14 awaits departure time from Welshpool on 4 September 1999. *ACB*

Channel Islands & Isle of Man

Steam Centre	**Alderney Railway**	Channel Islands

In 1997 the Alderney Railway was 150 years old, having opened on 14 July 1847. Queen Victoria was the only passenger until 1980
Location: Alderney, Channel Islands
Operating society/organisation: Alderney Railway Society, PO Box 75, Alderney, Channel Islands
Telephone: (01481) 822978
Car park: Yes
Access by public transport: Aurigny Air Services from Southampton
On site facilities: Station at Braye Road (tickets & souvenirs)
Public opening: Weekends and Bank Holidays, Easter to end of September
Special events: Alderney Week August. Easter Egg Specials on

Easter Saturday. Santa Specials, Saturday before Christmas
On site facilities: Miniature railway (7.25in gauge), quarter-mile circuit operates at Mannez in connection with standard gauge line
Length of line: 2 miles
Facilities for disabled: Yes

Industrial locomotives

Name	No	Builder	Type	Built
Elizabeth	—	Vulcan (D2271)	0-4-0DM	1949
Molly 2	—	R/Hornsby	0-4-0DM	1958

Stock
4 Wickham trolleys
2 Goods wagons
2 ex-London Underground 1938 Stock tube cars, Nos 10177/11177 (locomotive-hauled)
2 Wickham Flats
NB: all Wickhams privately owned

President: Frank Eggleston
Chairman: Anthony le Blanc (tel: 01481 822978)
Hon Sec: Mike Taylor
Notes: New shed at Quarry. Three Wickham 'trains' to operate 2000 low season; *Elizabeth* and tube cars high season and Easter

Groudle Glen Railway

Location: Groudle Glen Railway, Isle of Man
Officer in charge: Tony Beard
Operating company: Groudle Glen Railway Ltd (managed by the Isle of Man Steam Railway Supporters' Association) of 29 Hawarden Avenue, Douglas, Isle of Man IM1 4BP
Telephone: (01624) 622138 (evenings); (01624) 670453 (weekends)
Car park: Yes
Access by public transport: Manx Electric Railway (Groudle Hotel)
On site facilities: Sales shop
Length of line: 0.75-mile, 2ft gauge

Locomotives

Name	No	Builder	Type	Built
Dolphin	1	H/Hunslet (4394)	4wDM	1952
Walrus	2	H/Hunslet (4395)	4wDM	1952
Sea Lion	—	Bagnall (1484)	2-4-0T	1896
Annie	—	Booth/GGR	0-4-2T	1998

Public opening: Easter Sunday and Monday, May to September (11.00-16.30), Wednesday evening services July/August (19.00-21.00); Santa Trains — December (11.00-15.30)
Facilities for disabled: Due to the line's location, those who are disabled will have some difficulty. It is suggested that they telephone for advice
Further information and membership details: From above address
Membership journal: *Manx Steam Railway News* — quarterly

Isle of Man Railway

The 3ft gauge Isle of Man Railway is a survivor of a system which covered the whole island. Almost continuous operation since 1873 makes it one of the oldest preserved railways in the British Isles. The railway has changed little since the turn of the century and retains much of its Edwardian atmosphere. It runs for over 15 miles between Douglas and Port Erin through the island's rolling southern countryside
Director of Public Transport: David R. Howard
Operations Superintendent: M. P. Ogden
Engineering Superintendent: G. F. Lawson
Headquarters: Isle of Man Railways, Transport Headquarters, Banks Circus, Douglas, Isle of Man IM1 5PT
Telephone: Douglas (01624) 663366
Fax: (01624) 663637
Main station: Douglas
Other public stations: Port Soderick, Santon, Castletown, Ballasalla, Port St Mary and Port Erin
Car parks: Douglas, Ballasalla, Castletown, Port Erin
Access by public transport: Isle

Locomotives

Name	No	Builder	Type	Built
Sutherland	1*	B/Peacock (1253)	2-4-0T	1873
Peveril	6	B/Peacock (1524)	2-4-0T	1875
G.H. Wood	10*	B/Peacock (4662)	2-4-0T	1905
Maitland	11*	B/Peacock (4663)	2-4-0T	1905
Hutchinson	12*	B/Peacock (5126)	2-4-0T	1908
Kissack	13	B/Peacock (5382)	2-4-0T	1910
Caledonia	15*	Dubs & Co (2178)	0-6-0T	1885
Viking	17*	Schottler (2175)	0-4-0DH	1958
—	19*†	Walker (GNR (I))	diesel railcar	1950
—	20*†	Walker (GNR (I))	diesel railcar	1951
—	—*	M/Rail (22021)	4wDM	1959
—	—*	M/Rail (485280)	4wDM	1966
—	—	Wickhams	4wPM	1956
—	—*	Wickhams	4wPM	1961

*operational, Nos 6 and 13 stored out of use
†undergoing restoration to full working order

On display in museum at Port Erin

Name	No	Builder	Type	Built
Loch	4	B/Peacock (1416)	2-4-0T	1874
Mannin	16	B/Peacock (6296)	2-4-0T	1926

Owned by IoM Railway & Tramway Preservation Society Ltd (not on display)

Name	No	Builder	Type	Built
Mona	5	B/Peacock (1417)	2-4-0T	1874
Tynwald*	7	B/Peacock (2038)	2-4-0T	1880
Fenella†	8	B/Peacock (3610)	2-4-0T	1894
Douglas	9	B/Peacock (3815)	2-4-0T	1896

*chassis only
†undergoing restoration to working order. Work temporarily suspended as boiler is being used in No 1 for three years from 1998

of Man Transport bus to main centres

Special events: Gala 2000 — 5-19 August

Refreshment facilities: Port Erin and Douglas

Souvenir shops: Douglas and Port Erin stations and Douglas — Lord Street Travel Shop

Museum: Port Erin

Depot: Douglas

Length of line: 15.5 miles, 3ft gauge

Rolling stock
Gibbons crane (on display at the former Union Mills station/owned by IoMR&TPS), 20 coaches, 20 runners, 3 vans, 2 'M' type wagons, 1 well wagon

Passenger trains: Douglas-Port Erin

Period of public operation: Daily Daily 1 April-29 October

Facilities for disabled: Level access throughout Douglas and Port Erin stations including refreshment area. Carriages able to carry wheelchairs, ramps provided. Advance notice helpful

---

| Timetable Service | Manx Electric Railway | Isle of Man |

The 3ft gauge Manx Electric Railway is a unique survivor of Victorian high technology. A mixture of railway and tramway practice, it was built in 1893 and was a pioneer in the use of electric traction. Two of the original cars are still in service, making them the oldest tramcars still in operation in the British Isles. After leaving Douglas, the railway passes the Groudle Glen Railway before reaching the charming village of Laxey, home of the Snaefell Mountain Railway. The line continues over some of the most breathtaking coastal scenery in the island before reaching its terminus at Ramsey nearly 18 miles from Douglas

Director of Public Transport: David R. Howard

Operations Superintendent: M. P. Ogden

Engineering Superintendent: G. F. Lawson

Headquarters: Isle of Man Railways, Transport Headquarters, Banks Circus, Douglas, Isle of Man IM1 5PT

Telephone: Douglas (01624) 663366

Fax: (01624) 663637

Main station: Douglas (Derby Castle)

Other public stations: Groudle, Laxey, Dhoon Glen, Ballaglass, Ramsey and numerous wayside stops

Car parks: Douglas, Laxey, Ramsey (nearby)

Access by public transport: Isle

Motor Cars

Nos	Type	Seats	Body	Built
1, 2	Unvestibuled saloon	34	Milnes	1893
5, 6, 7, 9	Vestibuled saloon	32	Milnes	1894
14, 15, 17, 18	Cross-bench open	56	Milnes	1898
16	Cross-bench open	56	Milnes	1898
19-22*	Winter saloon	48	Milnes	1899
23†	Centre-cab locomotive	—	IOMT & EP6	1900
25-27	Cross-bench open	56	Milnes	1898
28-31	Cross-bench open	56	ERTCW	1904
32, 33	Cross-bench open	56	UEC	1906

*22 re-bodied 1991, McArd/MER
†owned by IoM Railway & Tramway Preservation Society Ltd

Trailers

13	Cross-bench open	44	Milnes	1893
36, 37	Cross-bench open	44	Milnes	1894
40, 41, 44	Cross-bench open	44	EE Co	1930
42, 43	Cross-bench open	44	Milnes	1903
45-48	Cross-bench open	44	Milnes	1899
49-50, 53, 54	Cross-bench open	44	Milnes	1893
52	pw flatcar (ex trailer)	—	Milnes	1893
55, 56*	Cross-bench open	44	ERTCW	1904
57, 58	Saloon	32	ERTCW	1904
59	Special Saloon	18	Milnes	1895
60	Cross-bench open	44	Milnes	1896
61, 62	Cross-bench open	44	UEC	1906

*rebuilt as invalid carriage in 1993

of Man Transport buses to main centres

Special events: Gala 2000 — 5-19 August

Depots: Douglas, Laxey, Ramsey

Refreshment facilities: Laxey

Museum: Ramsey

Souvenir shops: Ramsey and Douglas — Lord Street Travel Shop

Length of line: 17.5 miles, 3ft gauge

Passenger service: Douglas-Ramsey

Period of public operations: Daily 1 April-29 October. Limited winter service November-March

Special notes: Folded wheelchairs can be carried. Please notify in advance. One trailer (capable of carrying wheelchairs) with built-in lift. Please notify in advance

The 3ft 6in gauge Snaefell Mountain Railway is unique. It is the only electrically-driven mountain railway in the British Isles. Almost all the rolling stock is original and dates back to 1895. The railway begins its journey at the picturesque village of Laxey where its terminus is shared with the Manx Electric Railway. The climb to the summit of Snaefell (2,036ft) is a steep one and the cars travel unassisted up gradients as steep as 1 in 12. From the summit, the views extend to Wales, Scotland, England and Ireland.
Director of Public Transport: David R. Howard
Operations Superintendent: M. P. Ogden
Engineering Superintendent: G. F. Lawson
Headquarters: Isle of Man

Trams

Nos	Type	Seats	Body	Built
1-4, 6	Vestibuled saloon	48	Milnes	1895
5 (rebuild)	Vestibuled saloon	48	MER/ Kinnin	1971

Railways, Transport Headquarters, Banks Circus, Douglas, Isle of Man IM1 5PT
Telephone: Douglas (01624) 663366
Fax: (01624) 663637
Main station: Laxey
Other public stations: Bungalow, Summit
Car parks: Laxey, Bungalow (nearby)
Access by public transport: Manx Electric Railway or Isle of Man Transport bus to Laxey
Special events: Gala 2000 — 5-19 August

Depot: Laxey
Refreshment facilities: Laxey, Summit
Museum: Ramsey
Souvenirs shops: Summit and Douglas — Lord Street Travel Shop
Length of line: 5 miles, 3ft 6in gauge
Passenger service: Laxey-Snaefell summit
Period of public operation: Daily 17 April-1 October
Special notes: No 5 fitted with wheelchair lift for disabled passengers. Advance notice helpful

Ireland

Restoration work commenced in June 1993 and to date some half-mile of line has been rebuilt, water tower and engine shed refurbished and new workshops and carriage shed constructed. The ultimate objective is to rebuild a further 5.75 miles of line to Mohill
Location/headquarters: The Narrow Gauge Station, Dromod, Co Leitrim, adjacent to the Irish Rail station
Telephone: 00353 78-38599 (from UK)
General Manager: Michael Kennedy
Main station: Dromod
Other stations: Clooncolry Halt
Car park: At Dromod terminus

Locomotives

Name	No	Builder	Type	Built
Dromod	1	K/Stuart (3024)	0-4-2ST	1916
—	1	R/Hornsby (326051)	4wDM	1952
Nancy*	1	Avonside (3024)	0-6-0T	1908
—	9	M/rail (115U093)	4wDH	1970
—	(D5)*	H/Hunslet (2659)	4wDM	1942
Dinmor	F511	Fowler (3900011)	4wDM	1947
—	LM11	Ruhrthaler (1082)	4wDM	1936
—	LM87	R/Hornsby (329696)	4wDM	1952
—	LM91	R/Hornsby (371962)	4wDM	1954
—	LM131	R/Hornsby (382809)	4wDM	1955
—	LM141	R/Hornsby (392142)	4wDM	1955
—	LM142	R/Hornsby (392145)	4wDM	1955
—	LM178	Deutz (57120)	0-4-0DM	1960
—	LM180	Deutz (57122)	0-4-0DM	1960
—	LM186	Deutz (57132)	0-4-0DM	1960
—	LM187	Deutz (57133)	0-4-0DM	1960
—	LM260	Deutz (57841)	0-4-0DM	1960

Access by public transport: Rail service to Dromod (Irish Rail) on the Dublin/Sligo line. Bus Eireann and Ulsterbus routes also call at Dromod
Refreshment facilities: Meals and snacks available at nearby 'Brandywell' Bar
Souvenir shop: Dromod
Length of line: Half-mile (3ft gauge)
Museum: Large collection of locomotives, rolling stock and road vehicles, many still awaiting restoration
Period of public operation: Daily all year round. Steam trains Sundays 1 May-31 October or by special arrangement
Special events: Annual Vintage Rally — second Sunday in May; Ghost Trains — 31 October; Santa Specials — weekends in December
Contact address for operating

	LM350	Simplex (60SL748)	4wDM	1980

*2ft gauge
Nancy under restoration at Alan Keef Ltd, Ross-on-Wye

Railcars

Name	No	Builder	Type	Built
—	5	Drewry Car (1945)	4wDM	1927
—	C11	Bord Na Mona	4wPM	–
—	C42	Wickham (7129)	4w	1955
—	C56	Wickham (7681)	4wPM	1957
—	W6/11-4	Wickham (9673)	4wPM	1963

5 built as 5ft 3in gauge inspection car for Great Southern Railway, regauged in 1994
C42 used as unpowered p-way trolley

Rolling stock
Includes West Clare railway trailer 47c, Tralee & Dingle coaches 7T and 10T and Alan Keef-built No 13

Co: Cavan & Leitrim Railway Co Ltd, Dromod, Co Leitrim, Republic of Ireland
Membership journal: *Cavan &*

Leitrim News – quarterly newsletter of C&L R Supporters' Association (address as above)

Museum	**County Donegal Railway Restoration Society**	County Donegal

Members: HRA
Location/Headquarters: Old Station House, Donegal Town, Ireland
Telephone: (00353-73 [from UK]) (073 [from Ireland]) 22655
Contacts: Anne Temple, Margaret Ward
Public opening: Old Station House opened as a permanent Railway Museum & Heritage Centre from Easter 1995
Membership details: From above address
Membership journal: *The Phoenix*
Special notes: Outline planning

Locomotives

Name	No	Origin	Class	Type	Built
*Drumboe**	5	CDR	5	2-6-4T	1907

*on loan from the Foyle Valley Railway

Stock
1 CDR brake/third coach No 28
1 CDR railcar No 14
1 CDR trailer No 5
1 CDR combined goods/cattle and horse van (247 of 1893)
1 goods van

Viewing of all rolling stock is by arrangement only

permission has been received for a 3/4-mile long line from the station to Correus crossing

---

Steam Centre	**Cumann Traenach Gaeltrachta Lair**	County Donegal

This stretch of track has been laid on the formation of the Fintown-Glenties line. The railway runs along the shore of Lough Finn and

for 1998 it is planned to have a dual ride, out by rail and return by boat.
Location/headquarters: Fintown

Railway Station, Fintown, Co Donegal, Eire
Telephone: 00353 46280 (from UK)

Manager: Anne-Marie Bonner
Main station: Fintown Station
Car park: Located at station area
Access by public transport: Local buses
Refreshment facilities: Local café at top of station lane
Souvenir shop: Located at station area
Length of line: 2.5 miles (3ft gauge)
Museum: Not in operation but a collection of antiquated farm machinery is being restored
Period of public operation: June — Monday/Sunday 13.00-17.00; July-September 11.00-18.00
Special events: Easter Specials,

Locomotives

Name	No	Builder	Type	Built
—	LM77	R/Hornsby (329680)	4wDM	1952
—	—	Simplex	4wDM	

Rolling stock
3 Belgian tramcars

Halloween Train, Santa Train
On site facilities: Toilet, it is also hoped to have a playground in operation
Membership details: Bernadette McGee, (Membership Secretary), c/o above address
Membership journal: *An Mhuc Dhubh* — annual

Downpatrick Railway Museum

Timetable Service

County Down

Members: HRA
Location: The Railway Station, Market Street, Downpatrick, Co Down BT30 6LZ
OS reference: J483444
Operating society/organisation: Downpatrick & Ardglass Railway Co Ltd, with the support of the Downpatrick Railway Society
Telephone: (028) 4461 5779
Car park: Free parking adjacent to station
Access by public transport: A regular service is operated by Ulsterbus from Belfast Europa bus centre (next to Great Victoria Street railway station). Tel: (028) 9032 0011
Refreshment facilities: Buffet carriage open on operating days
On site facilities: Souvenir shop, toilets
Length of line: 1.75-miles open to public traffic. Current terminus: King Magnus's Halt. Track is extending southwards towards Balldugan and north to Inch Abbey
Public opening: Operating days: — 17 March (St Patrick's Day); Easter Sunday, Monday; Sundays in July and August; first two Sundays in September. 14.00-17.00 Station tours — Monday-Friday June-August (static) 11.00-14.00
Journey time: 30min return journey from Downpatrick town to

Diesel locomotives

Name	No	Origin	Class	Type	Built
W. F. Gillespie OBE	E421	CIE	421	C	1962
—	E432	CIE	421	C	1962
—	G611	CIE	611	B	1962
—	G613	CIE	611	B	1962
—	G617	CIE	611	B	1962

Steam locomotives

Name	No	Builder	Type	Built
Guinness	3BG	H/Clarke (1152)	0-4-0ST	1919
—	1	O&K (12475)	0-4-0T	1934
—	3	O&K (12662)	0-4-0T	1935

Rolling stock
2 CIE Brake open standards (Nos 1918 & 1944); CIE Travelling Post Office (No 2978); 1 CIE Brake open standard generating steam van (No 3223); CIE Buffet open standard (No 2419); NIR '70' class railcar brake open standard intermediate (No 728); NIR '70' class railcar brake open standard driving trailer (No 713); B&CDR 'Royal Saloon' (No 153); B&CDR 1st/2nd composite (No 152); B&CDR 3rd open (ex-railmotor); B&CDR 6-wheeled 2nd (No 154); B&CDR 6-wheeled brake 3rd (No 39); GS&WR 3rd open (No 836); GSWR 6-wheeled brake first (No 69); Ulster Railway Family Saloon (No 33); GNR 6-wheeled third; 4 LMS (NCC) parcels vans; 2 LMS (NCC) open wagon; LMS (NCC) brake van; CIE closed van; 2 GNR closed vans; GNR brake van; GSWR ballast hopper; GSWR ballast plough; LMS (NCC) steam crane; 2 private oil company tankers, CIE Track Inspection Vehicle No 712; selection of carriage and wagon underframes for internal use

Owners
1 and 3 the Irish Sugar Locomotive Group
3BG on loan from the Railway Preservation Society of Ireland
G611 and G617 the Irish Traction Group
G613 privately owned

134

Ireland

Downpatrick Loop Platform and King Magnus's Halt
Special events: Ghost Trains — Halloween weekend, travel to the Loop Platform and visit Merlin the Magician on board his own Grotto Train. Children receive a present; Santa Specials — December weekends, travel to the Loop Platform and visit Santa Claus on board his own Grotto Train. Children receive a present

Facilities for disabled: All station facilities at Downpatrick accessible for disabled
Membership details: The Secretary, Downpatrick Railway Society, The Railway Station,

Steam Centre — Foyle Valley Railway — County Londonderry

Members: HRA

The Foyle Valley Railway Centre is a museum of narrow gauge railways in the north-west of Ireland, adjoining, and associated with, an operating pleasure railway. The centre contains a number of items and rolling stock from the former County Donegal and Lough Swilly railways. It is housed in a modern building in an attractive, newly developing riverside park. Plans exist for the line to run along the former Great Northern Railway (Ireland) formation to Carrigans, and then on towards St Johnston, a total distance of 8 miles.

Location: Foyle Valley Railway Centre, Foyle Road, Londonderry BT48 6AQ
Main station: Waterside Railway station
Car park: Adjacent to the station
Access by public transport: By NI Railways to Londonderry station (quarter-mile). By Ulsterbus from various centres (three-quarter-mile)
Souvenir shop: Operated by North West of Ireland Railway Society at railway museum
Operating group: A combined project operated by Derry City Council and the North West of Ireland Railway Society (responsible under Council control

Locomotives and railcars

Name	No	Origin	Class	Type	Built
Meenglas	4	CDRJC	5	2-6-4T	1907
Columbkille	6	CDRJC	5	2-6-4T	1907
—	12	CDRJC	—	Diesel Railcar	1934
—	18	CDRJC	—	Diesel Railcar	1940

Industrial locomotives

Name	No	Origin	Type	Built
—	—	Simplex	0-4-0DH	1974

Rolling stock
1 ex-CDRJC carriage No 12, 1 ex-Londonderry & Lough Swilly Railway carriage, 1 ex-Ballymena & Larne Railway carriage, 1 ex-Clogher Valley Railway Box wagon No 19, 2 ex-CDRJC goods wagons

for the rail service)
Museum: At Foyle Valley Railway Centre
Facilities for disabled: Yes
Operating society: North West of Ireland Railway Society, 8 Letterkenny Road, Londonderry BT48 9XG
Telephone: (028) 7126 5358 or (028) 7126 4865
Membership details: Secretary, D. W. Mason, 7 Nicholson Terrace, Londonderry BT48 7LW
General Manager: R. Gallagher, telephone (028) 7126 5234
Society journal: *The Starter* published once a year

Refreshment facilities: None on site but city centre quarter-mile away
On site facilities: Souvenir shop, museum, toilets and 3ft gauge railway
Period of public operation: April-September, Tuesday-Saturday and public holidays 10.00-17.00, Sunday 14.00-18.00. October-March, Tuesday-Saturday 10.00-17.00. Special opening times Easter and Christmas
Length of line: 2.5 miles operated by diesel railcars of the former County Donegal Railways

Steam Centre — Irish Steam Preservation Society — County Laois

Members: HRA, NTET
Location: Stradbally Hall, eight miles from Athy, six miles from Portlaoise (on N80 road).

Telephone: 00353 502 25444 (from UK)
Access by public transport: Irish Rail train to Athy or Portlaoise.

Kavanagh's Bus Portlaoise-Stradbally-Athy also Portlaoise-Stradbally-Kilkenny (both routes twice daily Monday-Saturday)

On site facilities: 3ft gauge railway
Catering facilities: None on site but town centre quarter-mile away
Length of line: 1km
Public opening: Easter Sunday & Monday — 23/24 April; May Bank Holi lday Sunday & Monday — 30 April, 1 May; June Bank Holiday Sunday & Monday — 4/5 June; National Steam Rally, August Bank Holiday Sunday & Monday — 6/7 August; Sunday 17 September; October Bank Holiday — 29/30 October.
1430-17.00 on all dates except 6/7 August when 12.00-18.30
Special notes: This is the longest established steam railway in

Industrial locomotives

Name	No	Builder	Type	Built
—	2	Barclay (2264)	0-4-0WT	1949
—	—	Hunslet (2281)	4wDM	1941
Nippy	—	Planet (2014)	4wDM	1936
—	4	R/Hornsby (326052)	4wDM	1952

Stock
1 Passenger coach; 2 Ballast wagons; 1 Brake van

Ireland, now in its 32nd year. It is hoped to reopen the Steam Museum in Stradbally in 2000. Please contact Rally Secretary, ISPS, Bunnacrannagh, Timahoe Road, Stradbally, Co Laois for further details or telephone above number

---

Museum — Irish Traction Group — County Tipperary

Member: HRA
Location: The former goods store adjacent to Carrick-on-Suir railway station
Operating society/organisation: Irish Traction Group, 31 Hayfield Road, Bredbury, Stockport, Cheshire SK6 1DE, England
Telephone: (0161) 285 5836 (Mon-Fri 18.00-21.00 only)
Car park: Available in station goods yard
Access by public transport: Infrequent train service. Services operated by Bus Eireann from Dublin, Limerick and Waterford
Facilities: Toilets on IE station. Site is located quarter-mile from town centre
Special events: Operation of railtours over IE/NIR systems
Opening times: Premises open occasional weekends throughout the year, although most locomotives are stabled outside. Please telephone above number before visiting

Locomotives/Railcar

Name	No	Origin	Class	Manufacturer	Type	Built
—	1	NIR	DH	E/Electric (D1266)	6wDH	1969
—	2	NIR	DH	E/Electric (D1267)	6wDH	1969
—	3	NIR	DH	E/Electric (D1268)	6wDH	1969
-	A3R	CIE	001/A	M/Vickers (889)	Co-Co	1955
-	A39	CIE	001/A	M/Vickers (925)	Co-Co	1956
-	B103	CIE	101/B	BRCW (DEL22)	A1A-A1A	1956
—	226	CIE	201/C	M/Vickers (972)	Bo-Bo	1957
—	C231	CIE	201/C	M/Vickers (977)	Bo-Bo	1957
—	G601	CIE	601/G	Deutz (56119)	4wDH	1956
—	G611	CIE	611/G	Deutz (57225)	4wDH	1962
—	G616	CIE	611/G	Deutz (57227)	4wDH	1962
—	G617	CIE	611/G	Deutz (57229)	4wDH	1962
—	712	CIE	—	Wickham (8919)	4wDH	1962

Notes:
A3R and A39 are kept at IEÍ Inchicore Works between railtour duties
G611 and G617 currently on loan to Downpatrick Steam Railway
C231 is in the UK for restoration

A3R departs Castlerea on 12 June 1999 on its first railtour duty. *A. J. Marshall/ITG*

Ireland

Members: HRA, TT

The RPSI was formed in 1964, making it one of the older preservation societies in these islands. It has always specialised in main line steam operations, and runs an intensive summer programme of trips out of both Belfast and Dublin. The main maintenance base is situated at Whitehead, 15 miles north of Belfast on the NIR route to Larne Harbour. Here not only are the traffic locomotives shedded, but the locomotive shed is also used for heavy maintenance; currently the society is completing the full rebuilding of its fifth boiler 'in-house'. A large engineering workshop has just been constructed for the Locomotive Department, with the 100-year-old overhead crane which was originally in the Belfast & County Down Railway Locomotive Erecting Shop at Queen's Quay in Belfast. This workshop, which will undertake all heavy engineering for the Society, has still to be fitted out, and will be commissioned hopefully during the course of 2000. A large carriage shed is also on site where traffic vehicles are maintained and coaches are fully rebuilt. There are also heavy lifting facilities on site, and access may occasionally be limited for safety reasons when these are in use. Annual operations commence with 'Easter Bunny' trains out of Belfast, usually on Easter Monday. In May the 'International Railtour' is the main event, a three-day steam extravaganza, which in 2000 will visit Cork. During June there are main line trips out of both Belfast and Dublin, including a Midsummer Barbecue train and a Musical Special. July and August see the 'Portrush Flyers' from Belfast to Portrush and back, around 180 miles of main line steam, as well as the 'Sea Breeze' excursions from Dublin to Rosslare and back, covering 205 miles. During June, July and August there are steam train rides on site at

Locomotives

Name	No	Origin	Class	Type	Built
Merlin	85*	GNR (I)	V	4-4-0	1932
Slieve Gullion	171	GNR (I)	S	4-4-0	1913
—	4††	LMS (NCC)	WT	2-6-4T	1947
—	184†	GS&WR	J15	0-6-0	1880
—	186†	GS&WR	J15	0-6-0	1879
—	461**	D&SER	K2	2-6-0	1922
Lough Erne	27	SL&NCR	Z	0-6-4T	1949

Industrial locomotives

Name	No	Builder	Type	Built
Guinness	3§	H/Clarke (1152)	0-4-0ST	1919
R. H. Smyth	3	Avonside (2021)	0-6-0ST	1928
—	23	Planet (3509)	0-4-0DM	1951
—	4	R/Hornsby	0-4-0DM	1954

* on loan from Ulster Folk & Transport Museum
** currently based in Dublin for regular operations
† awaiting restoration
§ on loan to Downpatrick & Ardglass Railway Society
†† returning to traffic in 2000

Stock

The Society also owns some 20 operational coaches, normally divided between Whitehead and Dublin. Further coaches are awaiting restoration and a small number of freight wagons are also preserved, as well as a steam crane. A serious fire due to vandalism a couple of years ago destroyed several vehicles, and any rebuilding is likely to be some years in the future at best. The Society plans to purchase Craven steel-bodied coaches from Irish Rail as soon as these become available. The Society's secondary maintenance base is at Mullingar, Co Westmeath, but there is **no** access to the public.

Whitehead on Sunday afternoons, and at the end of July there will be an Open Day in conjunction with the Whitehead Community Association when not only will there be train rides but also at least two locomotives will be in steam and there will be access to the workshop areas. The season usually ends with further excursions in September to Rosslare and Whitehead. Halloween shuttles between Belfast and Whitehead. November sees the operation of a Coleraine Christmas shopper special out of Belfast, with a Santa Special out of Coleraine, before Santa Specials out of both capital cities

Location: Whitehead Excursion Station, Co Antrim, Northern Ireland

Operating society: Railway Preservation Society of Ireland, Castleview Road, Whitehead, Carrickfergus, Co Antrim BT38 9NA

Telephone/fax: (028) 9335 3567 (from UK).
(01) 837 4533 (from Eire)

Car park: Public car parking is readily available adjacent to the Society premises, with a further large car park less than 5min walk away on the sea front. Both car parks are normally free

Access by public transport: Northern Ireland Railways or Ulsterbus to Whitehead

On site facilities: Souvenir shop (operating days only)

Public opening: Visitors welcome most weekends. Site not open during the week (except public holidays) or when main line trains are operating from Whitehead or

Belfast. Special opening for parties, or in the evening, may be arranged by telephoning in advance
Special notes: The RPSI is noted for its main line excursions and traditional rolling stock. For details: RPSI Railtours, c/o 141 Cavehill Road, Belfast BT15 5BL (9x4 SAE please).
Facilities for disabled: Please note that wheelchair facilities can be provided on trains, with advance notice if possible. A dedicated coach for carrying wheelchairs operates out of Whitehead on Belfast-based trains. Wheelchair access around the workshops at Whitehead is possible, but difficult, and advanced warning is requested of any visitors who may need special facilities
Operations Officers:
Evan Pamley (Belfast),
Charles McDonnell (Dublin)
Membership details: Membership Secretary, 148 Church Road, Newtownabbey, Co Antrim BT36 6HJ
Future developments: Completion of a new heavy engineering workshop is planned, as well as a projected extension to the Carriage Shed and additional stores and maintenance areas, and there are further developments in the pipeline which will hopefully improve access. Additional locomotive and coach restoration is proposed

---

| Museum | Ulster Folk & Transport Museum | County Down |

Forty-five acres are devoted to the Transport Galleries. Permanent exhibitions include the earliest forms of transport, horse-drawn vehicles, bicycles, motor cars and the Museum's *Titanic* exhibition.

The Irish Railway Collection is displayed in an award-winning purpose-built gallery — the largest Transport Museum gallery in Ireland.

The collection features *Maedb* — the largest locomotive run in Ireland. The display includes narrow gauge and standard gauge rolling stock, locomotives, carriages, goods wagons, railcars and railbuses along with new, previously undisplayed material and memorabilia
Location: Ulster Folk & Transport Museum, Cultra, Holywood
Operating organisation: Ulster Folk & Transport Museum, Cultra, Holywood BT18 0EU
Telephone: (028) 9042 8428
Fax: (01232) 9042 8728
Access: By car or bus the museum is about 7 miles from Belfast city centre on the A2 Belfast-Bangor Road. You can also reach the museum by train
Car park: Extensive free parking
On site facilities: Shops, toilets, tearoom
Opening times: All year round. Opening times vary with season check with the Museum for details

Locomotives (5ft 3in)

Name	No	Origin	Class	Type	Built
—	93	GNR(I)	JT	2-4-2T	1895
—	30	BCDR	I	4-4-2T	1901
Dunluce Castle	74	LMS(NCC)	U2	4-4-0	1924
Maedb	800	GSR	B1A	4-6-0	1939
—	1	R/Stephenson (2738)	—	0-6-0ST	1891
Merlin	85	GNR(I)	V	4-4-0	1932
—	1	GNR(I)	—	Railbus	1932

Locomotives (narrow gauge)

Name	No	Origin	Class	Type	Built
Blanche	2	CDRJC	5A	2-6-4T	1912
Kathleen	2	CLR	—	4-4-0T	1887
Phoenix	11	CVR	—	4wD	1928
—	20	Industrial	—	0-4-0	1905
—	2	Industrial	—	0-4-0	1907

Stock
1 Dublin, Wicklow & Wexford Railway coach; 1 Dundalk, Newry & Greenore Railway coach; 1 Midland & Great Western Railway director's saloon (ex-private vehicle); 1 Electric tramcar of Bessbrook-Newry Tramway; 2 trams from Giant's Causeway Tramway, Great Northern Railway Ireland Fintona tram, 1 Cavan-Leitrim Railway coach; 2 County Donegal Railway railcars; 1 County Donegal Railway director's coach; 1 County Donegal Railway trailer coach (bodywork ex-Dublin & Lucan Railway coach); 1 Giant's Causeway (P&BVR) saloon trailer; 1 Castlederg & Victoria Bridge Tramway 1st/3rd coach; 1 County Donegal Railway 7-ton open wagon, 3 Belfast trams, 1 Belfast trolleybus, 1 Belfast double-deck bus. Extensive collection of cars, motorcycles, bicycles, commercial vehicles, fire-fighting equipment and industrial railway vehicles

Miniature Railways

Audley End Railway, Essex

Audley End, Saffron Walden, Essex. Tel: (01799) 541354 or 541956
General Manager: A. W. P. Granger
Opening details: Saturdays, Sundays and Bank Holidays April-October; daily running during school holidays; Santa Specials run on two weekends before Christmas. Trains run from 14.00
10.25in gauge; 1.5 miles long; 4 steam, 3 diesel locomotives
Public access: Rail to Audley End (1-mile), car park
Site facilities: Station building under construction for 2000. Ticket office, shop and light refreshments, toilets, large picnic area
Note: (Postal address) Audley End Estate Office, Brunketts, Wendens Ambo, Saffron Walden, Essex CB11 4JL

Dobwalls Family Adventure Park

Dobwalls, Nr Liskeard, Cornwall PL14 6HD. Tel: (01579) 320325/321129. Infoline (01579) 320578. Fax: (01579) 21345
General Manager: J. B. Southern
Opening details: Daily Easter-30 September. 10.00-18.00 (last admissions 16.30)
7.25in gauge; two 1-mile long routes; 6 steam and 4 diesel locomotives
Public access: By train to Liskeard — 3 miles; by bus — National Express coaches to/from Cornwall via Plymouth stop in Dobwalls village; By car — signposted off A38
Site facilities: Refreshments, toilets inc disabled, mother & baby facilities, picnic area, souvenirs, radio-controlled boats and trucks, crazy golf, children's adventure playground, wildlife gallery
Facilities for disabled: Wheelchair access throughout (free loan, subject to availability), toilets

Great Cockcrow Railway, Surrey

Hardwick Lane, Lyne, Chertsey, Surrey. Tel: Mon-Fri (01932) 255500; Sun (01932) 565474
Opening details: Every Sunday May to October inclusive, 14.00-17.30
7.25in gauge; choice of two routes, each approx 2 miles; 20 steam locomotives, 1 electric, 3 petrol (6 normally in service). Journey time about 15-20min. Unique signalling system worked from 4 signalboxes
Public access: BR Chertsey (1.25 miles); London Buslines 561, 586 Holloway Hill (half-mile), free car park
Site facilities: Toilet, light refreshments, picnic area, free car park
Special note: Sponsored by Ian Allan Group. Send 19p SAE for brochure

Kerr's Miniature Railway

West Links Park, Arbroath, Angus. Tel: (01241) 879249
(Along the sea front to the west of town)
General Manager: Mathew B. Kerr
Opening details: Easter-end of September — weekends (14.00-17.00). All of July and first half of August — daily 11.30-14.00-17.00, but trains usually run from noon onwards. All times weather permitting
10.25in gauge; 400yd (alongside ScotRail line); 3 steam, 2 diesel, 2 petrol
Public access: ScotRail Arbroath station 1.5 miles; Strathtay Buses route A92
Site facilities: None, but park has toilets, snack bar, etc

Lightwater Valley Theme Park, North Yorkshire

North Stainley, Nr Ripon, North Yorkshire. Tel: (01765) 635368 (24 hours), 635321 (administration/party bookings)
Opening details: Easter-October (daily in June/July/August). Telephone for details
Operations & Maintenance Dept: J. Connall
15in gauge; 1-mile long; 1 diesel
Public access: Main line station Harrogate (12 miles) and Thirsk (9 miles), free car park
Site facilities: 125 acres of country park featuring unique white knuckle rides including the world's biggest rollercoaster, live family entertainment, leisure pursuits, skill-testing activities. Wide range of catering facilities and themed shopping malls

Moors Valley Railway, Dorset

Moors Valley Country Park, Horton Road, Ashley Heath, Nr Ringwood, Dorset. Tel: (01425) 471415
General Manager: Mr J. A. W. Haylock
Opening details: Sundays all year; Saturdays March-October; daily all school holidays and Spring Bank Holiday to mid-September. Santa Specials in December.
Special events: Railway Open Day — 9 April; Summer Gala — 10/11 June. American Weekend — 1/2 July, Hornby Railways Weekend — 22/23 July, Model Railway Weekend — 9/10 September, Tinkerbell Rally — 7/8 October, Santa Specials — 10, 17 December
7.25in gauge; 1-mile long; 10 steam locomotives
Public access: Wilts & Dorset bus X2, from Bournemouth/Ringwood to Ashley Heath
Site facilities: Picnic areas, lakeside walks, adventure playground, railway shop and refreshments all set in the beautiful Moors Valley Country Park. Car park and toilets (including disabled)

Heritage Railway Association

Company Limited by Guarantee and not having a share capital.
Registered in England No 2226245
(Registered Office: 2 Littlestone Road, New Romney, Kent TN28 8PL)
President: Dame Margaret Weston DBE
Vice Presidents: Ian Allan OBE, Allan Garraway MBE

Private Membership Secretary:
Dr John Oakley, Winchet Lodge, Winchet Hill, Goudhurst, Cranbrook, Kent TN17 1JX.
Tel: (01580) 211773

Corporate Membership Secretary:
Frank Sheppard, The Old Station, Egloskerry, Launceston, Cornwall PL15 8ST. Tel: (01566) 785492

Journal Editors:
Jackie and Michael Cope, 30 Gledhow Drive, Oxenhope, Keighley, West Yorkshire BD22 9SA

Members of the Heritage Railway Association

UK Affiliate Members

Britt Alcroft (Thomas) Ltd:
3 Grovenor Square, Southampton, Hampshire SO1 2BE

Dartmoor Railway Ltd: Mr D. Payne, Meldon Quarry, Okehampton, Devon, EX20 4LT

Edmondson Ticket Printing Co: Mr I. Wilks, Ty Celyn, Axton, Holywell, Flintshire CH48 9DH

Guild of Railway Artists: Mr F. Hodges, Chief Executive Officer, 45 Dickins Road, Warwick CV34 5NS

Lloyd's Railway Society:
Mr P. Wood, 30 Beechwood Avenue, Caterham, Surrey CR3 6NA

Locomotive Club of Great Britain: Mr R. L. Patrick, 8 Wolviston Ave, Bishopgate, York YO1 3DD

London Transport Museum Library: see main entry

J. & H. Marsh & McLennan Ltd: Mr D. Tarr, Corporate Division, Aldgate House, 33 Aldgate High Street, London EC3 1AQ

Railworld: Oundle Road, Peterborough PE3 9NR

Transport Trust: Mr D. Muirhead, 202 Lambeth Road, London SE1 7JW

Westinghouse Signals Ltd: Helen Webb, PO Box 79, Pew Hill, Chippenham, Wiltshire SN15 1ND

Overseas Affiliate Members

AJECTA: M Phillippe Tomatis, Depot des Machines, Boite Postale No 1, F-77650, Longeville, France

Association of Preservation Groups: Mr R. Jowett, Treasurer, New South Wales Inc, 43 Gara Drive, Mt Riverview, NSW 2774, Australia

Australian Railway Historical Society: Mr R. Jowett, New South Wales Division, 67 Renwick St, Redfern, NSW 2016, Australia

Puffing Billy Railway: M. M. Elliot, PO Box Belgrave, Victoria 3160, Australia

Stoomscentrum Maldegem: Rik Degruyter, De Streep 19, B-8340 Damme-Sysele, Belgium

Stoompoorlijn Dendermonde-Puurs: Mr Jaak Serckx, Station Baasrode Noord, Fabrieksstraat 118, B-9200, Baasrode, Belgium

Additional Corporate Members not in the main part of the book

Almond Valley Heritage Trust: Dr R. Chesters, Millfield, Livingstone Village, West Lothian EH54 7AR

Aln Valley Railway Society: Mr S. Manley, Alnwick Station, Alnwick, Northumberland NE66 2NP

Bahamas Locomotive Society: Mr K. J. Tait, 73 Derby Road, Heaton Moor, Stockport, Cheshire SK4 4NG

Battle of Britain Locomotive Preservation Society: Mr J. Gartside, 66 Hawthorn Hill, Letchworth, Herts SG6 4HQ

Britain's Great Little Railways: Mr M. B. Beevers, 64 Bullar Road, Southampton SO18 1GS

Britannia Locomotive Society: Mr A. Sixsmith, 6 Vermont Grove, Peterborough PE3 6BN

Bulleid Society Ltd: Mr D. A. Foale, Namron, South Chailey, Lewes, East Sussex BN8 4AD

Caerphilly Railway Society Ltd:
Mr A. Smith, 51 Worcester
Crescent, Newport, NP9 7NX

Camelot Locomotive Society:
Mr P. W. Gibbs, 54 Latimer
Gardens, Pinner, Middx HA5 3RA

Class 45/1 Preservation Society:
Mr N. Burden, 97 Richmond Park
Crescent, Handsworth, Sheffield
S13 8HF

*Cornish Steam Locomotive
Preservation Society Ltd*:
Mr M. Orme, 3 Jubilee Terrace,
Goonhavern, Truro, Cornwall TR4
9JY

Cravens Heritage Trains:
Mr G. Thorp, The Thatched Cottage,
High Wych Lane, Sawbridgeworth,
Herts CM2 0JN

Devon Diesel Society Ltd: Mr D.
Martin, 89 Osprey Park, Thornbury,
Bristol BS35 1LZ

Diesel and Electric Group:
Mr R. Jones, 32 Ty Wern Road,
Rhiwbina, Cardiff CF4 6EB

*Diesel Unit Preservation Associates
Ltd:* Mr M. Cornell, 24 Ashbury
Drive, Marks Tey, Colchester, Essex
SS6 9AR

Eden Valley Railway Society:
Mr A. R. Nunn, 15 Frith Drive,
St Bees, Cumbria CA27 0EY

EPB Preservation Group: Mr R.
Baines, 73 Woodhurst Avenue, Petts
Wood, Orpington, Kent BR5 1AT

Errol Station Museum Trust: David
Tough, 48 Moyness Park Drive,
Blairgowrie, Perthshire PH10 6LX

Forest Pannier Tank Fund:
Mr J. S. Metherall, 15 Sudbrook
Way, Gloucester GL4 4AP

Foxcote Manor Society:
Mr M. Whitton, Meadow Brook,
Station Lane, Mickle Trafford,
Chester CH2 4EH

Galatea Locomotive Trust Ltd:
Mrs I. H. Evans, 26 Deanwater
Close, Locking Stumps, Warrington,
WA3 6ER

Gloucester Railcars Trust Ltd:
Mr M. Hancocks, 19 Abbots Road,
Abbots Langley, Herts WD5 0AY

Gresley Society (The):
Mr P. J. Coster, Pendoggett Farm, St
Kew, Bodmin, Cornwall PL30 3HH

Grimsby-Louth Railway Society:
Mr N. Brown, 12 Cambridge Road,
Grimsby, NE Lincs DN34 5EA

GWR 813 Preservation Fund:
Mr P. Goss, 23 Hatchmere,
Thornbury, Bristol BS12 3EU

*Hampshire & Sussex Units
Preservation Society:*
Mr N. Wilkinson, 39 Dryden Road,
Popley, Basingstoke, RG24 9DL

Hastings Diesels Ltd:
Mr G. Smith, 15 Orchard Glade,
Headcorn, Nr Ashford, Kent
TN27 9SS

*Hull & Barnsley Railway Stock
Fund:* Mr A. E. Hallman,
6 Chequerfield Court, Pontefract,
West Yorkshire WP8 2TQ

*Keith & Dufftown Railway
Association:* Mrs M. H. Webster, 36
Low Shore, Whitehills, Banff
AB45 2NN

*Kingdom of Fife Railway
Association (The):*
Mr A. Sawson, 54 Townend Place,
Kirkcaldy, Fife KY1 1HB

Lambton No 29 Syndicate:
Mr J. M. Richardson, 5 Ravine Hill,
Filey, North Yorkshire YO14 9EU

*Lancashire & Yorkshire Railway
Preservation Society:* Mr E. Ring,
111 Huddersfield Road, Elland,
West Yorks HX5 0EE

*Lincolnshire Coast Light Railway
Historical Vehicles Trust:*
Mr H. L. Goy, 12 Giles Street,
Cleethorpes DN35 8AE

*Llangollen Great Western
Locomotive Group:*
Mr C. R. Cooksley, 21 Allanson
Road, Colwyn Bay LL28 4HN

*Locomotive Owners Group
(Scotland) Ltd:* Mr H. Stevenson, 4
Queens Road, Blackhall, Edinburgh
EH4 2BY

London & North Western Society:
Mr A. Lowe, 15 Park Road,
Loughborough, Leics LE11 2ED

Lynton & Barnstaple Light Railway:
Mr D. Tooke, 3 Torrs Walk Ave,
Ilfracombe, Devon EX34 8AU

Maid Marian Locomotive Fund:
Mr H. Johns, 139 Stoops Lane,
Doncaster DN4 7RG

*Manston Locomotive Preservation
Society:* Mr J. Cleverdon, PO Box
169, Ramsgate, Kent CT12 6GG

*Market Drayton Railway
Preservation Society:*
Mr R. Pitt, 1 Queens Drive,
Newport, Shropshire TF10 7EU

Maunsell Locomotive Society:
Mr J. S. Pilcher, 312 Riverside
Mansions, Garnett Street, Wapping,
London E1 9SZ

*Merchant Navy Locomotive
Preservation Society Ltd:*
Mr R. Abercrombie, 12 Inglewood
Avenue, Heatherside, Camberley,
Surrey GU15 1RJ

Modern Railway Society of Ireland:
Mr M. A. McFerran, 54 Prince's
Drive, Newtownabbey, Northern
Ireland BT37 0AZ

*North Eastern Locomotive
Preservation Group:*
Mr C. Hatton, 20 Sorrell Court,
Marton, Middlesbrough TS7 8RZ

*North Gloucestershire Railway Co
Ltd:* Mr R. H. Wales,Wellesbourne',
Oakfield Street, Tivoli, Cheltenham,
Gloucestershire GL33 8HR

*North London Locomotive
Preservation Society:*
Mr R. T. Moore, 7 Woodbine Grove,
Enfield, Middlesex EN2 0EA

North Somerset Railway Co Ltd:
Mr D. G. Edwards, 40 Belvedere,
Lansdown Road, Bath, Somerset
BA1 5HR

*Ongar Railway Preservation
Society:* Mr B. Ayton, 75 Highland
Road, Nazeing, Essex EN9 2PU

*Princess Royal Locomotive Trust
Ltd:*
Mr H. Routledge, 112 Larch Drive,
Stanwix, Carlisle, Cumbria
CA3 9FL

Red Rose Society:
Mr G. Jones, Astley Green Colliery
Museum, Higher Green Lane,
Astley, Tyldesay, Manchester
M29 7JB

*Rother Valley Railway (East Sussex)
Ltd:* Mr G. S. Crawley, Penny
Cottage, Yelsted, Sittingbourne,
Kent ME9 7UT

*Salisbury Steam Locomotive
Preservation Trust:* Mr E. J. Roper,
33 Victoria Road, Wilton, Salisbury,
Wiltshire SP2 0OZ

*Scottish Locomotive Preservation
Trust Fund:* Mr F. Landrey, 45
Sycamore Drive, Hamilton
ML3 7HF

South Wales Pannier Group:
Mr J. Melhuish, 74 Coychurch
Road, Bridgend, Mid Glamorgan
CF31 2AP

South West Main Line Steam Co:
Mr P. Gould, 8 Parcroft Gardens,
Yeovil, Somerset BA20 2BS

Southern Electric Group:
Mr J. M. Cousins, 51 Primrose
Walk, Shortcroft Road, Ewell,
Surrey KT17 2EZ

Southern Locomotives Ltd:
Mr S. Kerley, 369 Wimborne Road, Poole, Dorset BH15 3ED

Southport Railway Centre:
Mr D. W. Watkin, 3 Lincoln Drive, Liverpool, Merseyside, L10 3LJ

Southwold Railway Society (The):
Mr J. Bennett, 1 Barnaby Green, Southwold, Suffolk IP15 6AP

Stanier 8F Locomotive Society Ltd:
Mr D. R. McIntosh, 1 The Hawthornes, Comberton Road, Kidderminster, Worcs DY10 3DH

Steam Power Trust '65:
Mr A. R. Thompson, The Station House, Penshaw, Houghton le Spring DH4 7PQ

Stephenson Locomotive Society: Mr B. F. Gilliam, 25 Regency Close, Chigwell, Essex IG7 5NY

Stratford on Avon, Broadway Railway Society:
Mr G. Turner, Manor Lodge, Penelope Gardens, Manor Road, Wickhamford, Evesham, Worcs WR11 6SG

Suburban Electric Railway Association:
Mr R. Davidson, 6 Coombfield Drive, Darenth, Dartford, Kent DA2 7LQ

Underground Railway Rolling Stock Trust: Mr D. C. Alexander, 13 Irvine Drive, Stoke Mandeville, Aylesbury HP22 5UN

Urie Locomotive Society:
Mr A. Ball, 'Lavenham', Adams Lane, Selborne, Alton, Hants GU34 3LJ

Wainwright 'C' Preservation Society: Mr N. W. DeMaid, 11 Meadow Close, Catford, London SE6 3NW

Weardale Railway Society:
Mr G. Chatsfield, Stanhope Station, Bondisle, Bishop Aukland, Co Durham DL13 2YS

Western Locomotive Association:
Mr D. H. Tompkins, 23 Haytor Drive, Newton Abbot, Devon TQ12 4DR

Worcester Locomotive Society Ltd:
Mr A. T. Dowling, 9 Queens Court, Ledbury, Herefordshire HR4 9DN

1708 Locomotive Preservation Trust Ltd: Mr G. W. Kingham, 106 Stanford Road, Luton, Beds LU2 0QA

1857 Society: Mr K. R. Bowen, 18 Lochmore Close, Hollycroft, Hinckley, Leicestershire

4247 Ltd: Mr N. Powles, Station House, Station Road, Lower Heyford, Oxon OX6 3PD

48624 Locomotive Soc: G. Robb, 26 Old Gardens Close, Tunbridge Wells, Kent TN2 5ND

6024 Preservation Society Ltd:
Mr C. K. Hargreaves, Spencer Lodge, Back Lane, Chapel Brampton, Northampton NN6 8AJ

6201 Princess Elizabeth Society Ltd:
Mr A. Harries, 1 Ormerod Close, Sandbach, Cheshire CW11 4HA

35006 Locomotive Co Ltd: Mr G. Chidley, 29 Gatehouse, The Moorings, Leamington Spa, CV13 3QA

71000 Duke of Gloucester Steam Locomotive Trust Ltd: Mr F. Reid, 2 Bodmin Avenue, Marthside, Southport PR4 9TU

8E Association: Mr A. Ashurst, 149 St Mary Street, Latchford, Warrington, Cheshire WA4 1EL

A1 Steam Locomotive Trust Ltd: Mr B. Wilson, St Melior, Portlet Bay, St Brelade, Jersey JE3 8AT

A4 Locomotive Society Ltd: Mr A. Pitt, 30 Barham Road, Stevenage, Herts SG2 9HX

LM2MT 46464 Trust: Mr D. Fraser, 6 Westbury Lodge Close, Pinner, Middx HA5 3FG

Applicant Organisations

Amman Valley Railway Society

Bridgend Valleys Railway Society

Cambrian Railways Trust

Corporate Blue Traction Ltd

Cumann Traenach Gaeltrachta Lair

Epping Ongar Railway

Great Yorkshire Railway Preservation Society

Gwendraeth Valley Railways Co Ltd

Hollycombe Steam Collection (see main section)

Kirklees Light Railway Co Ltd (see main section)

Llanelli & Mynydd Mawr Railway Co Ltd

Port Road Railway Society

Rhondda & Cynon Valleys Railway Society

The Royal Deeside Railway Preservation Society

South Eastern & Chatham Railway Preservation Society

Timothy Hackworth Victorian & Railway Museum

Wensleydale Railway Society

Britain's Great Little Railways (contact addresses given)

Brookside Miniature Railway:
Mr C. Halsall, Brookside Garden Centre, Macclesfield Road, Poynton, Cheshire SK12 1BY

Cleethorpes Coast Light Railway (see main section)

Eastleigh Lakeside Railway:
Mr C. Upton, Fletchwood House, Quayside Road, Southampton, Hants SO18 1DP

Exmoor Steam Railway:
Mr T. Stirland, Cape of Good Hope Farm, Bratton Fleming, Barnstaple, Devon EX32 7JN

Fairbourne & Barmouth Railway (see main section)

Haigh Hall Railway: Mr T. Sharratt, Haigh Hall Country PArk, Haigh, Wigan, Lancs WN2 1PE

Little Giant Railways:
Mr J. Crosskey, 18 Frogmore Gardens, North Cheam, Surrey SM3 9RZ

Moors Valley Railway (see miniature section)

Mull Rail (see main section)

Perrygrove Railway: Mr M. Crofts, Perrygrove Farm, Coleford, Glos GL16 8QB

Road, Rail & Waterway:
Mr J. Shackell, 27 Witney Road, Duckington, Witney, Oxon OX8 7TX

Rudyard Lake Railway:
 Mr P. Hanton, Four Winds, Crawford Road, Eaton, Cheshire CW12 2NN

Shibden Miniature Railway:
Mr K. Norris, 3 Nettle Grove, Stump Cross, Halifax, W. Yorks HX3 7AR

Further details, including locations and opening times, can be found in *abc Miniature Railways* published by Ian Allan Publishing Ltd

INDEX

143

Association of Independent Railways & Preservation Societies Ltd

To a person actively interested in nationwide railway preservation as opposed to one particular preservation scheme, PRIVATE MEMBERSHIP of the HERITAGE RAILWAY ASSOCIATION offers many advantages. Five major meetings are organised annually, some at the railway site of a leading Member Society. Here one can meet well-known personalities in the railway preservation world, and the host railway invariably lays on a full day's programme which is both stimulating and enjoyable.

The *Heritage Railway Journal* (published quarterly) is sent to members, containing information on Association activities from member organisations, book reviews and wants, etc.

Railways Restored is made available at a reduced price.

Private members receive Transport Trust Travel Back cards yearly enabling them to visit transport museums or travel on steam railways at reduced charges (and in some cases free). Some 120 sites are covered and are listed in Railways Restored and Steam Heritage Yearbook. In addition to annual membership, a two-year Inter Rail and membership package is available which includes travel facilities on most member railways.

**Private Membership
Application Form (2000)**

Send this form (or photostat of) to: Membership Secretary, HRA, Winchet Lodge, Winchet Hill, Goudhurst, Cranbrook, Kent TN17 1JX.

Name
....

(*BLOCK LETTERS PLEASE*)
Address
....

....

....

Post Code
....

Telephone
....

Subscription enclosed
....

Donation enclosed
....

Private membership costs:

	UK	Overseas
Annual (1 April-31 March)	£15	£20
Life	£200	£250
Two-year package	£40	N/A

HERITAGE RAILWAYS
2000

NATIONAL TIMETABLE OF
SCHEDULED SERVICES

Price £1

This timetable has been produced in collaboration with the Heritage Railway Association, *Railway World* and Ian Allan Publishing Ltd and was printed by Ian Allan Printing Ltd of Hersham, Surrey.

NOTES TO THE TIMETABLE

Throughout the Timetable, the 24 hour clock is used.

Days of operation are shown on the grid at the head of most entries. The letter, or in some cases number, contained in each square denotes the service pattern for that day, and the appropriate letter or number is shown against 'service' in the timetable columns below.

Many trains have refreshment facilities. These are not shown herein as availability may vary according to staffing conditions and seasons of the year.

For details of Wine and Dine, Thomas the Tank Engine, Santa Specials and other out-of-the-ordinary facilities, please enquire of the appropriate railway company for details. Operating days for these are shown by the letter X on the grids.

The telephone number and postal address of each railway operator is shown at the head of each entry so that specific enquiries can be made direct.

The entries are mostly in alphabetical order but in some cases there has been a slight variation to meet space requirements.

It would be helpful if this timetable was read in conjunction with the annual publication *Railways Restored,* obtained from booksellers or direct from Ian Allan Publishing Ltd.

DISCLAIMER

This timetable has been compiled from information received from operating companies and is believed to be accurate. However, neither the publisher nor HRA accept any responsibility for any loss, damage or delay which may be caused by variances between this brochure and actual operations or any other cause.

© Ian Allan Publishing Ltd 2000

MARKS OF QUALITY

Some railways excel in certain fields, and in this timetable special merit markings are applied as has been thought appropriate. The symbols represent individual quality; a double symbol represents excellence. Winners in the 1999 Ian Allan Independent Railway of the Year Awards are highlighted.

 Award winner 1999   Interesting Rolling Stock   On-board catering

 On-shore catering   Interesting Engines   Interesting Stations and Signals

 Big Engines   Loos   Views from the train

INDEX TO TIMETABLES

* *Narrow Gauge Railway*   † *1999 Award Winners*

Cover illustration by Alan P. Barnes.

AVON VALLEY RAILWAY
Bitton Station, Bath Road, Willsbridge, Bristol BS30 9YZ   **0117 932 7296**

2000	1	2	3	4	5	6	7	8	9	10	11	12	13	14	15	16	17	18	19	20	21	22	23	24	25	26	27	28	29	30	31
Jan	C																														
Apr																					B	B	X	X						B	
May	B					T	T								A						A						B	B			
June			A							A							A							A							
July		A							A							A							A							A	
Aug	C				A				C				A			C				A			C			B	B	B			C
Sept			A							A							A							A						T	
Oct	T																														
Dec		S	S	S				S	S							S	S						S	S							C

X denotes special service, S denotes Santa Specials, T denotes Thomas event.   *No service in February, March and November.*

Service A & B   ★

Bitton	dep	11.00	12.15	13.30	14.45	16.00	17.00
River Boyd	No alightening or boarding (Reverse)						
Bitton	dep	11.20	12.35	13.50	15.05	16.20	17.20
Oldland	dep	11.40	12.55	14.10	15.25	16.40	17.40
Bitton	arr	11.45	13.00	14.15	15.30	16.45	17.45

Service C

11.00	12.30	14.00	15.30
11.20	12.50	14.20	15.50
11.40	13.10	14.40	16.10
11.45	13.15	14.45	16.15

★ Service B only.

BALA LAKE RAILWAY
The Station, Llanuwchllyn, Bala, Gwynedd LL23 7DD   **01678 540666**

This railway is one of the Great Little Trains of Wales. The 2ft gauge line offers a nine mile return journey along the shore of Bala Lake through the beautiful scenery of the Snowdonia National Park. The trains give excellent views of the lake and its surrounding pastoral and woodland scenery.

The line's main station, Llanuwchllyn, has adequate car parking and there is a well-stocked buffet and souvenir shop. Bala Station has only limited roadside car parking and is some 12 minutes walk from the town centre.

2000	1	2	3	4	5	6	7	8	9	10	11	12	13	14	15	16	17	18	19	20	21	22	23	24	25	26	27	28	29	30	31
Apr															A	A	A	A	A	A	A	A	A	A	A	A	A	A	A	A	
May	A	A	A	A		A	A		A	A	A		A	A		A	A	A		A	A		A	A		A	A		A	A	A
June	A	A	A	A		A	A	A		A	A		A	A	A		A	A		A	A	A		A	A		A	A		A	A
July	A	A	A	A	A	A	A	A	A	A	A	A	A	A	A	A	A	A	A	A	A	A	A	A	A	A	A	A	A	A	A
Aug	A	A	A	A	A	A	A	A	A	A	A	A	A	A	A	A	A	A	A	A	A	A	A	A	A	A	A	A	A	A	A
Sept	A	A	A		A	A	A		A	A		A	A	A		A	A		A	A	A		A	A		A	A		A		
Oct	A																														

No service in January, February, March, November and December except Santa weekend (9/10 December).

Service A

Llanuwchllyn	dep	11.15	12.50	14.25	16.00
Bala	dep	11.50	13.25	15.00	16.35

Journey times:

Llanuwchllyn–Bala: Return trip 1 hour; single trip 25 minutes. Break of journey allowed at any station.

Bala–Llanuwchllyn: Return trip 1 hour 30 minutes as train stops at Llanuwchllyn to take on coal and water etc. Single journey 25 minutes.

All trains arrive at and depart from Llangower 10 minutes after leaving Llanuwchllyn and 15 minutes after leaving Bala. Trains also call by request at Pentrepiod, Glanllyn and Bryn Hynod halts. To join the train please signal clearly to the Driver. To alight, inform the Guard when you board the train.

BLUEBELL RAILWAY
Sheffield Park Station, Uckfield, East Sussex TN22 3QL   **01825 723777**

Trains run between
SHEFFIELD PARK – HORSTED KEYNES – KINGSCOTE

Bus service 473 operates between Kingscote and East Grinstead, connecting with Connex South Central services from London Victoria and East Croydon.

TRAINS RUN EVERY WEEKEND.
DAILY FROM MAY TO SEPTEMBER AND DURING SCHOOL HOLIDAYS

Please phone for details:
Talking timetable 01825 722370 **General Enquiries** 01825 723777

BATTLEFIELD LINE (SHACKERSTONE RLWY)   01827 880754
Shackerstone Station, Shackerstone, nr Nuneaton, Warks CV13 6NW

Please phone for timetable details.

BODMIN & WENFORD RAILWAY
Bodmin General Station, Bodmin, Cornwall PL31 1AQ   01208 73666

Enjoy a relaxing journey viewing the Cornish countryside on the only Heritage standard gauge railway in Cornwall and the only railway in the country that operates two branch lines from the terminus at Bodmin General. Travel to Bodmin Parkway by main line train with cross platform interchange, also walk to Lanhydrock House (N.T.). Our other branch goes to Boscarne Junction for the Camel Trail. Total route mileage is 6½ miles and the ruling gradient for much of the way is 1 in 40.

We have a buffet serving light meals, sandwiches, hot/cold drinks as well as a souvenir shop at Bodmin General, and a bar operates on most train services.

2000	1	2	3	4	5	6	7	8	9	10	11	12	13	14	15	16	17	18	19	20	21	22	23	24	25	26	27	28	29	30	31
Mar	A							A							A							A			X	X			A		
Apr		A			A			A			A					A	A	A	A	A	X	X	X	X	A	A	A	A	A	A	
May	A	A	A			A			A			A				A				A				A			X	X	X	A	A
June	A	A	A	A	A	A	A	A	A	A	A	A	A	A	A	A	A	A	A	A	A	A	A	A	A	A	A	A	A	A	
July	A	A	A	A	A	A	A	A	A	B	B	B	B	X	X	X	X	B	B	B	X	X	X	X	B	B	B	B	A	A	B
Aug	B	B	B	B	A	A	B	B	B	B	B	B	A	A	B	B	B	B	B	A	A	B	B	B	B	B	B	A	B	B	B
Sept	B	X	X	A	A	A	A	A	A	A	A	A	A	A	A	A	A	A	A	A	A	A	A	A	A	A	A	A	A	X	
Oct	X			A				A				A				A				A	A	A	A	A	A	A	A	A			
Dec		S	S						S	S						S	S						S	S	A	A					A

X denotes special service, S denotes Santa Specials, see local announcements.   *No service in January, February and November.*

Service A
★

		★				
Bodmin General	dep	10.25	11.20	12.20	14.10	15.10
Bodmin Parkway	arr	10.37	–	12.37	–	15.27
Boscarne Junction	arr	–	11.35	–	14.25	–
Boscarne Junction	dep	–	11.45	–	14.35	–
Bodmin Parkway	dep	10.40	–	12.48	–	15.38
Bodmin General	arr	10.52	12.02	13.10	14.52	16.00

Service B
†

10.25	11.15	12.10	13.15	14.10	15.15	16.10
10.37	–	12.27	–	14.27	–	16.27
–	11.30	–	13.30	–	15.30	–
–	11.38	–	13.38	–	15.38	–
10.40	–	12.35	–	14.35	–	16.35
10.52	11.55	12.57	13.55	14.57	15.55	16.57

★ Only runs Mondays to Fridays 30th May to 7th July, 4th-29th September (Diesel Train).   † Diesel Train.

BO'NESS & KINNEIL RAILWAY
Union Street, Bo'ness, West Lothian EH51 9AQ   01506 822298

2000	1	2	3	4	5	6	7	8	9	10	11	12	13	14	15	16	17	18	19	20	21	22	23	24	25	26	27	28	29	30	31
Apr	B	B						B	B							B	B				A	A	A	A					A	A	
May	A					A	A						A	A						X	X					A	A			A	
June			A	A					A	A					A	A					A	A									
July	A	A		A	A	A	A	A	A		A	A	A	A	A	A		A	A	A	A	A		A	A	A	A	A	A	A	A
Aug	A	A	A	A	A	A		A	A	A	A	X	X		A	A	A	A	A	A		A	A	A	A	A	A				
Sept		X	X					A	A						A	A					A	A								A	
Oct	A					A	A						A	A						A	A										
Dec		S	S					S	S						S	S						S	S							X	X

X denotes Gala days and other non-standard timetables,
S denotes Santa Specials, see local announcements.   *No service in January, February, March and November.*

Service A
Bo'ness	dep	12.15	13.45	15.00	16.15

Service B
11.00	12.15	13.45	15.00	16.15

BRECON MOUNTAIN RAILWAY
Pant Station, Merthyr Tydfil CF48 2UP　　　　　**01685 722988**

Please phone for timetable details.

BURE VALLEY RAILWAY – See page 11

CHASEWATER LIGHT RAILWAY – See page 30

CHURNET VALLEY RAILWAY PLC – See page 12

CLEETHORPES COAST LIGHT RAILWAY
Lakeside Station, Kings Road, Cleethorpes, Lincs DN35 0AG　　01427 604657

2000	1	2	3	4	5	6	7	8	9	10	11	12	13	14	15	16	17	18	19	20	21	22	23	24	25	26	27	28	29	30	31
Jan	A	A						A	A						A	A						A	A						A	A	
Feb				A	A						A	A				A	A						A	A	A	A					
Mar	A	A	A	A	A					A	A				A	A						A	A								
Apr	A	A						A	A						A	A	A	A	A	A	A	B	B	A	A	A	A	A	A	B	
May	B	A	A	A	A	A	B	A	A	A	A	A	X	X	A	A	A	A	A	A	B	A	A	A	A	A	X	X	X	A	A
June	A	A	X	X	A	A	A	A	A	X	X	A	A	A	A	A	A	B	A	A	A	A	A	A	B	A	A	A	A	A	
July	X	X	A	A	A	A	A	A	B	A	X	A	A	A	A	A	B	A	A	A	A	A	B	A	A	A	A	A	A	B	A
Aug	A	A	T	T	T	T	A	A	A	A	A	A	B	A	A	A	A	A	A	B	A	A	A	A	A	X	X	X	A	A	A
Sept	A	A	B	A	A	A	A	A	X	X	A	B	A	A	A	X	X	A	A	A	A	A	A	A	A	A	A	A	A	A	
Oct	A					A	A					A	A						A	A	A	A	A	A	A	A	A	A			X
Nov			A	A					A	A				A	A						A	A									
Dec		A	A				A	A				A	A								S	S	S		A	A	A	A	A	A	

Service A: trains every 40 mintes from Lakeside Station.
Service B: trains every 20 minutes from Lakeside Station.
Service X, T, SL: Special Events. For more information please ring 01472 604657.

Timetables subject to change during 2000 due to opening of extension.

DEAN FOREST RAILWAY
Norchard Railway Centre, Forest Road, Lydney, Glos GL15 4ET　　01594 843423

2000	1	2	3	4	5	6	7	8	9	10	11	12	13	14	15	16	17	18	19	20	21	22	23	24	25	26	27	28	29	30	31
Feb																							B	B							
Apr		A							A							A						B	B	A	A					B	A
May	A				A					A						A						A				B	A	A		X	X
June	X	X	X	X			B		B	A			B			B	A		B			B		B	A			B			
July	B	A			B			B	A			B			B	A			B			B	A			B	B	B		B	A
Aug	B	B	B		B	A		B	B	B		B	A		B	B	B		B	A		B	B	B		B	A	A	B	B	B
Sept	X	X	X						A							A							A							B	
Oct	A							A								X						A		B	B	B			A		
Dec		S						S	S							S	S						S	S						X	X

X denotes special service, S denotes Santa Specials, see local announcements.　　*No service in January, March and November.*

Service A

Norchard	dep	11.00	12.00	13.30	14.30	15.30	16.30
Lydney Junction	arr	11.15	12.15	13.45	14.45	15.45	16.38
Lydney Junction	dep	11.25	12.25	13.55	14.55	15.55	16.55
Norchard	arr	11.40	12.40	14.10	15.10	16.10	17.10

Service B

11.00	12.00	13.30	14.30	15.30
11.15	12.15	13.45	14.45	15.45
11.25	12.25	13.55	14.55	15.55
11.40	12.40	14.10	15.10	16.10

Trains call at St Mary's Halt (in both directions) eight minutes after leaving Norchard and three minutes after leaving Lydney Junction.

COLNE VALLEY RAILWAY
Castle Hedingham, Halstead, Essex CO9 3DZ   **01787 461174**

2000	1	2	3	4	5	6	7	8	9	10	11	12	13	14	15	16	17	18	19	20	21	22	23	24	25	26	27	28	29	30	31
Mar					D							D							D							A					
Apr		A						A								A			B		A	A	A	A		B	D		D	A	
May	A				A								A				E	A							A	A	A	D	B		
June	D		D	A							E	M	T	T	T	T	T	T	T	T	T	T	T	T	T						
July	E	A						A								A			E	A				D	B	B	D	D	A		
Aug	D	B	B	D	D	A			D	B	B	B	D	D	A		D	B	B	B	D	D	A		D	B	B	B	D	A	A
Sept		E	A						A							E	A							A							
Oct	A		V	V	V	V		A								A								A	D	B	D			D	
Dec							S						S	S					S				S	S		S					

No service in January, February and November.

Service A – Steam Service (12.00–16.00)
Service B – Steam Service (11.00–15.00)
Service D – Heritage Diesel Service (11.00-15.00)
Service E – Evening Murder Mystery Wine & Dine
Service M – Model Engineering Exhibition
Service S – Santa Specials
Service T – Friends of Thomas
Service V – Victorian Special

DIDCOT RAILWAY CENTRE
Didcot, Oxfordshire OX11 7NJ   **01235 817200**

See the steam trains of the Great Western Railway in an original engine shed, branch line station and signalling, a re-creation of Brunel's broad gauge trackwork and much more.

On Steamdays there are rides in the 1930s trains.

DIDCOT STEAM 2000 27th May–4th June – the Great Western steam event of the millennium with up to 2,000 locomotives, full size and models.

Entrance at Didcot Parkway rail station, signed from M4 (junction 13) and A34.

2000	1	2	3	4	5	6	7	8	9	10	11	12	13	14	15	16	17	18	19	20	21	22	23	24	25	26	27	28	29	30	31
Jan	S	S	S					W	W						W	W					W	W							W	W	
Feb				W	W						W	W					W	S	W	W	S	W	W	W	W						
Mar			T	T	T						O	O						O	O								O	S			
Apr	O	S	O	O	O	O	O	O	O	O	O	O	O	O	O	O	O	O	O	O	O	S	S	S	S	O	O	O	O	S	
May	S	O	O	O	O	O	S	O	O	O	O	O	O	O	O	O	O	O	O	O	O	O	O	O	O	O	X	X	X	X	X
June	X	X	X	X	O	O	O	O	O	O	O	O	O	O	O	O	O	O	O	O	O	O	O	O	O	O	O	O	O	O	
July	O	S	O	O	O	O	O	O	S	O	O	S	O	O	O	S	O	O	S	O	O	O	S	O	O	O	S	O	O	S	O
Aug	O	S	O	O	O	S	O	O	S	O	O	O	S	O	O	O	S	O	O	O	S	O	O	O	S	O	O	S	S	S	O
Sept	O	O	S	O	O	O	O	O	O	O	O	O	O	O	O	O	O	O	O	O	O	O	S	S	O	O	O	O	O	O	
Oct	S				T	T	T						O	O							O	O	O	O	O	O	X	X	S		
Nov			O	S						O	O						O	O					O	S							
Dec		O	O					O	O				T	T	T					T	T					O	O	O	O	S	

O	Open 10.00-17.00	T	Day out with Thomas	W	Winter opening 10.00 – 16.00
S	Steamday – trains run continuously		Steamday/Thomas Santa Special	X	Special event

EAST LANCASHIRE RAILWAY
Bolton Street Station, Bury, Lancs BL9 0EY   **0161-764 7790**

This railway operates mainly at weekends. Trains run from Bury to Rawtenstall, journey time 41 minutes. Please phone or write for timetable details.

EAST SOMERSET RAILWAY
Cranmore Station, Shepton Mallet, Somerset   **01749 880417**

This two mile railway operates a limited service throughout the year based on departures from Cranmore Station near Shepton Mallett. Please phone for timetable details.

FAIRBOURNE & BARMOUTH RAILWAY
Beach Road, Fairbourne, Gwynedd LL38 2PZ   **01341 250362**

2000	1	2	3	4	5	6	7	8	9	10	11	12	13	14	15	16	17	18	19	20	21	22	23	24	25	26	27	28	29	30	31
Apr												A	A	A	A	A	A	A	A	A	A	B	B	B	B	B	B	B	B	B	
May	B	B	A	A	A	A	A	A	A	A	A	A	A	A	A	A	A	A	A	A	A	A	A	A	A	A	B	B	B	B	B
June	B	B	B	B	A	A	A	A	A	A	A	A	A	A	A	A	B	B	B	A	A	A	A	A	A	A	A	A	A	A	
July	A	A	A	A	A	A	A	B	B	B	B	B	B	B	B	B	B	B	B	B	B	B	B	B	B	B	B	B	B	B	B
Aug	B	B	B	B	B	B	B	B	B	B	B	B	B	B	B	B	B	B	B	B	B	B	B	B	B	B	B	B	B	B	B
Sept	A	A	A	A	A	A	A	A	A	A	A	A	A	A	A	A	A	A	A	A	A	A	A	A							
Oct																					A	A	A	A	A	A	A	A	A		
Dec																S	S														

S denotes Santa Specials, please telephone for details.   *No service in January, February, March and November.*

Service A

Fairbourne	dep	11.00	12.30	14.15	15.45
Penrhyn Point	dep	11.45	13.15	15.00	16.30

Service B

10.40	11.20	12.00	12.40	13.40	14.20	15.00	15.40	16.20
11.20	12.00	12.40	13.40	14.20	15.00	15.40	16.20	17.00

FFESTINIOG RAILWAY
Harbour Station, Porthmadog, Gwynedd LL49 9NF   **01766 512340**

The steam-hauled narrow gauge Ffestiniog Railway runs from the picturesque harbour town of Porthmadog, through the Snowdonia National Park, to the historic slate mining town of Blaenau Ffestiniog. On their journey, the trains pass through tranquil pastures and forests, past lakes and waterfalls, round horseshoe bends and even round a complete spiral, sometimes clinging to the mountainside, sometimes tunnelling through it. Amongst its various motive power are the unique Double Farlie locomotives. Special events run throughout the year.

2000	1	2	3	4	5	6	7	8	9	10	11	12	13	14	15	16	17	18	19	20	21	22	23	24	25	26	27	28	29	30	31
Feb																			A	A	A	A	A	A	A	A	A				
Mar				B	B						B	B						B	B						B	B	B	B	B	B	B
Apr	C	C	D	D	D	D	D	C	C	C	D	D	D	D	D	D	C	C	D	D	D	D	E	E	E	E	E	E	D	D	
May	D	D	D	D	D	C	C	D	D	D	D	D	D	C	C	D	D	D	D	D	C	C	D	D	D	D	C	E	F	F	F
June	F	E	C	C	D	D	D	D	D	D	C	C	D	D	D	D	D	C	C	D	D	D	D	D	C	C	D	D	D	D	
July	C	C	D	D	D	D	D	C	C	D	D	D	D	D	C	C	D	D	D	D	D	E	E	F	F	F	F	E	E	E	F
Aug	F	F	F	E	E	E	F	F	F	F	E	E	E	F	F	F	F	E	E	E	F	F	F	F	E	E	E	F	F	F	F
Sept	E	E	C	D	D	D	D	D	D	C	C	D	D	D	D	D	C	C	D	D	D	D	D	C	D	D	D	D	D	D	
Oct	D	D	D	D	D	D	D	D	D	D	D	D	D	D	D	D	D	D	D	D	D	D	D	D	D	D	D	D	B	B	B
Nov	B	B	B	B	B			B	B									B	B					B	B				B	B	
Dec										S	S							S	S						B	B	B	B	B	B	

X denotes special service, S denotes Santa Specials, see local announcements.

Service A

		D	D
Porthmadog	dep	10.25	13.45
Blaenau	arr	11.40	14.55
Blaenau	dep	11.55	15.10
Porthmadog	arr	13.10	16.20

Service B

D	D
10.25	13.45
11.40	14.55
11.55	15.10
13.10	16.20

Service C

10.25	12.45	13.45	16.00
11.40	13.50	14.55	17.05
11.55	14.00	15.10	17.30
13.10	15.05	16.20	18.35

Service D

	D		D
10.25	12.45	13.45	16.00
11.40	13.50	14.55	17.05
11.55	14.00	15.10	17.30
13.10	15.05	16.20	18.35

Service E

			D		D
Porthmadog	dep	10.25	11.35	12.45	13.45	14.55	16.00
Blaenau	arr	11.40	12.50	13.50	14.55	16.05	17.05
Blaenau	dep	11.55	13.00	14.00	15.10	16.15	17.30
Porthmadog	arr	13.10	14.10	15.05	16.20	17.30	18.35

Service F

D							D
09.10	10.25	11.35	12.45	13.45	14.55	16.00	18.10
10.10	11.40	12.50	13.50	14.55	16.05	17.05	19.20
10.25	11.55	13.00	14.00	15.10	16.15	17.30	19.50
12.05	13.10	14.10	15.05	16.20	17.30	18.35	20.55

D denotes diesel hauled service.

All trains call at intermediate stations: Minffordd (10), Penrhyn (15) and Tan-y-Bwlch (35) minutes after leaving Porthmadog and at Tan-y-Bwlch (25), Penrhyn (40) and Minffordd (55) minutes after leaving Blaenau.

EMBSAY & BOLTON ABBEY RAILWAY
Embsay Station, Embasy, Skipton, Yorks BD23 6AX **01756 795189**

This railway operates a service between Embsay and Bolton Abbey during the summer. Please phone or write for timetable details.

FOXFIELD STEAM RAILWAY
Blythe Bridge, Stoke-on-Trent ST11 9EA **01782 396210**

This railway was constructed in 1883 to carry coal from Foxfield Colliery to the North Staffordshire Railway at Blythe Bridge. Following the closure of the colliery in 1965 the line was rescued by the volunteers of the Foxfield Light Railway Society, who today operate the line as a passenger carrying railway.

   The steam train makes a five mile round trip through scenic Staffordshire countryside, and drinks are available on the train, meals are available in our licensed buffet, and you may visit the Souvenir Shop and a selection of our locomotives and rolling stock in the Museum. Ample free car parking.

2000	1	2	3	4	5	6	7	8	9	10	11	12	13	14	15	16	17	18	19	20	21	22	23	24	25	26	27	28	29	30	31
Apr		A							A								A						A	A	A					A	A
May	A					A							A						A						A	A	A				
June				A						A						A	A							A							
July		A							A								A						A						X	X	
Aug				A						A					A	A							A	A	A						
Sept		A							A							A							A						A	A	
Dec		S	S						S	S						S	S						S	S							

X denotes special service, S denotes Santa Specials, see local announcements.   *No service in January, February, March and November.*

Service A

Blythe Bridge	dep	11.30	13.00	14.00	15.00	16.00

GOLDEN VALLEY LIGHT RAILWAY
Butterley Station, Ripley, Derbyshire DE5 3QZ **01773 747674**

2000	1	2	3	4	5	6	7	8	9	10	11	12	13	14	15	16	17	18	19	20	21	22	23	24	25	26	27	28	29	30	31
Mar				X	X																										
Apr	B	B					B	B							B	B							B	B	B	A	A	A	A	B	B
May	B					B	B						X	X					B	B					X	X	X	X	X		
June	X	X	X	X			A			B	B		A			B	B			A			B	B		A					
July	B	B			A			B	B		A			B	B		A		X	B	B			A			X	X	X		
Aug	X	X	X	X	X	X	A	A	A	A	A	X	X	A	A	A	A	A	B	B	A	A	A	A	A	B	B	A	A	A	A
Sept	A	B	B		A			B	B		A			B	B		A			B	B		A					B				
Oct	B				B	B						B	B				B	B				X	B								
Nov			X																												

X denotes special service, see local announcements.   *No services in January, February and December.*

Service A

		★				★	
Butterley Park	dep	11.45	12.30	13.15	14.00	14.45	15.30
Newlands Inn	arr	11.55	12.40	13.25	14.10	14.55	15.40
Newlands Inn	dep	12.05	12.50	13.35	14.20	15.05	15.50
Butterley Park	arr	12.15	13.00	13.45	14.30	15.15	16.00

All trains from Newlands Inn call at Brands Crossing (5 minutes).

★ Runs as required.

Service B

							★
Butterley Park	dep	12.30	13.15	14.00	14.45	15.30	16.15
Newlands Inn	arr	12.40	13.25	14.10	14.55	15.40	16.25
Newlands Inn	dep	12.50	13.35	14.20	15.05	15.50	16.35
Butterley Park	arr	13.00	13.45	14.30	15.15	16.00	16.45

GLOUCESTERSHIRE WARWICKSHIRE RAILWAY
The Railway Station, Toddington, Gloucs GL54 5DT   **01242 621405**

2000	1	2	3	4	5	6	7	8	9	10	11	12	13	14	15	16	17	18	19	20	21	22	23	24	25	26	27	28	29	30	31
Jan		D	E						D							D							D							D	
Feb										D									D								D				
Mar				D	F					D	F					F	F						X	X	X						
Apr	C	C					C	C							X	X						C	C	A	A	E	E	E	E	C	A
May	A					C	C					C	C						C	C							C	A	A	E	E
June	E	E	C	C					C	C						C	C						C	C							
July	C	C			D			C	C			D			B	B		X	X	X		B	B			E	E	E		B	B
Aug	E	E	E	X	C	A		E	E	E		X	X		E	E	E		A	A		E	E	E	X	A	A	A	E	E	E
Sept		C	C					C	C							C	C						C	C						C	
Oct	C					C	C					X	X				X	X	X			D	D	D			D	D			
Nov				D									D									C	D								
Dec		S	S						S	S													S	S			E	X		E	E

X denotes special service, S denotes Santa Specials, see local announcements.

Services A & B

Toddington	dep	10.45	11.30 ★	12.15	13.30 ★	14.15	15.00 ★	15.45	16.30 ★
Winchcombe	dep	10.58	11.43	12.27	13.43	14.28	15.13	15.58	16.42
Winchcombe	dep	11.45	12.30	13.05	14.30	15.15	16.00	16.45	17.20
Toddington	arr	11.56	12.41	13.16	14.41	15.26	16.11	16.56	17.31

★ Diesel trains on Service B only.
† Diesel train on 13.40.

Service C

Toddington	dep	10.45	12.10	13.40 †	15.00	16.25
Winchcombe	dep	10.57	12.22	13.52	15.12	16.37
Winchcombe	dep	11.35	13.00	14.27	15.50	17.15
Toddington	arr	11.46	13.11	14.38	16.01	17.26

Service D (diesel railcar)

10.45	11.45	14.00	15.00	16.00
10.56	11.56	14.11	15.11	16.11
11.20	12.20	14.35	15.35	16.35
11.30	12.30	14.45	15.45	16.45

Service E

Toddington	dep	10.45	12.15	14.15	15.45
Winchcombe	dep	10.57	12.27	14.27	15.57
Winchcombe	dep	11.35	13.05	15.05	16.35
Toddington	arr	11.46	13.16	15.16	16.46

Service F

10.45	12.15	14.15	15.45
11.05	12.35	14.35	16.05
11.35	13.05	15.05	16.35
11.40	13.10	15.10	16.40

All trains proceed to and return from Gotherington which is beyond Winchcombe but at which there is no passenger access or egress.

Not all trains are steam hauled.

GREAT CENTRAL RAILWAY
Great Central Road, Loughborough, Leicestershire LE11 1RW   **01509 230726**

Train services may be altered during engineering work in connection with the commissioning of Double Track Operation. This work will commence in April 2000 and visitors are advised to telephone 01509 230726 for advice of train times from May 2000 onwards.

Trains between Loughborough Central and Leicester North until further notice.

Weekdays only from 26th to 28th April 2000 and from 30th May to 21st September 2000

			B	
Loughborough Central	dep	11.00	13.15	15.30	19.30
Leicester North	arr	11.29	13.48	15.59	20.26
Leicester North	dep	11.50	14.05	16.20	20.45
Loughborough Central	arr	12.20	14.35	16.50	22.15

Saturdays, Sundays and Bank Holiday Mondays throughout the year. Also Good Friday and Easter Tuesday

	D	A			C
09.30	10.15	11.45	13.15	14.00	15.30	17.00	19.30
09.59	10.44	12.14	13.48	14.29	15.59	17.29	20.25
10.20	11.05	12.36	14.05	14.50	16.20	17.50	20.45
10.50	11.35	13.05	14.35	15.20	16.50	18.20	22.15

All trains call at intermediate stations: Quorn (8) and Rothley (17) minutes after leaving Loughborough and at Rothley (9) and Quorn (22) minutes after leaving Leicester North.

A – **"The Silver Jubilee"** runs on Saturdays, Sundays and Bank Holiday Mondays to provide a First Class traditional luncheon service.
B – **"The Master Cutler"** runs on Wednesday evenings to provide a First Class traditional dining service.
C – **"The Charnwood Forester"** runs on most Saturday evenings, as advertised, to provide a First Class prestigious dining service.
D – This train will be hauled by a classic diesel locomotive during the months of March and April.

Additional trains run during "Gala" days and Bank Holiday Mondays.

SEE ADVERTISEMENT ON OUTSIDE BACK COVER

GROUDLE GLEN RAILWAY
29 Hawardine Avenue, Douglas, Isle of Man IM1 4EP   01624 622138 (evenings only)

Operation days

Sundays	23rd April–24th September	11.00–16.30
Easter Monday	24th April	11.00–16.30
Wednesdays	5th July–16th August	19.00–21.00
Tuesdays	1st, 8th, 15th August	19.00–21.00

Trains operate at 30 minute intervals between the stated times.

GWILI RAILWAY
Bronwydd Arms Station, Bromwydd Arms, Carmarthen SA33 6HT   01267 230666

2000	1	2	3	4	5	6	7	8	9	10	11	12	13	14	15	16	17	18	19	20	21	22	23	24	25	26	27	28	29	30	31
Apr																					T	T	T	T					A	A	
May	A					A				A				A							A							A	A	A	A
June	A	A		A		A				A				A				A			A					A			A		
July		A			A				A			A				A			A			A	A	A	A	A	A	A	A	A	A
Aug	A	A	A	A	A	A	A	A	A	A	A	A	A	A	A	A	A	A	A	A	A	A	A	A	A	A	A	A	A	A	A
Sept			A							A								A							A						
Oct																					A					A	A				
Dec									S	S						S	S			S	S	S	S	S							

T denotes Thomas event, S denotes Santa Specials,
A denotes normal operating, please phone for timetable details.

No service in January, February, March and November.

ISLE OF MAN STEAM RAILWAY
Isle of Man Transport, Transport Headquarters, Banks Circus,
Douglas, Isle of Man IM1 5PT (as from March 2000)   **01624 663366**

Trains run daily from 1st April to 29th October 2000.

Address and phone number above from March 2000. Until then the address is:
Strathallan Crescent, Douglas, Isle of Man IM2 4NR. Tel: 01624 663366.

Service A

Douglas	dep	10.00	10.35	12.00	14.00	14.35 ★	16.15
Port Erin	arr	11.00	11.35	13.00	15.00	15.35	17.15
Port Erin	dep	10.15	11.40	12.15	14.15	15.55 ★	16.30
Douglas	arr	11.17	12.42	13.17	15.17	16.57	17.32

★ Runs Mondays to Thursdays 17th July – 24th August 2000.

All trains call at intermediate stations: Port Soderick (12), Ballasalla (32), Castletown (39), Colby (49) and Port St Mary (57) minutes after leaving Douglas and at Port St Mary (4), Colby (12), Castletown (23), Ballasalla (30) and Port Soderick (50) minutes after leaving Port Erin.

ISLE OF WIGHT STEAM RAILWAY
The Station, Havenstreet Village, Ryde, IOW PO33 4DS   01983 882204

Trains operate over a five mile stretch of the former Ryde–Cowes line closed in 1966, using vintage carriages dating back to 1864, and locomotives, the oldest of which was built in 1876. The unique atmosphere of the Island's once extensive railway system under Southern Railway ownership, has been carefully preserved for future generations to experience. There are four stations, Wootton, Ashey, Havenstreet, and Smallbrook Junction, where there is an interchange with the Ryde–Shanklin electric trains. Shop, Museum, Cafeteria, Children's play area, Woodland Walk, and the Company's headquarters and workshops are all based in Havenstreet.

2000	1	2	3	4	5	6	7	8	9	10	11	12	13	14	15	16	17	18	19	20	21	22	23	24	25	26	27	28	29	30	31
Mar																				B			B							B	
Apr		B			B			B				B				B				A	A	A	A	A	A	A	A	A	A	A	
May	A	B	B	B	B	B	B			A	A		B	B			A	A		B	B			A	A		B	B	A	A	A
June	A	B	B	B	B	A	A	A	B	B	B	B	A	A	A	B	B	B	B	A	A	A	B	B	B	B	A	A	A	B	
July	B	B	B	A	A	A	B	B	B	B	A	A	A	B	B	B	B	A	A	A	B	B	B	B	A	A	A	A	A	A	A
Aug	A	A	A	A	A	A	A	A	A	A	A	A	A	A	A	A	A	A	A	A	A	A	A	A	A	X	X	X	X	X	A
Sept	B	B	B	B	A	A	A	B	B	B	B	A	A	A	B	B	B	B	A	A	A	B	B	B	B	A	A	A	B	B	
Oct	B				A		B	B				A			B	B				A		B	B			A	A	A		B	B
Nov					A																										
Dec																	S	S	S	S	S	S	S	S							

X denotes special service, S denotes Santa Specials, see local announcements.   *No service in January and February*

Service A

Smallbrook Jct	dep	–	10.56	11.56	12.56	14.33	15.33	16.33
Havenstreet	arr	–	11.07	12.07	13.07	14.44	15.44	16.44
Havenstreet	dep	–	11.09	12.09	13.09	14.46	15.46	16.46
Wootton	arr	–	11.15	12.15	13.15	14.52	15.52	16.52
Wootton	dep	–	11.21	12.21	13.21	14.58	15.58	16.58
Havenstreet	arr	–	11.26	12.26	13.26	15.03	16.03	17.03
Havenstreet	dep	10.33	11.38	12.38	14.15	15.15	16.15	
Smallbrook Jct	arr	10.49	11.49	12.49	14.26	15.26	16.26	

Service B

–	10.56	12.12	–	14.14	15.55
–	11.07	12.23	–	14.25	16.06
–	11.09	12.25	–	14.27	16.08
–	11.15	12.31	–	14.33	16.14
–	11.21	12.37	–	14.39	16.20
–	11.26	12.42	–	14.44	16.25
10.33	11.54	–	13.56	15.35	–
10.49	12.05	–	14.07	15.46	–

BURE VALLEY RAILWAY
Aylsham Station, Norwich Road, Aylsham, Norfolk NR11 6BW   01263 733858

2000	1	2	3	4	5	6	7	8	9	10	11	12	13	14	15	16	17	18	19	20	21	22	23	24	25	26	27	28	29	30	31
Apr																B	B	B	B	B	B	A	A	A	B	B	B			B	
May	A	B	B	B			B	B	B	B	B			B	B	B	B	B		B	B	B	B	B				T	T	A	A
June	A	B	B	A	A	A	A	A		A	A	A	A	A		A	A	A	A	A		A	A	A	A	A	A	A	A	B	
July	B	A	A	A	A	A	A	A	X	A	A	A	A	A	A	A	A	A	A	A	A	A	A	A	A	A	A	A	A	A	A
Aug	A	A	A	A	A	A	A	A	A	A	A	A	A	A	A	A	A	A	A	A	A	A	A	A	A	A	A	A	A	A	A
Sept	A	A	A	B	B	B	B		B	B	B	B	B		B	B	B	B	B		T	T	B	B	B	B					
Oct																	B	B	B	B	B		B	B	B	B	B	B			
Nov																									S	S					
Dec	S	S			S	S		S	S			S	S			S	S	S	S	S	S	S	S	S							

X denotes special service, S denotes Santa Specials,
T denotes Thomas events, please phone for details.   *No service in January, February and March.*

Service A

Aylsham	dep	10.15	11.30	12.45	14.00	15.15	16.30
Wroxham	arr	11 00	12.15	13.30	14.45	16.00	17.15
Wroxham	dep	10.15	11.30	12.45	14.00	15.15	16.30
Aylsham	arr	11.00	12.15	13.30	14.00	16.00	17.15

Service B

10.15	12.45	15.15
11.00	13.30	16.00
11.30	14.00	16.30
12.15	14.45	17.15

All trains call at intermediate stations: Brampton (12), Buxton (17) and Coltishall (30) minutes after leaving Aylsham and at Coltishall (15), Buxton (28) and Brampton (33) minutes after leaving Wroxham.

KEIGHLEY & WORTH VALLEY RAILWAY
Haworth Station, Keighley, West Yorkshire BD22 8NJ　　　　**01535 645214**

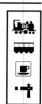

2000	1	2	3	4	5	6	7	8	9	10	11	12	13	14	15	16	17	18	19	20	21	22	23	24	25	26	27	28	29	30	31
Jan	X	X	X					B	C						B	C						B	C					B	C		
Feb					B	C						B	C						B	C						B	C				
Mar			B	B						B	B						B	B								B	B				
Apr	B	B						B	B					B	X					B	B	A	A	E	E	E	E	B	A		
May	A					B	B						X	X					B	B							B	A	A	E	E
June	E	E	X	X					B	A						B	A	E	E	E	E	E	B	A	E	E	E	E	E		
July	B	A	E	E	E	E	E	B	A	E	E	E	E	E	B	A	E	E	E	E	E	X	X	E	E	E	E	E	B	A	E
Aug	E	E	E	E	B	A	E	E	E	E	E	E	B	A	E	E	E	E	E	E	B	A	E	E	E	E	E	B	A	E	E
Sept	E	B	A						B	A						B	A						X	X						B	
Oct	B					B	X						B	B						X	X	X	X	X	X	B	B				
Nov			B	C						B	C						B	C						B	C						
Dec		S	S					S	S						S	S						S	S			C	C	C	C	B	C

X denotes special services, see local announcements.

Service A
Oxenhope	dep		D 09.10		D 10.25	11.05		D 11.50	12.35	13.20	14.05	14.50	15.35	16.20	17.05
Oxenhope	dep	09.10	10.25	11.05	11.50	12.35	13.20	14.05	14.50	15.35	16.20	17.05
Keighley	arr	09.30	10.45	11.30	12.15	13.00	13.45	14.30	15.15	16.00	16.45	17.30
Keighley	dep	09.50	11.10	11.50	12.35	13.20	14.05	14.50	15.35	16.20	17.05	17.50
Oxenhope	arr	10.10	11.30	12.15	13.00	13.45	14.30	15.15	16.00	16.45	17.30	18.15

(D markers above Service A departures: D over 09.10, D over 10.25, D over 11.50)

Service C
Oxenhope	dep	11.05	12.35	14.05	15.35
Keighley	arr	11.30	13.00	14.30	16.00
Keighley	dep	11.50	13.20	14.50	16.20
Oxenhope	arr	12.15	13.45	15.15	16.45

Service B
Oxenhope	dep	D 09.10	D 10.25	11.05	12.35	14.05	15.35	17.05
Keighley	arr	09.30	10.45	11.30	13.00	14.30	16.00	17.30
Keighley	dep	09.50	11.10	11.50	13.20	14.50	16.20	17.50
Oxenhope	arr	10.10	11.30	12.15	13.45	1515	16.45	18.15

Service S
	09.00	09.55	11.15	12.25	13.35	14.45	15.55
	09.25	10.15	11.40	12.50	14.00	15.10	16.20
	09.30	10.48	11.58	13.08	14.18	15.28	–
	09.50	11.10	12.17	13.27	14.37	15.47	–

Service E
Oxenhope	dep	11.25	13.00	14.35	16.10
Keighley	arr	11.50	13.25	15.00	16.35
Keighley	dep	12.10	13.45	15.20	16.55
Oxenhope	arr	12.35	14.10	15.45	17.20

D Diesel Trains

All trains call at intermediate stations: Haworth (6), Oakworth (9), Damems (14) and Ingrow West (18) minutes after leaving Oxenhope and at Ingrow West (4), Damems (6), Oakworth (10) and Haworth (15) minutes after leaving Keighley.

CHURNET VALLEY RAILWAY (1992) PLC
Cheddleton Station, Cheddleton, Staffordshire ST13 7EE　　　　**01538 360522**

2000	1	2	3	4	5	6	7	8	9	10	11	12	13	14	15	16	17	18	19	20	21	22	23	24	25	26	27	28	29	30	31
Feb																			C	C			C								
Apr		A							A						B	A					B	A	A		B				B	A	
May	A					A							A							A					B	A	A				
June			A						A							A								A							
July	B	A					B	A							B	A					B	A			B				C	C	
Aug		C				B	A		B			B	A						B			B	A			B		B	C	C	
Sept			A						C	C						A							A								
Oct	A																														
Dec		S	S						S	S						S	S						S	S							

S denotes Santa Specials, see local announcements.

No service in January, March and November.

Service A
Cheddleton	dep	11.00	12.10	13.20	14.30	15.40	16.50

Service B
	12.00	13.10	14.20	15.30	16.40

Service C
Cheddleton	dep	10.30	11.35	12.45	13.55	15.05	16.15	17.25

All trains call at Consall (7) and Leekbrook (5) minutes after leaving Cheddleton. Overall journey time 55 minutes. For details of forthcoming events please contact Cheddleton Station on 01538 360522.

It is recommended that customers phone to check timetable details.

KENT & EAST SUSSEX RAILWAY
Tenterden Town Station, Tenterden, Kent TN30 6HE   01580 765155

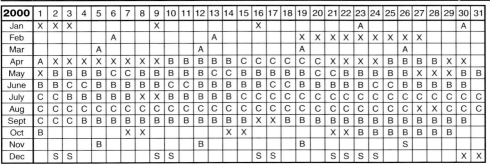

2000	1	2	3	4	5	6	7	8	9	10	11	12	13	14	15	16	17	18	19	20	21	22	23	24	25	26	27	28	29	30	31
Jan	X	X	X						X							X							A							A	
Feb					A							A				X	X	X	X	X	X	X	X								
Mar				A							A								A							A					
Apr	A	X	X	X	X	X	X	X	X	B	B	B	B	B	C	C	C	C	C	C	X	X	X	X	B	B	B	B	X	X	
May	X	B	B	B	B	C	C	B	B	B	B	B	B	C	C	B	B	B	B	B	C	C	B	B	B	B	B	X	X	X	B
June	B	B	C	C	B	B	B	B	C	C	B	B	B	B	B	C	C	B	B	B	B	B	B	C	C	B	B	B	B	B	
July	C	C	B	B	B	B	B	X	X	B	B	B	B	B	C	C	C	C	C	C	C	C	C	C	C	C	C	C	C	C	C
Aug	C	C	C	C	C	C	C	C	C	C	C	C	C	C	C	C	C	C	C	C	C	C	C	C	C	C	X	X	C	C	C
Sept	C	C	C	B	B	B	B	B	B	B	B	B	B	B	B	B	X	X	B	B	B	B	B	B	B	B	B	B	B	B	
Oct	B						X	X						X	X							X	X	B	B	B	B	B	B	B	
Nov				B								B							B								S				
Dec		S	S						S	S						S	S						S	S	S	S				X	X

X denotes special events, S denotes Santa Specials (see below), also see local announcements.

Service A

		★	★
Tenterden Town	dep	11.00	13.15	15.30
Northiam	arr	11.35	13.50	16.05
Northiam	dep	11.50	14.05	16.20
Tenterden Town	arr	12.30	14.35	16.50

Service B

			★	★	★
Tenterden Town	dep	10.40	13.15	15.30
Northiam	arr	11.15	13.53	16.05
Bodiam	arr	11.30	14.05	16.20
Bodiam	dep	11.45	14.20	16.30
Northiam	arr	11.58	14.33	16.43
Tenterden Town	arr	12.35	15.10	17.20

Service C

	★	†	★	†	★	†
	10.40	11.45	13.15	14.20	15.30	16.30
	11.15	12.20	13.53	15.00	16.05	17.05
	11.30	12.35	14.05	15.12	16.20	17.25
	11.45	12.45	14.20	15.30	16.30	17.30
	11.58	12.57	14.33	15.42	16.43	17.40
	12.35	13.45	15.10	16.20	17.20	18.20

Santa Specials: Meet Father Christmas on a full-size steam train. There's a present for every child and Sherry and mince pies for grown-ups. Advance booking essential. Bookings open August.

Notes for all timetables
★ – steam train of 1930s and '50s carriages with first class accommodation and on-board refreshment facilities.
† – steam train including carriages dating from Victorian times.

LAKESIDE & HAVERTHWAITE RAILWAY
Haverthwaite Station, Ulverston, Cumbria LA12 8AL   015395 31594

From the old Victorian station at Haverthwaite, by the main A590 road, hard working steam locomotives haul the trains on this steeply graded railway. Comfortable coaching stock ensures that our passengers have a pleasant and leisurely journey through the contrasting lake and river scenes of the beautiful Leven Valley.

Originally this Furness Railway branch line carried passengers and freight from the old market town of Ulverston (seven miles away) to Lakeside, but now the only part remaining is the 3½ mile section from Haverthwaite through Newby Bridge to the terminus at Lakeside where connections are made with Windermere Lake Cruises' boats which ply the 10½ mile length of England's longest lake, Windermere. At Haverthwaite station there is ample coach and car parking, shop, and licensed restaurant.

2000	1	2	3	4	5	6	7	8	9	10	11	12	13	14	15	16	17	18	19	20	21	22	23	24	25	26	27	28	29	30	31
Apr															A	A	A	A	A	A	A	A	A	A	A	A	A	A	A		
May	A	A	A	A	A	A	A	A	A	A	A	A	A	A	A	A	A	A	A	A	A	A	A	A	A	A	A	A	A	A	A
June	A	A	A	A	A	A	A	A	A	A	A	A	A	A	A	A	A	A	A	A	A	A	A	A	A	A	A	A	A	A	
July	A	A	A	A	A	A	A	A	A	A	A	A	A	A	A	A	A	A	A	A	A	A	A	A	A	A	A	A	A	A	A
Aug	A	A	A	A	A	A	A	A	A	A	A	A	A	A	A	A	A	A	A	A	A	A	A	A	A	A	A	A	A	A	A
Sept	A	A	A	A	A	A	A	A	A	A	A	A	A	A	A	A	A	A	A	A	A	A	A	A	A	A	A	A	A	A	
Oct	A	A	A	A	A	A	A	A	A	A	A	A	A	A	A	A	A	A	A	A	A	A	A	A	A	A	A	A	A		

No service in January, February, March, November and December except Santa weekend (16/17 December).

Service A

							★
Haverthwaite	dep	10.35	11.45	13.00	14.05	15.10	16.15	17.20
Lakeside	arr	10.53	12.03	13.18	14.23	15.28	16.33	17.38
Lakeside	dep	11.15	12.30	13.35	14.40	15.45	16.50	17.48
Haverthwaite	arr	11.33	12.48	13.53	14.58	16.03	17.08	18.06

★ Operates 28th May to 4th June and 23rd July to 3rd September.

All trains call at Newby Bridge (12) after leaving Haverthwaite and (6) minutes after leaving Lakeside.

LEIGHTON BUZZARD RAILWAY
Page's Park Station, Billington Road, Leighton Buzzard LU7 8TN 01525 373888

The Leighton Buzzard Railway takes you on a 65-minute journey into the Bedfordshire countryside, to discover the vanished world of the English narrow-gauge light railway. Built in 1919 to carry sand traffic, it features sharp curves, steep gradients, level crossings, and a unique stretch of roadside running. It is home to the largest collection of narrow-gauge locomotives in Britain – steam, diesel and petrol – and a new attraction is the 1999-built diesel, *Beaudesert*.

2000	1	2	3	4	5	6	7	8	9	10	11	12	13	14	15	16	17	18	19	20	21	22	23	24	25	26	27	28	29	30	31
Mar																			A							A					
Apr		A							A							A					A	B	B			A			A	B	
May	B						A							B					A						A	B	B				A
June			A			C				X	X			C			A	A			C			B			C				
July		X			A				B			A				B			A				B			A				B	
Aug	A	A	A		A	B		A	A	A		A	B		A	A	A		A	B		A	A	A		A	B	B	A	A	A
Sept	D	X	X						B							A							A								
Oct	A							A							A						A		A						A		
Dec		S	S						S	S						S	S					S	S			S	S				

X denotes special service, S denotes Santa Specials, see local announcements.   *No service in January, February and November.*

Service A

Page's Park	dep	11.15	12.45	14.15	15.45 ★
Stonehenge Wks	arr	11.40	13.10	14.40	16.10

Stonehenge Wks	dep	11.55	13.25	14.55	16.25
Page's Park	arr	12.20	13.50	15.20	16.50

Service C

10.30	12.00	13.30
10.55	12.25	13.55

11.10	12.40	14.10
11.35	13.05	14.35

Service D

17.15	18.45
17.40	19.10

17.55	19.25
18.20	19.50

★ Does not run in October.

Service B

Page's Park	dep	11.15	12.00	12.45	13.30	14.15	15.00	15.45	16.30
Stonehenge Wks	arr	11.40	12.25	13.10	13.55	14.40	15.25	16.10	16.55

Stonehenge Wks	dep	11.55	12.40	13.25	14.10	14.55	15.40	16.25	17.10
Page's Park	arr	12.20	13.05	13.50	14.35	15.20	16.05	16.50	17.35

LLANBERIS LAKE RAILWAY
Padarn Country Park, Llanberis, Gwynedd LL55 4TY   01286 870549
E-mail: llr@lake-railway.freeserve.co.uk Web: www.lake-railway.freeserve.co.uk

2000	1	2	3	4	5	6	7	8	9	10	11	12	13	14	15	16	17	18	19	20	21	22	23	24	25	26	27	28	29	30	31
Mar																				A	A	A					A	A	A	A	
Apr			A	A	A	A				A	A	A	A				B	B	B	B	B	B	B	B	B	B	B				B
May	B	B	B	B	B			B	B	B	B	B	B		B	B	B	B	B	B		B	B	B	B	B	B	B	C	C	C
June	C	B			B	B	B	B	B			B	B	B	B	B	B		B	B	B	B	B		B	B	B	B	B	B	

New extension planned to open June 2000. Train timetables available late spring (see our web site).

No service in January and February.

Service A

Llanberis	dep	11.30	13.00	14.00	15.00

Service B

★	★				†
11.00	11.45	13.00	14.00	15.00	16.00

Service C

Llanberis	dep	11.00	11.45	12.30	13.00	13.30	14.00	14.30	15.00	15.30	16.00	16.30

★ Not Saturdays or Sundays except Bank Holiday weekends.
† Not Fridays in April and May.

LLANGOLLEN RAILWAY

The Station, Abbey Road, Llangollen, Denbighshire LL20 8SN   **01978 860979**

Fax: 01978 8609??. Talking Timetable: 01978 860951

2000	1	2	3	4	5	6	7	8	9	10	11	12	13	14	15	16	17	18	19	20	21	22	23	24	25	26	27	28	29	30	31
Jan	A	A																													
Feb				E	E							A	A					X	X	B	B	B	B	X	X						
Mar			A	A					A	A							A	A							A	A					
Apr	X	X				A	C				A	C	A	A	A	A	A	C	C	C	B	B	B	B	B	E	E				
May	C				A	C	A	A	A	A	A	A	C	A	A	A	A	A	X	X	A	A	A	A	D	D	D	B	B	B
June	B	B	B	C	A	A	A	A	A	A	C	A	A	A	A	A	A	C	A	A	A	A	A	C	A	A	A	A	A		
July	X	X	B	B	B	B	B	B	D	D	B	B	B	B	B	B	C	B	B	B	B	B	B	C	B	B	B	B	X	X	B
Aug	B	B	B	B	C	C	B	B	B	B	C	C	B	B	B	B	C	C	B	B	B	B	B	D	C	D	B	B	B		
Sept	B	B	C	B	B	B	B	B	B	C	A	A	A	A	X	X	A	A	A	A	A	B	A	A	A	A	A	A			
Oct	B	A	A	A	A	C	A	A	A	A	A	A	A	A	A	A	A	A	A	X	X	B	B	B	B	B	X	X			
Nov				A	A																										
Dec		S	S						S	S					S	S				S	S	S	S		A	A	A	A	A	A

X denotes special service, S denotes Santa Specials, see local announcements.

Service A

Llangollen	dep	11.00	13.00	15.00
Carrog	dep	11.50	13.50	15.50

Service B

10.45	12.30	14.15	16.00
11.35	13.25	15.05	16.50

Service C

Llangollen	dep	11.00	12.00	13.00	14.00	15.00	16.00	17.00
Carrog	dep	11.15	12.20	13.00	14.00	15.00	16.00	17.00

Service D

Timetable D as timetable C but with DMU running at 12.25 and 14.25

Overall journey time 30 minutes end to end.

MANX ELECTRIC RAILWAY

**Isle of Man Transport, Transport Headquarters, Banks Circus,
Douglas, Isle of Man IM1 5PT (as from March 2000)**   **01624 663366**

Trains run daily from 1st April to 29th October 2000.

Address and phone number above from March 2000. Until then the address is:
Strathallan Crescent, Douglas, Isle of Man IM2 4NR. Tel: 01624 663366.

Services A

			■			■	▲			★	●	●	●
Douglas Derby Castle	dep	09.45	10.15	10.45	11.45	12.45	13.45	14.15	14.45	15.15	16.15	17.15	18.15	19.50	21.15
Groudle	dep	09.57	10.27	10.57	11.57	12.57	13.57	14.27	14.57	15.27	16.27	17.27	18.27	20.02	21.27
Laxey	dep	10.15	10.45	11.15	12.15	13.15	14.15	14.45	15.15	15.45	16.45	17.45	18.45	20.20	21.45
Dhoon	dep	10.30	11.00	11.30	12.30	13.30	14.30	15.00	15.30	16.00	17.00	18.00			
Ballaglass	dep	10.40	11.10	11.40	12.40	13.40	14.40	15.10	15.40	16.10	17.10	18.10			
Ramsey Tram Station	arr	11.00	11.30	12.00	13.00	14.00	15.00	15.30	16.00	16.30	17.30	18.30			

		■			■	▲			★	●	●	●
Ramsey Tram Station	dep	10.15	11.15	11.45	12.15	13.45	14.45	15.15	15.45	16.15	16.45	17.45			
Ballaglass	dep	10.35	11.35	12.05	12.35	14.05	15.05	15.35	16.05	16.35	17.05	18.05			
Dhoon	dep	10.45	11.45	12.15	12.45	14.15	15.15	15.45	16.15	16.45	17.15	18.15			
Laxey	dep	11.00	12.00	12.30	13.00	14.30	15.30	16.00	16.30	17.00	17.30	18.30	19.00	20.30	22.00
Groudle	dep	11.18	12.18	12.48	13.18	14.48	15.48	16.18	16.48	17.18	17.48	18.48	19.18	20.48	22.18
Douglas Derby Castle	arr	11.30	12.30	13.00	13.30	15.00	16.00	16.30	17.00	17.30	18.00	19.00	19.30	21.00	22.30

★ Runs 1st May to 1st October ONLY.
■ Runs 29th May to 10th September ONLY.
● Runs Monday to Saturday 17th July to 26th August ONLY.
▲ Runs Monday to Thursday 17th July to 24th August ONLY.

Illuminated Tram – Groudle Shuttle. In connection with Groudle Glen Railway Evening Services.

Tuesdays	Douglas	dep	18.45	19.15	19.45	20.15	20.45
1st, 8th and 15th August	Groudle	arr	18.57	19.27	19.57	20.27	20.57
Wednesdays	Groudle	dep	19.00	19.30	20.00	20.30	21.15
5th July to 16th August	Douglas	arr	19.12	19.42	20.12	20.42	21.27

MID-HANTS RAILWAY ('WATERCRESS LINE')

The Railway Station, Alresford, Hants SO24 9JG **01962 733810**

Web: www.watercressline.co.uk

2000	1	2	3	4	5	6	7	8	9	10	11	12	13	14	15	16	17	18	19	20	21	22	23	24	25	26	27	28	29	30	31
Jan	X	X	X																												
Feb						A							A						A								A				
Mar				X	X							A						A							B	A					
Apr	B	X					B	E							B	E					X	X	X	X	X	X	X	X	X	X	
May	X					B	E						C	D						B	E						B	D	C	A	A
June	A	A	B	E		A	A	A			B	D		A	A	A	X	X		A	A	A		X	E		A	A	A		
July	C	E		C	C	C		C	E		C	C	C		C	D		C	C	C		C	X	C	C	C	C	C	C	D	C
Aug	C	C	C	C	X	X	X	X	X	X	X	X	C	C	C	C	C	C	E	C	C	C	C	C	C	D	C	C	C	C	C
Sept	C	C	D							B	E						B	D								C	E			B	
Oct	D						B	D						B	E						B	D						X	X		
Nov				X																											
Dec		S	S						S	S							S	S		S	S	S	S	S			X				X

X denotes special service, see local announcements or website.

Service A

Alresford	dep	10.50	12.35	14.20
Alton	arr	11.23	13.09	14.54
Alton	dep	11.35	13.35	15.28
Alresford	arr	12.05	14.05	15.57

Service B

–		10.50	12.35	14.20	16.07	17.40
–		11.23	13.09	14.54	16.39	18.11
10.11		11.35	13.35	15.28	16.50	–
10.40		12.05	14.05	15.57	17.19	–

Service C

Alresford	dep	–	10.51	11.51	12.29	13.29	14.29	15.29	16.29	17.20
Alton	arr	–	11.26	12.26	13.07	14.07	15.07	16.07	17.07	17.55
								★	★	
Alton	dep	10.40	11.40	12.40	13.40	14.40	15.40	16.40	17.29	–
Alresford	arr	11.11	12.11	13.11	14.11	15.11	16.11	17.09	17.58	–

All trains call at intermediate stations: Ropley (10) and Medstead and Four Marks (25) minutes after leaving Alresford and at Medstead (14) and Ropley (24) minutes after leaving Alton.

★ Saturdays and Bank Holidays only.

Service D

Alresford	dep	–	10.41	11.20	12.20	13.20	14.20	15.20	16.20	17.20
Alton	arr	–	11.16	11.58	12.58	13.58	14.58	15.58	16.58	17.54
Alton	dep	10.30	11.30	12.30	13.30	14.30	15.30	16.30	17.10	–
Alresford	arr	11.01	12.01	13.01	14.01	15.01	16.01	17.01	17.39	–

Service E

Alresford	dep	–	10.41	11.19	12.19	13.29	14.39	15.23	16.24	16.59
Alton	arr	–	11.16	11.58	12.58	14.08	15.16	16.00	17.00	17.37
Alton	dep	10.30	11.30	12.30	13.40	14.30	15.33	16.14	17.10	–
Alresford	arr	11.01	12.01	13.02	14.18	15.02	16.04	16.45	17.41	–

MIDDLETON RAILWAY
The Station, Moor Road, Hunslet, Leeds LS10 2JQ   **0113 271 0320**

2000	1	2	3	4	5	6	7	8	9	10	11	12	13	14	15	16	17	18	19	20	21	22	23	24	25	26	27	28	29	30	31
Mar																									X	X					
Apr	X	X						A	B						A	B					X	X	X	X							
May	B					A	B						X	X						A	B						A	B			
June			A	B						A	B						X	X						A	B						
July	A	B						A	X						A	B						A	B						A	B	
Aug					A	X						A	B						A	B						A	B				
Sept		A	B						A	B						A	B						X	X						A	
Oct	B							B							B							B							B		
Nov				X	X						X	X						B								B					
Dec			S						S	S						S	S						S	S							

X denotes special events, S denotes Santa Specials, please phone for details, or see Website: www.personal.leeds.ac.uk/mph6mip/mrt/mrt.htm   *No service in January and February.*

Service A

Moor Road	dep	13.00	13.40	14.20	15.00	15.40	16.20
Park Halt	arr	13.08	13.48	14.28	15.08	15.48	16.28
Park Halt	dep	13.15	13.55	14.35	15.15	15.55	16.35
Moor Road	arr	13.20	14.03	14.43	15.23	16.03	16.43

Service B

11.00	11.40	12.20	13.00	13.40	14.20	15.00	15.40	16.20
11.08	11.48	12.28	13.08	13.48	14.28	15.08	15.48	16.28
11.15	11.55	12.25	13.15	13.55	14.35	15.15	15.55	16.35
11.23	12.03	12.43	13.20	14.03	14.43	15.23	16.03	16.43

MIDLAND RAILWAY CENTRE
Butterley Station, Ripley, Derbys DE5 3QZ   **01773 747674**

2000	1	2	3	4	5	6	7	8	9	10	11	12	13	14	15	16	17	18	19	20	21	22	23	24	25	26	27	28	29	30	31
Jan	X	X	X																		A	A							A	A	
Feb				A	A						A	A						A	A	A	A	A	A	A	A						
Mar			C	C							B	B						B	B						X	X					
Apr	B	C		A			B	B		A			B	C	B	B	B	B	B	B	C	C	B	B	B	B	C	C			
May	C		A			B	B		A			X	X		A			B	C			A				C	C	C	C	C	
June	C	C	C	C			B			B	C			B			B	C			B			B	C			B	B	B	
July	B	C		B	B	B		B	C		B	B	B	B	B	C		B	B	B	B	B	C	B	B	B	B	B	C	C	C
Aug	C	C	C	C	C	C	B	B	B	B	B	B	C	C	B	B	B	B	B	B	B	C	B	B	B	B	B	B	C	C	B
Sept	B	B	B	B		B			B	B		A			B	B		A			B	B	C			A				B	
Oct	B			A			B	C			A			X	X			B	B	A	A	A	A	A	X	A					
Nov			X	A						A							A						S	S							
Dec		S	S					S	S			S			S	S			S	S	S	S	S		S	S	X	X	X	X	X

X denotes special service, S denotes Santa Specials, see local announcements.

Service A

Butterley	dep	11.15	12.30	14.00	15.10
Hammersmith	arr	11.55	13.10	14.40	15.50
Hammersmith	dep	12.05	13.20	14.50	16.05
Butterley	arr	12.07	13.22	14.52	16.07

Service B

11.15	12.30	14.00	15.10	16.20
11.55	13.10	14.40	15.50	17.10
12.05	13.20	14.50	16.05	17.20
12.07	13.22	14.52	16.07	17.22

All trains call at intermediate stations: Riddings Junction (14) and Swanwick Junction (32) minutes after leaving Butterley.

Service C

Butterley	dep	10.45	11.20	11.55	12.30	13.05	14.00	14.35	15.10	15.45	16.20
Hammersmith	arr	11.30	12.05	12.40	13.15	13.50	14.45	15.20	15.55	16.30	17.05
Hammersmith	dep	11.40	12.15	12.50	13.25	14.00	14.55	15.30	16.05	17.40	17.15
Butterley	arr	11.42	12.17	12.52	13.27	14.02	14.57	15.32	16.07	17.42	17.17

MULLRAIL
Old Pier Station, Craignure, Isle of Mull PA65 6AY   **01680 812494**

Though Mullrail is only 1¼ miles long, it is unique as Scotland's first island passenger railway. The fact that it links with CalMac ferries from Oban makes destination Torosay Castle and gardens also unique in UK and arguably in Europe.

The 260mm gauge railway follows a spectacularly scenic route with an unfolding panorama of sea and mountains, the backdrop being Ben Nevis, Ben Cruachan and the Glencoe Hills.

The trains, steam and diesel hauled, include a new locomotive for 2000 and the largest tank locomotive, *Victoria*, built in this gauge.

A great family expedition.

2000	1	2	3	4	5	6	7	8	9	10	11	12	13	14	15	16	17	18	19	20	21	22	23	24	25	26	27	28	29	30	31
Apr																				A	A	B	A	A	A	A	A	B	A		
May	A	A	A	A	A	B	A	A	A	A	A	A	B	A	A	A	A	A	A	B	A	A	A	A	A	A	B	A	C	C	C
June	C	A	B	A	C	C	C	C	A	B	A	C	C	C	C	A	B	A	C	C	C	C	A	B	A	C	C	C	C	A	
July	B	A	C	C	C	C	C	B	A	C	C	C	C	C	B	A	C	C	C	C	C	B	A	C	C	C	C	C	B	A	C
Aug	C	C	C	C	B	A	C	C	C	C	C	B	A	C	C	C	C	C	B	A	C	C	C	C	C	B	A	C	C	C	C
Sept	C	B	A	A	A	A	A	B	A	A	A	A	A	B	A	A	A	A	A	B	A	A	A	A	A	A	B				
Oct	A	A	A	A	A	A	B	A	A	A	A	A	B	A	A	A	A	A	A	B											

No service in January, February, March, November and December.

Service A

Craignure	dep	11.15	13.15	14.30‡	15.10	16.45	–
Torosay	dep	10.40	12.10	14.10	14.50‡	16.10	17.30†

Service B

	11.45	13.45	14.45	15.45	17.45
	11.10	13.10	14.10	15.10	17.10

Service C

Craignure	dep	11.10	11.20	11.50	12.30	13.10	13.30	14.20	15.10	15.25	15.55	16.35	17.00*
Torosay	dep	10.45	11.35	11.50	12.15	12.55	14.00	14.15	15.05	15.40	16.10	16.20*	17.30*

‡ Commences on 15th May and ceases on 10th September.   † Commences on 2nd July and ceases on 27th August.   * Does not run on Fridays.

PAIGNTON & DARTMOUTH RAILWAY
DART VALLEY RAILWAY PLC
Queens Park Station, Torbay Road, Paignton TQ4 6AF   **01803 553760**

2000	1	2	3	4	5	6	7	8	9	10	11	12	13	14	15	16	17	18	19	20	21	22	23	24	25	26	27	28	29	30	31
Apr		A							A		A		A			A	A	A	A	A	A	A	A	A	A	A	A	A	A	A	
May	A	A	A	A			A		A		A			A		A		A			A	A	A	A	A	A	A	A	A	A	A
June	A	A	A	A	A	A	A	A	A	A	A	B	B	B	B	B	B	A	A	B	B	B	B	B	A	A	B	B	B	B	
July	A	A	B	B	B	B	B	B	A	B	B	B	B	B	B	A	A	B	B	B	B	B	A	A	C	C	C	C	A	A	C
Aug	C	C	C	C	A	A	C	C	C	C	C	C	B	B	C	C	C	C	C	A	A	C	C	C	C	C	A	A	C	C	C
Sept	C	A	A	B	B	B	B	B	A	A	A	A	A	A	A	A	A	A	A	A	A	A	A	A	A	A	A	A	A	B	
Oct	A		A		A			A		A		A			A		A		A		A	A	A	A	A	A	A	A			
Dec								S	S				S	S		S	S	S	S												

S denotes Santa Specials, see local announcements.   *No service in January, February, March and November.*

Service A

Paignton	dep	10.30	12.15	14.15	16.15
Kingswear	arr	11.00	12.45	14.45	16.45
Kingswear	dep	11.15	12.55	15.15	17.00
Paignton	arr	11.45	13.25	15.45	17.30

Service B

10.15	11.35	13.30	14.50	16.15
10.45	12.05	14.00	15.20	16.45
10.55	12.15	14.10	15.30	17.00
11.25	12.45	14.40	16.00	17.30

All trains call at intermediate stations: Goodrington (5) and Churston (15) minutes after leaving Paignton and at Churston (15) and Goodrington (25) minutes after leaving Kingswear. Pullman Observation Car (supplement) runs on all trains in Services A and B and in alternate trains in Service C.

Service C

Paignton	dep	09.30	10.15	11.00	11.45	12.30	14.00	14.45	15.30	16.15	17.00
Kingswear	arr	10.00	10.50	11.35	12.20	13.05	14.35	15.20	16.05	16.50	17.30
Kingswear	dep	10.15	11.00	11.45	12.30	14.00	14.45	15.30	16.15	17.00	17.45
Paignton	arr	10.50	11.35	12.20	13.05	14.35	15.20	16.05	16.50	17.30	18.15

The Company operates a connecting ferry service to Dartmouth where passengers will arrive about 20 minutes after train arrival at Kingswear. Returning passengers should be ready to embark at Dartmouth at least 30 minutes before scheduled train departure from Kingswear.

NENE VALLEY RAILWAY
Wansford Station, Stibbington, Peterborough PE8 6LR   01780 784444

The Nene Valley Railway is a standard-gauge railway which runs for 7½ miles between Yarwell Junction and Peterborough in north Cambridgeshire. The Railway's headquarters at Wansford Station is home to a unique collection of locomotives and rolling stock from 11 different countries. Passenger services operate at weekends from Easter to the end of October; Wednesdays from May to the end of August plus other mid-week services in summer.

The Railway offers regular driving experience courses on both its own and visiting locomotives which are always popular gift ideas for birthdays, anniversaries and retirement surprises.

As an educational charity the Railway aims to bring back memories to those who knew, or to introduce to those who are too young, the experience of railway travel of the past.

2000	1	2	3	4	5	6	7	8	9	10	11	12	13	14	15	16	17	18	19	20	21	22	23	24	25	26	27	28	29	30	31
Jan	X	X							A							A							A							A	
Feb						A								A					A				A			A	A				
Mar					C							C						X	X							C					
Apr	X	X						C	C						C	C					A	C	B	B	A	A	A	A	B	B	
May	B		A			C	C		A				C	C			A			C	C						B	B	B	A	A
June	A	A	D	D		A		X	X				A	A			D	D			A		X	X	X			A			
July	D	D			A			X	X			A				D	D			A			D	D		A	A	A	A	D	D
Aug	A	A	A	A	X	X		A	A	A	A	D	D		A	A	A	A	D	D		A	A	A	A	B	B	B	A	A	A
Sept	A	X	X						C	C						C	C			A	A		C	C							C
Oct	C					A	A							A	A					A	A			A				A	A		
Nov																										S					
Dec		S	S			S			S	S			S			S	S			S		S	S	S		S			S	S	S

X denotes special service, S denotes Santa Specials, see local announcements.

Service A

Wansford	dep	11.00	12.45	14.30
Yarwell Junction	arr	11.05	12.50	14.35
Wansford	dep	11.20	13.05	14.50
Peterborough NV	arr	11.45	13.30	15.15
Peterborough NV	dep	12.00	13.45	15.30
Wansford	arr	12.25	14.10	15.55

Service B

10.30	11.30	12.30	13.30	14.30	15.30	16.30
10.35	11.35	12.35	13.35	14.35	15.35	16.35
10.45	–	–	–	–	–	16.45
11.10	12.10	13.10	14.10	15.10	16.10	17.10
11.20	12.20	13.20	14.20	15.20	16.20	17.20
11.44	12.44	13.44	14.44	15.44	16.44	17.44

Service C

Wansford	dep	11.00	12.45	14.30	16.30
Yarwell Junction	arr	11.05	12.50	14.35	16.35
Wansford	dep	11.20	13.05	14.50	16.45
Peterborough NV	arr	11.45	13.30	15.15	17.10
Peterborough NV	dep	12.00	13.45	15.30	17.20
Wansford	arr	12.25	14.10	15.55	17.44

Service D

10.30	12.00	13.30	15.00	16.30
10.35	12.05	13.35	15.05	16.35
10.45	12.15	13.45	15.15	16.45
11.10	12.40	14.10	15.40	17.10
11.20	12.50	14.20	15.50	17.20
11.44	13.14	14.44	16.14	17.44

All trains call at Ferry Meadows and Orton Mere.

NORTHAMPTON & LAMPORT RAILWAY
Pitsford Road, Chapel Brampton, Northampton NN6 8BA   **01604 820327**

Trains operate on Sundays and Bank Holidays March to November at frequent intervals. Please phone for details.

NORTH NORFOLK RAILWAY
The Station, Sheringham, Norfolk NR26 8RA   **01263 822045**

2000	1	2	3	4	5	6	7	8	9	10	11	12	13	14	15	16	17	18	19	20	21	22	23	24	25	26	27	28	29	30	31
Feb																			C	A	C	A	A	A	A	C	A				
Mar				X	X				C	A						C	A									C	A				
Apr	C	A						C	A						C	A	A	A	A	A	A	A	B	D	D	A	A	A	A	X	X
May	X	A	A	A	C	B	B	C	A	A	A	C	B	B	C	A	A	A	C	X	X	C	A	A	A	C	D	D	D	A	A
June	A	A	X	B	C	A	A	A	C	X	X	C	A	A	A	C	X	X	C	A	A	A	C	B	B	C	A	A	A	C	
July	B	B	B	B	B	B	B	X	X	B	B	B	B	X	X	B	B	B	B	B	B	B	B	B	D	D	B	D	D	D	D
Aug	D	D	D	D	B	D	D	D	D	D	D	D	B	D	D	D	D	D	D	D	B	D	D	D	D	D	D	B	D	D	D
Sept	D	B	A	A	A	A	A	A	X	X	X	A	A	A	A	A	B	A	A	A	A	A	A	X	X	A	A	A	A	A	B
Oct	A			A	A		C	A			A	A		C	A			A	A		C	A	A	A	A	A	A	X	X		
Nov				C								C						C							C						
Dec		S	S						S	S			S			S	S		S	S	S	S	S	S		X	X	X	X	X	X

X denotes special service, S denotes Santa Specials, see local announcements.   *No service in January.*
Not all services are steam hauled.

Service A
Sheringham	dep	11.00	12.30	14.00	15.30
Holt	arr	11.24	12.54	14.24	15.54
Holt	dep	11.40	13.15	14.40	16.15
Sheringham	arr	12.05	13.40	15.05	16.40

Service B
10.00	11.00	12.30	14.00	15.30	17.00
10.20	11.24	12.54	14.24	15.54	17.20
10.30	11.40	13.15	14.45	16.15	17.25
10.50	12.05	13.40	15.10	16.40	17.44

Service C
Sheringham	dep	11.00	12.00	13.00	14.00	15.00	16.00	17.00
Holt	arr	11.18	12.18	13.18	14.18	15.18	16.18	17.18
Holt	dep	11.20	12.20	13.20	14.20	15.20	16.20	17.20
Sheringham	arr	11.37	12.37	13.37	14.37	15.37	16.37	17.37

Service D
Sheringham	dep	09.20	–	10.15	11.00	11.45	12.30	13.15	14.00	14.45	15.30	16.15	17.20
Holt	arr	09.39	–	10.40	11.24	12.09	12.54	13.39	14.24	15.09	15.54	16.39	17.39
Holt	dep	09.41	10.15	11.00	11.45	12.30	13.15	14.00	14.45	15.30	16.15	16.50	17.41
Sheringham	arr	09.58	10.42	11.27	12.12	12.57	13.42	14.27	15.12	15.57	16.42	17.14	17.58

All trains call at Weybourne.

NORTH YORKSHIRE MOORS RAILWAY
Pickering, North Yorkshire YO18 7AJ 01751 472508

2000	1	2	3	4	5	6	7	8	9	10	11	12	13	14	15	16	17	18	19	20	21	22	23	24	25	26	27	28	29	30	31
Apr	B	B	A	A	A	A	A	B	B	A	A	A	A	A	A	A	B	B	B	B	B	B	B	A	A	B	B	B	B	B	
May	B	A	A	A	A	B	A	A	A	A	A	C	C	A	A	A	A	A	B	A	A	A	A	A	A	C	C	B	B	B	B
June	B	A	A	B	B	B	B	B	A	C	C	B	B	B	B	A	A	B	B	B	B	B	A	A	B	B	B	B	B	A	
July	B	B	B	B	B	B	A	B	B	B	B	B	B	B	A	B	C	C	C	C	C	A	B	C	C	C	C	C	A	B	C
Aug	C	C	C	B	B	C	C	C	C	C	B	B	C	C	C	C	C	B	C	C	C	C	C	B	B	C	C	C	C	C	C
Sept	B	B	B	B	B	B	B	B	C	C	A	A	A	A	A	A	B	A	A	A	A	A	B	A	A	A	A	A	A	A	
Oct	B	A	A	A	A	A	C	C	A	A	A	A	A	A	A	A	A	A	A	A	C	C	B	B	B	B	B	B	A	A	A
Nov	A	A	A	C	C							D							D								D				
Dec		S	S					S	S							S	S										D	D	D	D	D

Certain services on Saturdays in July and August will be diesel hauled. *No service in January, February and March.*
S denotes Santa Specials, see local announcements.

Service A

Grosmont	dep	–	09.50	11.50	12.50	14.50	16.50
Pickering	arr	–	11.00	13.00	14.00	16.00	18.00
Pickering	dep	10.20	11.20	13.20	14.20	16.20	–
Grosmont	arr	11.25	12.25	14.25	15.25	17.25	–

(★ above the 11.50/13.00 column)

Service D

	–	10.50	12.50	13.50	15.50
	–	12.00	14.00	15.00	17.00
	11.20	12.20	14.20	15.20	–
	12.25	13.25	15.25	16.25	–

Service B

Grosmont	dep	–	09.50	10.50	11.50	12.50	13.50	14.50	16.50
Pickering	arr	–	11.00	12.00	13.00	14.00	15.00	16.00	18.00
Pickering	dep	10.20	11.20	12.20	13.20	14.20	15.20	16.20	–
Grosmont	arr	11.25	12.25	13.25	14.25	15.25	16.25	17.25	–

(★ above the 12.50/14.00 column)

Service C

Grosmont	dep	–	09.50	10.50	11.50	12.50	13.50	14.50	15.50	16.50
Pickering	arr	–	11.00	12.00	13.00	14.00	15.00	16.00	17.00	18.00
Pickering	dep	10.20	11.20	12.20	13.20	14.20	15.20	16.20	17.20	–
Grosmont	arr	11.25	12.25	13.25	14.25	15.25	16.25	17.25	18.25	–

(★ above the 12.50/14.00 column)

★ On Sundays includes 'The Moorland Lunch Train'.

All trains call at intermediate stations: Goathland (15), Newtondale (35) and Levisham (50) minutes after leaving Grosmont and at Levisham (20), Newtondale (31) and Goathland (50) minutes after leaving Pickering.

PEAK RAIL
Matlock Station, Matlock, Derbys DE4 3NA 01629 580381

2000	1	2	3	4	5	6	7	8	9	10	11	12	13	14	15	16	17	18	19	20	21	22	23	24	25	26	27	28	29	30	31
Jan									A							A							A							A	
Feb						A							A							A							A				
Mar				A							A							A							A						
Apr	A	A				A	A						A	A					A	A	A	A							A	A	
May	A					A	A						A	A						A	A						A	A	A		
June			A	A			A	A		A	A			A	A		A	A		A	A		A	A			A	A			
July	A	A				A	A		A	A				A	A		A	A		A	A								A	A	A
Aug	X	X	X	X	X	X			X	X		X	X			X	X		X	X			X	X		X	X	X	X	X	X
Sept		A	A			A			A	A			A			A	A						A	A						A	
Oct	A						A	A						A	A					A	A					A	A		A	A	A
Nov						A							A							A							A				
Dec		S	S					S	S			S				S	S			S			S	S							A

S denotes Santa Specials, see local announcements.

Trains run on the above dates. Please phone for timetable details.

RAVENGLASS & ESKDALE RAILWAY
Ravenglass, Cumbria CA18 1SW   **01229 717171**

2000	1	2	3	4	5	6	7	8	9	10	11	12	13	14	15	16	17	18	19	20	21	22	23	24	25	26	27	28	29	30	31
Jan	B	B																													
Feb												B	B	B	B	B	B	B	B	B	A	A	A	A	A	B	B	A	A		
Mar	A	A	A	B	B	A	A	A	A	A	B	B	A	A	A	A	A	A	B	B	A	A	A	A	A	A	B	B	A	A	A
Apr	C	C	C	C	C	C	C	C	C	C	C	C	C	C	C	C	C	C	C	C	C	D	D	D	D	D	D	D	D	D	
May	D	C	C	C	C	C	C	C	C	C	C	C	C	C	C	C	C	C	C	C	D	D	D	D	D	D	E	E	E	E	E
June	E	D	D	D	D	D	D	D	D	D	D	D	D	D	D	D	D	D	D	D	D	D	D	D	D	D	D	D	D	D	
July	D	D	D	D	D	D	D	D	D	D	D	D	D	D	D	D	D	D	D	D	D	D	D	E	E	E	E	E	D	D	E
Aug	E	E	E	D	D	E	E	E	E	E	D	D	E	E	E	E	E	D	D	E	E	E	E	E	D	D	E	E	E	E	E
Sept	D	D	D	D	D	D	D	D	D	D	D	D	D	D	D	D	D	D	D	D	D	D	D	D	D	D	D	D	D	D	
Oct	D	C	C	C	C	C	C	C	C	C	C	C	C	C	C	C	C	C	C	C	C	C	C	C	C	C	C	C	C	C	C
Nov	C	C	C	C	C	A	A	A	A	A	B	B	A	A	A	A	A	B	B	A	A	A	A	A							
Dec																										B	B	B	B	B	B

Service A

Ravenglass	dep	16.20
Eskdale (Dalegarth)	arr	16.55
Eskdale (Dalegarth)	dep	07.30
Ravenglass	arr	08.05

Service B

11.30	13.50
12.10	14.30
12.50	14.50
13.25	15.25

Service C

–	09.10	10.30	11.30	12.50	13.50	14.50	16.20
–	09.45	11.10	12.10	13.30	14.30	15.30	16.55
†	x						
07.30	10.10	11.30	12.50	13.50	14.50	16.00	–
08.05	10.50	12.10	13.30	14.30	15.30	16.40	–

Service D

Ravenglass	dep	–	09.10	10.30	11.30	12.10	12.50	13.50	14.50	15.50	17.00
Eskdale (Dalegarth)	arr	–	09.45	11.10	12.10	12.50	13.30	14.30	15.30	16.30	17.35
Eskdale (Dalegarth)	dep	07‡30	10.10	11.30	12.30	13.30	13.50	14.50	15.50	17.00	–
Ravenglass	arr	08.05	10.50	12.10	13.10	14.10	14.30	15.30	16.30	17.40	–

† not Saturdays and Sundays
* not Fridays, Saturdays or Sundays
¶ not Fridays and Saturdays
‡ not Sundays
x Saturdays and Sundays only

Service E

			*			†			¶			¶			¶		*		
Ravenglass	dep	–	09.10	10.10	10.30	11.10	11.30	11.50	12.10	12.50	13.10	13.50	14.10	14.30	14.50	15.10	15.50	16.10	17.00	18.20
Eskdale	arr	–	09.45	10.50	11.10	11.50	12.10	12.30	12.50	13.30	13.50	14.30	14.50	15.10	15.30	15.50	16.30	16.50	17.35	18.55
		†		*			†			¶			¶			¶		*		
Eskdale	dep	07.30	10.10	11.10	11.30	12.10	12.30	13.10	13.30	13.50	14.10	14.50	15.10	15.30	15.50	16.10	17.00	17.20	18.00	–
Ravenglass	arr	08.05	10.50	11.50	12.10	12.50	13.10	13.50	14.10	14.30	14.50	15.30	15.50	16.30	16.50	17.40	18.00	18.40	–

All trains call at intermediate stations: Muncaster Mill (5), Irton Road (20), The Green (24), Fisherground (28) and Beckfoot – to set down only (33) minutes after leaving Ravenglass and at Beckfoot – to pick up only (2), Fisherground (6), The Green (10), Irton Road (14) and Muncaster Mill (28) minutes after leaving Eskdale.

ROMNEY, HYTHE & DYMCHURCH RAILWAY
New Romney Station, New Romney, Kent TN28 8PL   **01797 362353**

2000	1	2	3	4	5	6	7	8	9	10	11	12	13	14	15	16	17	18	19	20	21	22	23	24	25	26	27	28	29	30	31
Feb																			A	A	A	A	A	A	A	A	A				
Mar				A	A					A	A						A	A							A	A					
Apr	A	A	B	B	B	B	B	A	A	B	B	C	C	C	C	C	C	C	C	C	D	E	D	D	C	C	C	C	C	C	
May	C	B	B	B	B	C	C	B	B	B	B	B	B	C	X	B	B	B	B	B	C	C	B	B	B	B	B	E	D	D	D
June	D	D	E	C	C	C	C	C	C	C	C	C	C	C	C	C	C	C	C	C	C	C	C	C	C	C	C	C	C	C	
July	C	C	C	C	C	C	C	C	T	C	C	C	C	C	C	C	C	C	C	C	C	C	C	C	C	C	D	D	E	D	D
Aug	D	D	D	D	E	D	D	D	D	D	D	E	D	D	D	D	D	D	E	D	D	D	D	D	D	E	D	D	D	D	D
Sept	D	T	T	C	C	C	C	C	C	C	C	C	C	C	C	C	C	C	C	C	C	C	C	C	A	A	A	A	A	A	
Oct	A						A	X						A	A					A	A	A	A	A	A	A	A				

X denotes special service, T denotes Thomas Events, see local announcements.   *No service in January, November and December.*

Service A

Hythe	dep	10.30	12.00	14.00	15.20	16.45	18.00
New Romney	dep	11.08	12.38	14.38	15.58	17.20	18.35
Dungeness	arr	11.35	13.05	15.05	16.25	–	–
Dungeness	dep	–	–	12.05	13.35	15.25	16.50
New Romney	dep	09.35	11.05	12.35	14.05	15.55	17.20
Hythe	arr	10.10	11.40	13.10	14.40	16.30	17.55

Service B

Hythe	dep	11.10	12.40	14.20	17.10
New Romney	dep	11.48	13.15	14.58	17.45
Dungeness	arr	12.15	–	15.25	–
Dungeness	dep	–	–	12.55	15.55
New Romney	dep	10.00	11.55	13.25	16.25
Hythe	arr	10.35	12.30	14.00	17.00

Service C

Hythe	dep	–	10.30	11.30	12.30	13.30	14.30	15.30	16.30	17.30	18.15
New Romney	dep	10.30	11.08	12.08	13.08	14.08	15.08	16.08	17.05	18.05	18.50
Dungeness	arr	10.57	11.35	12.35	13.35	14.35	15.35	16.35	–	–	–
Dungeness	dep	–	–	11.05	12.05	13.05	14.05	15.05	16.05	17.05	–
New Romney	dep	09.35	10.35	11.35	12.35	13.35	14.35	15.35	16.35	17.35	–
Hythe	arr	10.10	11.10	12.10	13.10	14.10	15.10	16.10	17.10	18.10	–

Service D

Hythe	dep	10.20	11.05	11.50	12.35	13.20	14.05	14.50	15.35	16.20	16.55	17.30	18.15	–
New Romney	dep	10.58	11.43	12.28	13.13	13.58	14.43	15.28	16.13	16.58	17.30	18.05	18.50	–
Dungeness	arr	11.25	12.10	12.55	13.40	14.25	15.10	15.55	16.40	17.25	–	–	–	–
Dungeness	dep	–	–	–	–	11.40	12.25	13.10	13.55	14.40	15.25	16.10	16.55	17.40
New Romney	dep	09.25	10.10	10.55	11.40	12.10	12.55	13.40	14.25	15.10	15.55	16.40	17.25	18.10
Hythe	arr	10.00	10.45	11.30	12.15	12.45	13.30	14.15	15.00	15.45	16.30	17.15	18.00	18.45

Service E

Hythe	dep	10.20	11.05	11.50	12.35	13.20	14.05	14.20	15.20	16.20	16.40	17.30	18.15	–
New Romney	dep	10.58	11.43	12.28	13.13	13.58	–	14.58	15.58	16.58	17.15	18.05	18.50	–
Dungeness	arr	11.25	12.10	12.55	13.40	14.25	14.50	15.25	16.25	17.25	–	–	–	–
Dungeness	dep	–	–	–	–	11.40	12.25	13.10	13.55	14.55	15.35	15.55	16.55	17.40
New Romney	dep	09.25	10.10	10.55	11.40	12.10	12.55	13.40	14.25	15.25	–	16.25	17.25	18.10
Hythe	arr	10.00	10.45	11.30	12.15	12.45	13.30	14.15	15.00	16.00	16.20	17.00	18.00	18.45

Trains call at Romney Sands (15), Jefferstone Lane (38) and Dymchurch (45) minutes after leaving Dungeness and at Dymchurch (18), Jefferstone Lane (23) and Romney Sands (50) minutes after leaving Hythe.

SEATON TRAMWAY
Harbour Road, Seaton, Devon EX12 2NQ   **01297 20375**

Seaton Tramway operates in East Devon's glorious Axe Valley and is noted for panoramic views of the Axe estuary and its wading birds. The tramway originated as a portable system in 1949, evolving into the Eastbourne Tramway in 1954; the move to Seaton occurred in 1970 after the closure of the BR Seaton branch. The ten-strong fleet mainly comprises purpose-built heritage open toppers, although three vintage tramcars have been rebuilt as enclosed saloons.

Pre-booked groups are welcome anytime. The 30th Anniversary Fortnight (27th May–11th June 2000) will be packed with celebratory events. Tram driving lessons are available throughout the season.

2000	1	2	3	4	5	6	7	8	9	10	11	12	13	14	15	16	17	18	19	20	21	22	23	24	25	26	27	28	29	30	31
Apr								A	A	A	A	A	A	A	A	A	A	A	A	A	A	A	A	A	A	A	A	A	A	A	
May	A	A	A	A	A	A	A	A	A	A	A	A	A	A	A	A	A	A	A	A	A	A	A	A	A	A	X	X	X	X	X
June	X	X	X	X	X	X	X	X	X	X	X	A	A	A	A	A	A	A	A	A	A	A	A	A	A	A	A	A	A	A	
July	A	A	A	A	A	A	A	A	A	A	A	A	A	A	A	A	A	A	A	A	A	A	A	A	A	A	A	A	B	B	B
Aug	B	B	B	B	B	B	B	B	B	B	B	B	B	B	B	B	B	B	B	B	B	B	B	B	B	B	B	B	B	B	B
Sept	B	X	A	A	A	A	A	A	A	X	A	A	A	A	A	A	A	A	A	A	A	A	A	A	A	A	A	A	A	A	
Oct	A	A	A	A	A	A	A	A	A	A	A	A	A	A	A	A	A	A	A	A	A	A	A	A	A	A	A	A	A	C	
Nov				C	C					C	C						C	C						C	C						
Dec		C	C					C	X						X	X							X	X							

X denotes special service, see local announcements.   *No service in January, February and March.*

Service A

Seaton	dep	09.40	then at these minutes past each hour	00	20	40		17.20
Colyford	dep	09.53		13	33	53	until	17.33
Colyton	arr	10.03		23	43	03		17.43

Colyton	dep	10.10	then at these minutes past each hour	00	20	40		17.50
Colyford	dep	10.20		13	33	53	until	18.00
Seaton	arr	10.34		23	43	03		18.33

Service B

		09.40	then at these minutes past each hour	00	20	40		20.40
		09.53		13	33	53	until	20.53
		10.03		23	43	03		21.03

		10.10	then at these minutes past each hour	00	20	40		21.10
		10.20		13	33	53	until	21.20
		10.34		23	43	03		21.34

Service C

Seaton	dep	09.40	then at these minutes past each hour	00	20	40		16.00
Colyford	dep	09.53		13	33	53	until	16.13
Colyton	arr	10.03		23	43	03		16.33

Colyton	dep	10.10	then at these minutes past each hour	00	20	40		16.30
Colyford	dep	10.20		13	33	53	until	16.40
Seaton	arr	10.34		23	43	03		16.54

Pre-booked groups welcomed all year round.
Extra departures run according to demand at peak periods.

SEVERN VALLEY RAILWAY
The Railway Station, Bewdley, Worcs DY12 1BG   **01299 403816**

2000	1	2	3	4	5	6	7	8	9	10	11	12	13	14	15	16	17	18	19	20	21	22	23	24	25	26	27	28	29	30	31
Jan	B	B	B					A	A				A	A		A	A					A	A						A	A	
Feb					A	A							A	A					A	A	A	A	A	A	A	A	A				
Mar				A	A				A	A						X	X					B	B								
Apr	B	B						B	B				B	B	B	B	B	B	B	D	D	B	B	B	B	B	B	B	D		
May	D					B	B						X	X	B	B	B	B	B	X	X	B	B	B	B	B	B	C	D	D	B
June	B	B	C	B	B	B	B	B	B	B	C	B	B	B	B	B	B	C	B	B	B	B	B	B	C	B	B	B	B	B	
July	D	D	B	B	B	B	B	B	C	B	B	B	B	B	B	B	C	B	B	B	B	B	B	C	D	B	B	B	B	C	D
Aug	B	B	B	B	C	D	B	B	B	B	B	C	D	B	B	B	B	B	C	D	B	B	B	B	B	C	D	B	B	B	B
Sept	B	X	X	B	B	B	B	B	X	X	B	B	B	B	B	C	B	B	B	B	X	X	X						X	X	
Oct	X						B	D				B	B					B	B		B	B	B	B	B	B					
Nov				A	A					A	A					A	A						A	A							
Dec		S	S					S	S					S	S		S	S	S	S	S	S			A	A	A	A	A	A	

X denotes special service, S denotes Santa Specials, see local announcements.

Continued top of next page

SEVERN VALLEY RAILWAY (continued)

Service A

Kidderminster	dep	10.45	12.00	13.15	14.30	16.15
Bridgnorth	arr	11.54	13.09	14.24	15.36	17.17
Bridgnorth	dep	11.45	12.30	13.45	15.00	16.40
Kidderminster	arr	12.26	13.42	14.57	16.00	17.44

Service B ★

10.30	11.45	12.15	13.00	14.15	15.30	16.45
11.39	12.54	13.28	14.09	15.24	16.39	18.03
		★				
11.00	12.15	13.30	14.15	14.45	16.00	17.25
12.11	13.27	14.42	15.25	15.57	17.08	18.33

Service C †

Kidderminster	dep	09.45	10.30	11.15	12.45	13.30	14.15	15.00	16.30	–
Bridgnorth	arr	11.00	11.45	12.30	13.59	14.44	15.29	16.14	17.44	19.50
										†
Bridgnorth	dep	11.05	11.50	12.35	13.20	14.50	15.35	16.20	17.05	21.15
Kidderminster	arr	12.22	13.07	13.52	14.37	16.07	16.52	17.37	18.18	–

† Does not call at intermediate stations between Bewdley and Bridgnorth.
★ Sundays only. Restaurant car service.

Service D

Kidderminster	dep	10.30	11.15	12.00	12.45	13.30	14.15	15.00	15.45	16.30	17.15
Bridgnorth	arr	11.45	12.30	13.14	13.59	14.44	15.29	16.14	16.59	17.44	18.25
Bridgnorth	dep	11.05	11.50	12.35	13.20	14.05	14.50	15.35	16.20	17.05	17.50
Kidderminster	arr	12.22	13.07	13.52	14.37	15.22	16.07	16.52	17.37	18.18	18.56

All trains call at intermediate stations: Bewdley (20), Arley (38), Highley (47) and Hampton Loade (58) minutes after leaving Kidderminster and at Hampton Loade (22), Highley (34), Arley (47) and Bewdley (66) minutes after leaving Bridgnorth (except †).

SITTINGBOURNE & KEMSLEY LIGHT RAILWAY
PO Box 300, Sittingbourne, Kent ME10 2SG   **01227 369606**

2000	1	2	3	4	5	6	7	8	9	10	11	12	13	14	15	16	17	18	19	20	21	22	23	24	25	26	27	28	29	30	31
Apr		A							A								A				B	A	B	B					A	C	
May	B					A							A							A					A	B	B			A	
June			A						A					A				A				A									
July	C	C					C	C								A					A			A				A	A		
Aug		A			A	B		A			B	B		A			A	B			A			A	B	B		A			
Sept			A	A				A							A					A							A				
Oct	A						C																								
Dec		S	S					S	S					S	S					S				S			S				

S denotes Santa Specials, see local announcements.   *No service in January, February, March and November.*

Service A

Sittingbourne Viaduct	dep	13.00	14.00	15.00	16.00
Kemsley Down	arr	13.15	14.15	15.15	16.15
Kemsley Down	dep	13.35	14.35	15.35	16.35
Sittingbourne Viaduct	arr	13.50	14.50	15.50	16.50

Service B

11.00	11.40	12.20	13.00	14.00	15.00	16.00
11.15	11.55	12.35	13.15	14.15	15.15	16.15
11.20	12.00	12.40	13.35	14.35	15.35	16.35
11.35	12.15	12.55	13.50	14.50	15.50	16.50

Service C

Sittingbourne Viaduct	dep	11.00	11.40	12.20	13.00	13.40	14.20	15.00	16.00
Kemsley Down	arr	11.15	11.55	12.35	13.15	13.55	14.35	15.15	16.15
Kemsley Down	dep	11.20	12.00	12.40	13.20	14.00	14.40	15.35	16.35
Sittingbourne Viaduct	arr	11.35	12.15	12.55	13.35	14.15	14.55	15.50	16.50

All trains call at Milton Regis Halt by request.

SNAEFELL MOUNTAIN RAILWAY
Isle of Man Transport, Transport Headquarters, Banks Circus, Douglas, Isle of Man IM1 5PT (as from March 2000)   **01624 663366**

Trams run daily from 1st April to 29th October 2000.

Address and phone number above from March 2000. Until then the address is: Strathallan Crescent, Douglas, Isle of Man IM2 4NR. Tel: 01624 663366.

SOUTH DEVON RAILWAY
The Station, Buckfastleigh, Devon TQ11 0DZ

01364 642338
Web: www.southdevonrailway.org

The South Devon Railway preserved Country branch line runs for seven miles beside the River Dart between Buckfastleigh and Totnes. The line has been improving its services over the years and for 2000 can now offer a better service than ever before. During the summer holiday two train sets will be in operation passing at Staverton, the tiny wayside station half-way along the line, giving nine return journeys during the day. On these peak days a vintage bus will meet trains from Totnes to give a connecting service to the famous Buckfast Abbey.

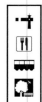

2000	1	2	3	4	5	6	7	8	9	10	11	12	13	14	15	16	17	18	19	20	21	22	23	24	25	26	27	28	29	30	31
Jan	A	A	A																												
Feb																					A		A	A	A			A			
Mar					A						B	B						A	A						A	A					
Apr	A	A		A	A			A	A		A	A			A	A	A	A	A	A	A	A	X	X	A	A	A	A	X	X	
May	X	A	A			A	A		A	A	A		X	X		A	A	A	A	A	A	B	A	A	A	A	A	X	X	A	A
June	A	A	A	A	A	A	A	A	A	A	X	X	A	A	A	A	A	A	A	A	A	A	A	B	A	A	A	A	A	A	
July	A	B	A	A	A	A	A	X	X	A	A	A	A	A	A	B	A	A	A	A	A	B	A	A	B	B	B	A	A	B	A
Aug	B	B	B	A	B	A	A	B	B	B	A	A	B	A	B	B	B	A	B	A	A	B	B	B	A	A	X	X	A	A	A
Sept	A	A	A	A	A	A	A	A	A	B	A	A	A	A	A	B	A	A	A	A	A	A	X	X	A	A	A	A	A	A	
Oct	A	A	A	A	A	A	A	A		A				A	A			A				X	X	A	A	A	A	A	B		
Dec		S							S	S						S	S				S	S	S							A	A

X denotes special service, S denotes Santa Specials, please phone for more details.   No service in November.

Service A

Buckfastleigh	dep	10.45	12.15	14.10	15.30
Totnes	dep	11.25	12.55	14.50	16.10

Service B

	D		D		D		D		D
Buckfastleigh dep	10.00	10.45	11.45	12.30	13.45	14.30	15.15	16.00	17.25
Totnes dep	10.45	11.45	12.30	13.45	14.30	15.15	16.00	16.45	18.00

D   May be Heritage diesel traction at weekends. The 17.25/18.00 does not run at weekends.

All trains call at intermediate station: Staverton (10) minutes after leaving Buckfastleigh and Totnes.

The Tuesday, Wednesday and Thursday peak service is all steam apart from the 17.25/18.00. There is also a vintage bus link to Buckfast Abbey on these days.

SOUTH TYNEDALE RAILWAY
Alston Station, Cumbria CA9 3JB

01434 382828

The South Tynedale Railway is a narrow-gauge line following part of the old Alston–Haltwhistle branch in the heart of the North Pennines Area of Outstanding Natural Beauty. It runs for 2¼ miles from Alston to Kirkhaugh. Preserved steam and diesel locomotives from Britain and overseas are used on this scenic route.

There is free parking beside the restored Victorian station at Alston. Refreshments are available on most trains, tea, coffee, soft drinks and snacks being sold from a converted brake-van on arrival at Kirkhaugh. Other refreshment facilities (not operated by the railway) are available at Alston station, and locally in Alston town centre.

2000	1	2	3	4	5	6	7	8	9	10	11	12	13	14	15	16	17	18	19	20	21	22	23	24	25	26	27	28	29	30	31
Apr		A							A							A	A				A	A	A	X	A	A	A	A	X	X	
May	X						A							A					A								A	A	A	A	
June	A	A	A	A					A	A						X	X						A	A							
July	A	A		A	A	A		A	A		A	A	A		A	A		A	A	A		A	A	A	A	A	A	A	A	A	A
Aug	A	A	A	A	A	A	A	A	A	A	A	A	A	A	A	A	A	A	A	A	A	A	A	A	A	A	A	A	A	A	A
Sept	A	X	X					A	A						A	A					A	A									
Oct	B						B							B				X	X			B	B	B			A	A			
Dec		S							S	S						S	S														

X denotes special service, S denotes Santa Specials, see local announcements.   No service in January, February, March and November.

Service A

Alston	dep	11.00	12.15	13.45	15.00	16.15
Kirkhaugh	arr	11.15	12.30	14.00	15.15	16.30

Kirkhaugh	dep	11.30	12.45	14.15	15.30	16.45
Alston	arr	11.45	13.00	14.30	15.45	17.00

Service B

11.00	12.15	13.45	15.00
11.15	12.30	14.00	15.15

11.30	12.45	14.15	15.30
11.45	13.00	14.30	15.45

On some dates, Kirkhaugh to Alston services may run approximately 15 minutes later than shown.

SNOWDON MOUNTAIN RAILWAY
Llanberis, Gwynedd LL55 4TY   01286 870223

Snowdon Mountain Railway is Britain's only public rack and pinion line. Starting from the picturesque lake-side village of Llanberis, the 4⅝-mile line climbs over 3,000ft at gradients of up to 1 in 5.5 to its terminus just below the Summit of Snowdon, the highest mountain in England and Wales. On clear days the trip offers spectacular views of Snowdonia. Cafeteria, gift shop and toilets are available at the Summit, but these facilities are only open from mid/late May until mid October (actual dates are weather-dependent).

Motive power on the line includes centenarian steam locomotives interworking with modern diesels.

DAYS OF OPERATION
Passenger trains run every day from **15th March** to **3rd November inclusive, weather permitting.**

TIMES OF TRAINS
Trains do not run to a strict timetable. Weather permitting, and if there are sufficient passengers, the **first train** of the day is scheduled to depart from Llanberis at **09.00**. Thereafter trains run at frequent intervals until mid-late afternoon.

At **Peak Periods (Bank Holidays** and from **Mid July to early September)** trains are scheduled to depart from Llanberis at **half hourly intervals** until **17.00** (15.30 on Saturdays), but always subject to weather and demand.

At periods of lesser demand the frequency is reduced and the time of last departure brought forward.

Each train can carry a maximum of 57 passengers and trains will not normally run with less than 25 passengers (but see also paragraph below).

The company uses its **best endeavours** to run **at least** three trains every day that the railway is open to the public, subject to considerations of safety and with the proviso that there are at least ten passengers on each of these trains.

JOURNEY TIMES
The train journey from Llanberis to the Summit takes approximately one hour. Each train waits empty at the Summit for ½ hour before leaving again for the descent to Llanberis. The downhill journey also lasts one hour making a total of 2½ hours for the round trip. Passengers with return tickets are entitled to a seat from the Summit on the same train by which they travelled to the Summit. Seats on later trains cannot be guaranteed.

In early (prior to mid/late May) and late (after mid October) season the upper section of the line and summit facilities are normally closed. Train services **then terminate at Clogwyn Station or Rocky Valley Halt.** Clogwyn is approximately ¾ of the way to the Summit. The round trip to Clogwyn and back lasts just under two hours including ½ hour stay at Clogwyn. If the destination is Rocky Valley, the round trip lasts just over 1½ hrs including 15 minutes at Rocky Valley.

STRATHSPEY RAILWAY
Aviemore Station, Dalfaber Road, Aviemore PH22 1PY   01479 810725
E-mail: laurence.grant@strathspey-railway.freeserve.co.uk

2000	1	2	3	4	5	6	7	8	9	10	11	12	13	14	15	16	17	18	19	20	21	22	23	24	25	26	27	28	29	30	31
Jan	A	A																													
Mar																						A	A		B	A			A	A	
Apr	A	A		A	A		A	A			A	A		A	A			A	A	A	A	A	A	A	A				X	X	
May	X		A	A		A	A			A	A		A	A			A	A		A	A			A	A		X	X	A	A	A
June		A	A	A	A	A	A	A	A	A	A	A	A	A	A	A	A	A	A	A	A	A	A	A	A	A	A	A	A	A	
July	A	A	A	A	A	A	A	A	A	A	A	A	A	A	A	A	A	A	A	A	A	A	A	A	A	A	A	A	A	A	A
Aug	A	A	A	A	A	A	A	A	A	A	A	A	A	A	A	A	A	A	A	A	A	A	A	A	A	A	A	A	A	A	A
Sept	A	X	X	A	A	A	A	A	A	A	A	A	A	A	A	A	A	A	A	A	A	A	A	A	A	A	A	A	A	A	
Oct	A			A	A		A	A			A	A		A	A		A	A		A	A			A	A			A	A		
Dec																	S						S	S		A					A

X denotes special service, S denotes Santa Specials, see local announcements.   *No service in February and November.*

Service A

Boat of Garten	dep	10.00	11.20	12.40	14.30	15.50
Aviemore	arr	10.20	11.40	13.00	14.50	16.10

Aviemore	dep	10.40	12.00	13.30	15.10	16.20
Boat of Garten	arr	11.00	12.20	13.50	15.30	16.40

TANFIELD RAILWAY
Old Marley Hill, Sunniside, Gateshead, Tyne & Wear NE16 5ET   0191-388 7545

Please phone for timetable details.

SWANAGE RAILWAY
Station House, Swanage, Dorset BH19 1HB   **01929 425800**

2000	1	2	3	4	5	6	7	8	9	10	11	12	13	14	15	16	17	18	19	20	21	22	23	24	25	26	27	28	29	30	31
Jan	A	A	A																												
Feb																			X	X	X	X	X	X	X	X	X				
Mar				A	A						A	A						A	A							X	X				
Apr	B	B	A	A	A	A	A	B	B	A	A	A	A	A	B	B	B	B	B	B	B	C	C	C	C	B	B	B	C	C	
May	C	B	B	B	B	B	B	B	B	B	B	B	B	B	B	B	B	B	B	B	B	B	B	B	B	B	C	C	C	B	B
June	B	B	B	B	B	B	B	B	B	B	B	B	B	B	B	B	B	B	B	B	B	B	B	B	B	B	B	B	B	B	
July	B	B	B	B	B	B	B	C	C	C	C	C	C	C	C	C	C	C	C	C	C	C	C	C	C	C	C	C	C	C	C
Aug	C	C	C	C	C	C	C	C	C	C	C	C	C	C	C	C	C	C	C	C	C	C	C	C	C	C	C	C	C	C	C
Sept	C	B	B	B	B	B	B	B	X	X	B	B	B	B	B	B	B	B	B	B	B	B	B	A	A	A	A	A	A	A	
Oct	A	A	A	A	A	A	A	A	A	A	A	A	A	A	A	A	A	A	A	A	A	A	A	A	A	A	A	A	A	A	A
Nov				A	A						A	A						A	A							S	S				
Dec		S	S						S	S							S	S	S	S	S	S	S	S	S	A	A	A	A	A	A

X denotes special timetable and fares apply, please phone for details.
S denotes Santa Specials. Special timetable and fares apply. See our special leaflet.

Service A

Swanage	dep	10.30	11.40	12.50	14.00	15.10
Norden	arr	10.55	12.05	13.15	14.25	15.35
Norden	dep	11.05	12.15	13.25	14.35	15.45
Swanage	arr	11.28	12.38	13.48	14.58	16.08

Service B ¶

Swanage	dep	10.30	11.40	12.50	14.00	15.10	16.20	17.30	19.10†	20.20†	22.00†
Norden	arr	10.55	12.05	13.15	14.25	15.35	16.45	17.55	19.30	20.40	22.20
Norden	dep	11.05	12.15	13.25	14.35	15.45	16.55	18.05	19.45‡	21.10‡	22.30‡
Swanage	arr	11.28	12.38	13.48	14.58	16.08	17.18	18.28	20.03	21.28	22.48

Service C

Swanage	dep	–	10.30	11.05	11.40	12.15	12.50	13.25	14.00	14.35	15.10	15.45	16.20
Norden	arr	–	10.55	11.30	12.05	12.40	13.15	13.50	14.25	15.00	15.35	16.10	16.45
Norden	dep	10.30	11.05	11.40	12.15	12.50	13.25	14.00	14.35	15.10	15.45	16.20	16.55
Swanage	arr	10.53	11.28	12.03	12.38	13.13	13.48	14.23	14.58	15.33	16.08	16.43	17.18

				★	★	★	★	★
Swanage	dep	16.55	17.30	18.05	19.10	20.20	22.00	23.00
Norden	arr	17.20	17.55	18.30	19.30†	20.40†	22.20†	23.18†
Norden	dep	17.30	18.05	18.35	19.45‡	21.10‡	22.30‡	23.25‡
Swanage	arr	17.53	18.28	18.57	20.03	21.28	22.48	23.42

All trains call at Corfe Castle 5 minutes before arriving at Norden.

★   Diesel service.
†   To Corfe Castle only.
‡   From Corfe Castle only.
¶   From 1st April to 26th May operates on Saturdays and Sundays only. From 30th May to 24th September operates daily.

All services operated by steam traction unless otherwise shown.

VALE OF RHEIDOL RAILWAY
Park Avenue, Aberystwyth SY23 1PG   **01970 625819**

2000	1	2	3	4	5	6	7	8	9	10	11	12	13	14	15	16	17	18	19	20	21	22	23	24	25	26	27	28	29	30	31
Apr																					A	A	A	A	A	A	A	A	A	A	
May	A	A	A	A		A	A	A	A	A	A		A	A	A	A	A	A		A	A	A	A	A		A	A	B	B	B	
June	B	A	A	A	A	A	A	A	A	A	A	A	A	A	A	A	A	A	A	A	A	A	A	A	A	A	A	A	A	A	
July	A	A	A	A	A	A	A	A	A	A	A	A	A	A	A	A	A	A	A	A	A	A	A	B	B	B	B	A	A	A	B
Aug	B	B	B	A	A	A	B	B	B	B	B	A	A	A	B	B	B	B	A	A	A	B	B	B	B	A	A	A	B	B	B
Sept	A	A	A	A	A	A	A		A	A	A	A	A	A		A	A	A	A	A		A	A	A	A	A	A		A		
Oct		A	A	A		A			A	A	A		A			A	A	A		A			A	A	A		A				

No service in January, February, March, November and December.

Service A

Aberystwyth	dep	11.00	14.30
Devil's Bridge	arr	12.00	15.30
Devil's Bridge	dep	13.00	16.30
Aberystwyth	arr	14.00	17.30

Service B

	10.45	12.15	14.00	15.45
	11.45	13.15	15.00	16.45
	12.30	14.15	16.00	17.30
	13.30	15.15	17.00	18.30

All trains call at intermediate stations on request.

TALYLLYN RAILWAY
Wharf Station, Tywyn, Gwynedd LL36 9EY

01654 710472

Fax: 01654 711755. Web: www.talyllyn.co.uk

2000	1	2	3	4	5	6	7	8	9	10	11	12	13	14	15	16	17	18	19	20	21	22	23	24	25	26	27	28	29	30	31
Jan	X	X																													
Feb																				A	A					A	A				
Mar					A							A							A							A					
Apr	A	A	A	A	A	A	A	A	A	A	A	A	A	A	A	A	A	A	A	A	A	A	C	C	C	C	C	C	C	C	
May	C	A	A	A	A	A	A	A	A	A	A	A	A	A	A	A	A	A	A	A	A	A	A	A	A	A	C	D	D	D	D
June	D	D	B	B	B	B	B	B	B	B	B	B	B	B	B	B	B	B	B	B	B	B	B	B	B	B	B	B	B	B	
July	B	B	B	B	B	B	B	B	B	B	B	B	B	C	C	C	C	C	C	C	C	D	D	D	D	D	D	C	C	C	D
Aug	D	D	D	D	C	C	D	D	D	D	D	D	C	C	D	D	D	D	D	X	C	D	D	D	D	D	D	C	D	D	D
Sept	D	B	B	B	B	B	B	B	B	B	B	B	B	B	B	B	B	B	B	B	B	B	B	B	B	B	B	B	B	X	
Oct	X	B	B	B	B	B	B	A	A	A	A	A	A	A	A	A	A	A	A	A	A	A	A	B	B	B	B	B	A	A	A
Nov	A	A	A	A																											
Dec																S	S						S	S		X	X	X	X	X	X

X denotes special service, S denotes Santa Specials, see local announcements.

Service A

Tywyn (Wharf)	dep	11.40	14.45
Nant Gwernol	arr	12.32	16.07
Nant Gwernol	dep	12.45	16.22
Tywyn (Wharf)	arr	14.05	17.15

Service B

10.30	11.40	13.55	15.00
11.25	12.32	14.47	16.12
11.40	12.45	15.00	16.22
12.55	14.05	16.15	17.15

Service C

10.30	11.40	13.25	14.30	16.10	19.30
11.25	12.32	14.17	15.22	17.17	★
11.40	12.45	14.30	15.35	17.27	★
12.55	14.05	15.45	16.50	18.20	22.05

Service D

Tywyn (Wharf)	dep	10.10	10.50	11.40	12.40	13.30	14.30	15.20	16.10
Nant Gwernol	arr	11.05	11.42	12.32	13.32	14.22	15.22	16.12	17.17
Nant Gwernol	dep	11.15	12.00	12.50	13.50	14.40	15.35	16.25	17.27
Tywyn (Wharf)	arr	12.21	13.21	14.11	15.11	16.01	16.51	17.45	18.20

★ Sundays only 23rd July to 20th August. *Also runs 1st and 27th August.* To and from Abergynolwyn only.

All trains call at intermediate stations: Rhydyronen (12), Dolgoch Falls (31) and Abegynolwyn (45) minutes approximately after leaving or before arriving at Tywyn.

WELLS & WALSINGHAM RAILWAY
Wells-next-the-Sea, Norfolk NR23 1QB

01328 710631

The longest 10¼" narrow-gauge steam railway in the world. Unique Garratt Locomotive *Norfolk Hero* which was specially built for this line . . . a great adventure for all the family in the delightful countryside of the North Norfolk Coast.

2000	1	2	3	4	5	6	7	8	9	10	11	12	13	14	15	16	17	18	19	20	21	22	23	24	25	26	27	28	29	30	31
Apr														C	C	C	C	C	C	C	B	B	B	B	B	B	B	B	B	B	
May	B	B	B	B	B	B	B	B	B	B	B	B	B	B	B	B	B	B	B	B	B	B	B	B	B	B	B	B	A	A	A
June	A	A	A	A	B	B	B	B	B	B	B	B	B	B	B	B	B	B	B	B	B	B	B	B	B	B	B	B	B	B	
July	A	A	A	A	A	A	A	A	A	A	A	A	A	A	A	A	A	A	A	A	A	A	A	A	A	A	A	A	A	A	A
Aug	A	A	A	A	A	A	A	A	A	A	A	A	A	A	A	A	A	A	A	A	A	A	A	A	A	A	A	A	A	A	A
Sept	B	B	B	B	B	B	B	B	B	B	B	B	B	B	B	B	B	B	B	B	B	B	B	B	B	B	B	B	B	B	
Oct	C	C	C	C	C	C	C	C	C	C	C	C	C	C	C	C	C	C	C	C	C	B	B	B	B	B	B	B	B	X	X

X denotes special service, please phone for details.   *No service in January, February, March, November and December.*

Service A

Wells	dep	10.15	11.45	13.30	15.00	16.30
Walsingham	dep	11.00	12.30	14.15	15.45	17.15

Service B

10.30	12.00	14.00	15.30
11.15	12.45	14.45	16.15

Service C

11.00	12.30	14.00
11.45	13.15	16.30

WELSHPOOL & LLANFAIR LIGHT RAILWAY
The Station, Llanfair Caereinion SY21 0SF   **01938 810441**

2000	1	2	3	4	5	6	7	8	9	10	11	12	13	14	15	16	17	18	19	20	21	22	23	24	25	26	27	28	29	30	31
Apr															A	A	A	A	A	A	A	A	A	B	B	A	A	A	A	A	
May	A			A	A								A	A						A	A						A	B	B	A	A
June	A	A	A	A		A	A	A		A	A		A	A	A		A	A		A	A		A	A		A	A	A		A	
July	X	X		A	A		A	A		A	A	A		A	A	A	A	A	A	A	A	A	A	A	A	A	A	A	A	A	A
Aug	A	A	A	A	A	A	A	A	A	A	A	A	A	A	A	A	A	A	A	A	A	A	A	A	A	A	B	B	A	A	A
Sept	A	X	X		A	A	A		A	A		A	A	A		A	A						A	A						A	
Oct	A																														

X denotes special service, please phone for details.   *No service in January, February, March, November and December.*

Service A

Llanfair	dep	10.15	13.15	16.15
Castle Caereinion	arr	10.40	13.40	16.40
Welshpool	arr	11.05	14.05	17.05
Welshpool	dep	11.30	14.30	17.15
Castle Caereinion	dep	11.50	14.50	17.35
Llanfair	arr	12.20	15.20	18.05

Service B

Llanfair	dep	09.15	10.15	11.45	13.15	14.45	16.15
Castle Caereinion	arr	09.40	10.40	12.15	13.40	15.15	16.40
Welshpool	arr	10.05	11.05	12.40	14.05	15.40	17.05
Welshpool	dep	10.20	11.30	12.55	14.30	15.55	17.15
Castle Caereinion	dep	10.40	11.50	13.15	14.50	16.15	17.35
Llanfair	arr	11.10	12.20	13.45	15.20	16.45	18.05

Trains will stop by request at Heniarth, Cyfronydd and Sylfaen

WEST LANCASHIRE LIGHT RAILWAY
Station Road, Hesketh Bank, Nr Preston PR4 6SP   **01772 815881**

The West Lancashire Light Railway is a two-foot gauge passenger carrying narrow gauge railway, located in the village of Hesketh Bank, midway between Preston and Southport.

The Railway dates from 1967, when it was constructed by a group of local enthusiasts, in an effort to preserve items of industrial equipment that were fast disappearing. The Railway has now become a working museum, with a variety of locomotives, ranging from some seven steam locomotives (five in working order) to a collection of over 20 petrol, diesel and electric powered locomotives, together with an extensive collection of rolling stock.

2000	1	2	3	4	5	6	7	8	9	10	11	12	13	14	15	16	17	18	19	20	21	22	23	24	25	26	27	28	29	30	31
Apr		X							A							A					A		A	A						A	
May	A						A							X		A													A	A	
June			A						A							X					A				A						
July		X							A							A					A									A	
Aug					A									X						A						A	A				
Sept			A						A						A					A											
Oct	X							A							A						A							A			
Dec																S	S						S								

X denotes Gala Day, S denotes Santa Specials, see local announcements.   *No service in January, February, March and November.*

Service A

Trains leave Beconsall at 12.30 and every 20 minutes until 17.30 returning from Delph at 12.40 and every 20 minutes until 17.40.

CHASEWATER LIGHT RAILWAY
Brownhills West Station, Hednesford Road, Walsall WS8 7LT   **01543 452623**

Founded in 1959 as the Railway Preservation Society (West Midlands District), the Chasewater Railway was reformed in 1985 as a Registered Charity. The railway operates as *The Colliery Line* to reflect its origins and location in the heart of the Cannock Chase Coalfield. The railway operates a regular timetabled service between Brownhills West Station and Norton Lakeside Station (which adjoins Chasewater's Wildfowl Reserve).

Public opening: Sundays and Bank Holiday Mondays from Easter to end of October.

Timetable: Trains depart from Brownhills West Station at 12 noon, 12.45, 13.30, 14.15, 15.00, 15.45, 16.30 and 17.15.

WEST SOMERSET RAILWAY
The Railway Station, Minehead, Somerset TA24 5BG   01643 704996

2000	1	2	3	4	5	6	7	8	9	10	11	12	13	14	15	16	17	18	19	20	21	22	23	24	25	26	27	28	29	30	31
Feb																															
Mar		E							E				A			E		A					E	X	X	X				E	
Apr	A	A		A	A	A		A	A		A	A	A		A	A		A	A	A	A	A	D	D	D	D	C	C	C	C	D
May	D	A	A	A		A	A		A	A	A		A	A		A	A	A		A	A	B	B	B	B	B	D	D	D	D	D
June	D	B	B	B	B	B	B	B	B	B	B	B	B	B	B	B	B	B	B	B	B	B	B	B	B	B	C	C	C	C	C
July	X	X	C	C	C	C	C	C	C	C	C	C	C	C	C	C	C	D	D	D	C	C	D	D	D	D	D	C	C	D	D
Aug	D	D	D	C	D	D	D	D	D	D	C	D	D	D	D	D	D	D	C	D	D	D	D	D	C	D	D	D	D	D	D
Sept	C	C	C	C	C	C	C	X	X	X	C	C	C	C	C	C	C	C	B	B	B	B	B	X	X	A	A	A	A	A	
Oct	A		A	A	A		A	A		A	A	A		A	A		A	A	A		A	A	B	B	B	B		A	A		A
Dec		X	X					X	X				X	X									X	X	X		A	A	A	A	A

X denotes special service, please phone for details.   *No service in January and November.*

Service A

			D		D
Minehead	dep	10.15	12.15	14.25	16.00
Bishops Lydeard	arr	11.29	13.26	15.37	17.06
			D		D
Bishops Lydeard	dep	10.25	12.25	14.35	16.05
Minehead	arr	11.32	13.34	15.42	17.13

Service B

Minehead	dep	10.15	12.15	14.00	15.55
Bishops Lydeard	arr	11.31	13.30	15.17	17.11
Bishops Lydeard	dep	10.25	12.25	14.10	16.05
Minehead	arr	11.38	13.36	15.21	17.15

Service C

				D1		D2		D
Minehead	dep	10.15	11.10	12.15	14.00	14.50	15.55	17.30
Bishops Lydeard	arr	11.31	–	13.30	15.17	–	17.11	18.33
			D		D3		D4	
Bishops Lydeard	dep	09.40	10.25	–	12.25	14.10	–	16.05
Minehead	arr	10.44	11.38	12.46	13.36	15.21	16.24	17.15

All services are steam hauled except those marked D.

D1+D2 Minehead to Wiliton, arrive 11.54 and 15.34
D3+D4 Wiliton to Minehead, depart 12.05 and 15.45
S1   Minehead to Wiliton, arrive 15.34
S2   Wiliton to Minehead, depart 15.45

Service D

				D		S1			D
Minehead	dep	10.15	11.10	12.15	14.00	14.50	15.55	16.45	17.30
Bishops Lydeard	arr	11.31	12.50	13.30	15.17	–	17.11	18.02	18.33
				D			D		S2
Bishops Lydeard	dep	09.40	10.25	11.35	12.25	13.05	14.10	–	16.05
Minehead	arr	10.44	11.38	12.46	13.36	14.31	15.21	16.24	17.15

Service E

Minehead	dep	14.00
Williton	arr	14.36
Williton	dep	14.50
Minehead	arr	15.30

All trains call at intermediate stations: Dunster (6), Blue Anchor (15), Washford (24), Watchet (34), Williton (44), Stogumber (56) and Crowcombe (66) minutes after leaving Minehead and at Crowcombe (15), Stogumber (23), Williton (35), Watchet (44), Washford (52), Blue Anchor (60) and Dunster (67) minutes after leaving Bishops Lydeard.

HERITAGE RAILWAY ASSOCIATION

PASSENGER & VISITOR CHARTER

Members of the Association will always endeavour to:

- *Provide a reliable and punctual service.*
- *Provide a clean and safe environment on trains and in its stations, museums and steam centres.*
- *Provide a professional and courteous service.*
- *Undertake to deal with any complaints in an efficient and courteous manner.*
- *In so far as is reasonably practicable, give advance notice of any changes to advertised services, connection facilities and operating hours.*

In the event of any disruption to advertised train services, each member will:

- *Do its utmost to advise when normal arrangements are resumed.*
- *Ensure that any inconvenience to passengers is kept to the minimum.*
- *Keep both passengers and prospective passengers as fully advised of the situation as circumstances permit.*
- *Help to organise alternative transport arrangements and facilities whenever necessary and practicable.*

"WE'RE TRAVELLING THE GREAT CENTRAL WAY"

PASSENGER TIMETABLE 2000

TRAINS BETWEEN LOUGHBOROUGH CENTRAL AND LEICESTER NORTH

UNTIL FURTHER NOTICE

Please refer to General Notes for explanation of symbols and operating days

			Summer Weekday Service					Saturdays, Sundays and Bank Holiday Mondays throughout the year							
			W	W	W	B		■	■	■D	■A	■	■	■	C
Miles			☕	✐	☕	✗		☕	✐	✐	✗	✐	✐	☕	✗
0	LOUGHBOROUGH CENTRAL	dep.	11.00	13.15	15.30	19.30	...	09.30	10.15	11.45	13.15	14.00	15.30	17.00	19.30
2¼	Quorn & Woodhouse	dep.	11.08	13.23	15.38	19.38		09.38	10.23	11.53	13.23	14.07	15.38	17.08	19.38
5½	Rothley	arr.	11.17	13.37	15.47	20.04	...	09.47	10.32	12.02	13.37	14.17	15.47	17.17	20.04
	Rothley	dep.	11.20	13.39	15.50	20.15		09.50	10.35	12.05	13.39	14.20	15.50	17.20	20.15
8	LEICESTER NORTH	arr.	11.29	13.48	15.59	20.25		09.59	10.44	12.14	13.46	14.29	15.59	17.29	20.25

Light refreshments are usually available at Loughborough Central Station every day and at other stations at weekends.

			W	W	W	B		■	■	■D	■A	■	■	■	C
Miles			☕	✐	☕	✗		☕	✐	✐	✗	✐	✐	☕	✗
0	LEICESTER NORTH	dep.	11.50	14.05	16.20	20.45	...	10.20	11.05	12.35	14.05	14.50	16.20	17.50	20.43
2½	Rothley	arr.	11.59	14.14	16.29	20.55		10.29	11.14	12.44	14.14	14.59	16.29	17.59	20.55
	Rothley	dep.	12.03	14.18	16.35	21.10		10.33	11.18	12.48	14.18	15.03	16.35	18.03	21.10
5¾	Quorn & Woodhouse	dep.	12.12	14.27	16.42	n/s		10.42	11.27	12.57	14.27	15.12	16.42	18.12	n/s
8	LOUGHBOROUGH CENTRAL	arr.	12.20	14.35	16.50	22.15	...	10.50	11.35	13.05	14.35	15.20	16.50	18.20	22.15

GENERAL NOTES TO TIMETABLES

■   **Trains run on Saturdays, Sundays and Bank Holiday Mondays throughout the year and Tuesday 25th April 2000.**

W   **Trains run on Weekdays only – 21st April 2000, 26th to 28th April 2000 and from 30th May to 21st September 2000.**

☕   **Buffet-Car** provided for the sale of snacks, hot and cold drinks etc.

✐   **Griddle-Car** provided for the sale of hot food including "all-day" breakfast, afternoon teas, snacks, hot and cold drinks etc.

✗   **Restaurant-Car** available from Loughborough Central for First Class ticket holders who have booked seats in advance.

A   The **"SILVER JUBILEE"** runs on Saturdays, Sundays and Bank Holiday Mondays, to provide a First Class traditional luncheon service for which advance booking is obligatory; please telephone 01509 230726 for details.

B   The **"MASTER CUTLER*"** runs on Wednesday evenings, from June to September to provide a First Class traditional dining service for which advance booking is obligatory; please telephone 01509 230726 for details.

C   The **"CHARNWOOD FORESTER"** runs on Saturday evenings to provide a First Class prestigious dining service for which advance booking is obligatory: please telephone 01509 230726 for details.

      Seats for non-dining passengers are available on all Restaurant-Car trains.

D   This train will be hauled by a classic diesel locomotive during the months of March and April.

n/s   No scheduled stop at this station.

      First Class accommodation is normally available on all trains.

Trains may be altered during the commissioning of Double Track Opertion in May 2000. Additional trains run during "Gala" days and Bank Holiday Mondays; please telephone 01509 230726 for information. Passengers are conveyed by the Company's trains in accordance with the Company's Conditions of Carriage of Passengers and their Luggage (copies of which are available for inspection in the Company's booking offices) and subject to the special condition that the Company reserves the right to cancel or amend any advertised train services.

* Use of the title The "MASTER CUTLER" is by arrangement with the Director of Passenger Rail Franchising.

GREAT CENTRAL RAILWAY
LOUGHBOROUGH, LEICESTERSHIRE
FOR MORE INFORMATION RING 01509 230726